NO MAN'S BLOOD

by
Gene Church

This book is based on the life of
Ron Lapin, M.D., Surgeon

Neither Doctor Lapin nor the Author
are members of the particular
religious group written about herein.

This book is dedicated to
all men in search of the Truth.

"First the Nazis went after the Jews, but I was not a Jew, so I did not object. Then they went after the Catholics, but I was not a Catholic, so I did not object. Then they went after the Trade-Unionists, but I was not a Trade-Unionist, so I did not object. Then they came after me, and there was no one left to object."

Martin Niemoller
German Theologian

PREFACE

Writing non-fiction can be a painful process. But along with the pain encountered while writing this book have come advantages and rewards. The craft, or art, depending on your perspective, has afforded me a unique opportunity to examine human conflicts and experience them from their most intriguing level: the vantage point of the individual himself.

In over ten years of writing about real people and real things, I cannot recall any as unusual as this individual and this story. The pain mentioned has evolved from spending seven months of my life with Dr. Ron Lapin, a surgeon. This man has devoted his entire life not only to saving others' lives in the surgical arena but also to defending the religious and civil rights of a well-known but little understood religious group.

These months were spent observing, examining, questioning, and learning about this man and his innately driven motives, and about the frustrating plight of a religious group. It centers around the struggle for just, equal treatment from the State of California and from the medical profession itself.

Why, friends and colleagues have asked, would this man challenge the medical community and risk his successful medical career daily for a group sometimes referred to as "nobody's people"? Is he simply a "good" person? A philanthropist?

As I pursued my subject and this story, I found my questions echoing their own. My eventual answer came with the rediscovery of an essay, "The Penalty of Leadership." An excerpt from the writing explains,

"When a man's work becomes a standard for the whole world, it also becomes a target for the shafts from the envious few."

My answers had been found. Dr. Ron Lapin, the surgeon, is not so fortunate. His battle continues, as does that of the religious group he so fervently defends.

The uniqueness of this story--the human conflict and the experience itself--is the battleground on which the war continues to wage. It's not on the streets-- with pickets carrying placards, pointing empty fingers of accusation, or hurling stones of denial. Rather, the battle goes on in the sterile arena of the operating room where the provocative weapons used in the quest for excellence and equality are faith, heart, and an electric knife.

Gene Church
September 8, 1982

Dirty, rotten air traffic controllers. . . . The thought was infuriating. It was burning, irritating. *I should have called,* he thought. *Should have called. . . .* Lapin was tired, empty, spent. And why shouldn't he be? After all, he'd worked late into the night on a patient that nobody else in Tucson would touch: an eighty-year-old woman who had to be emergency airlifted to Orange County. It was supposed to be the last trip of her life. At least that's what they'd all said--every single one of them, except, of course, Dr. Ron Lapin.

The diagnosis was acute lower gastro-intestinal bleeding, secondary to diffuse diverticulosis. She had a hemoglobin count of four and a half, one-third of what's normal, one-half of what's generally con- sidered safe for surgery.

The grueling, two-hour operation was a long one by his standards. The entire colon had to be removed under extremely adverse conditions, but that was normal for Lapin. He had come to expect cases that were abnormal or inoperable by anyone else's stan- dards.

The operation was a success. There was only minimal blood loss and the patient was recovering very nicely. Nevertheless, like so many times before, Lapin spent what little was left of the short California night at the hospital, monitoring the woman whose life he'd just prolonged . . . just to make sure. He slept on the couch in the physicians' lounge during those few precious hours, under the drone of the paging system as it called out doctors' names.

Dr. Lapin spent more and more time in the hospital these days. Showering and dressing there had become commonplace. His beard was more of a time-saving device than something related to vanity. By not shaving, he gained a few more valuable minutes each day to do what he did best: save people's lives.

"Good morning, Doctor Lapin." The intensive care nurse was unusually cheerful, considering she just drew the shift assignment for a holiday weekend.

"Morning, Susie. How's Mrs. Murdock?"

"You look tired. Did you stay here again last night?" She handed him Mrs. Murdock's chart and smiled. It was a smile of understanding--one that many people in the hospital shared with him, at least those who had the slightest idea of what this man was all about.

Lapin took the chart, ran his hand through his coal black hair, and smiled back. "There's no place like home," he quipped in his rich, thick accent.

Susie smiled again. "You're too much." She shook her head and went off to check another patient's IV.

Lapin's gait was totally confident as he took the few short steps to the patient's room.

"How are you feeling this morning, Mrs. Murdock?"

"Good. Can I go home now?" She was half serious.

Lapin studied the monitors and IV devices as he spoke. "Let you get away from me this soon? I've been lookin' for a woman like you all my life." His bedside manner bridged the gap between their forty-five year age difference and cemented her confidence in the man who only hours earlier had held her life in his hands. The vital signs were good, stable. The blood count was slowly rising. Mrs. Murdock would live to see eighty-one. Lapin had given her the greatest gift of all, life.

After a routine discussion with the hospital administrator about procedure, and after several impromptu hallway consultations with other staff physicians, Lapin was through for the day--pending emergencies, of course, that were becoming a regular, almost expected part of his hectic life.

He stepped outside and inhaled his first breath of fresh air in over twenty-eight hours. It felt great, even though the smog slowly crawled inland and stung his eyes like lingering ammonia. By the time Lapin reached the northbound San Diego freeway, the smog had become much thicker than usual for a Labor Day weekend. It hung motionless like a drab, gray quilt covering Los Angeles up ahead. Although most factories were closed for the holiday, the increased traffic and the lack of Santa Ana winds created an air quality index that sent asthma victims searching for hospitals and pure oxygen.

It just didn't seem right that the traffic heading north would be so uncommonly heavy, but nevertheless it was. It was like an endless parking lot, bumper to bumper, that seemed to become one solid mass of metal supported by Firestone and B.F. Goodrich. *Probably all going to the beach*, he thought; *maybe the mountains.*

Lapin checked his watch. The classical station playing on his car radio seldom interrupted Bach or Beethoven to announce the time. *It's close, but I'm still in good shape*, he thought, easing his way into the transient monster as it weaved its way northward.

Stop, then go . . . slow, then faster . . . but never reaching the magic fifty-five the entire way to the airport. Once there, he found carloads of people attempting a hurried exodus. He searched row by row for a parking space. He then walked to Worldway Avenue and waited for the light to change so he could cross over to the TWA terminal. Once he reached the information counter, he took his turn in the endless line of people because the flight number he wanted hadn't appeared on the monitors.

"Flight six-six-two from New Jersey?" Lapin finally asked. The sleepy-eyed man in the blue polyester blazer gave him an annoyed shrug across the counter and punched a few numbers into his terminal.

"Six-six-two?" the man repeated. Lapin nodded, his impatience growing. "In the air," the man said; "it'll be an hour and a half late."

The doctor gave the attendant an icy cold stare, almost inferring that he was personally responsible for the delay. In a low hissing whisper, Lapin carefully enunciated each word crisply, "Hour and a half late. . . ." His speech was exacting, much like his work with a knife or a suture.

The man was coldly unemotional. It wasn't his fault. It wasn't his job. He just worked there. "Air traffic controllers. They've got everything all screwed up. It's the strike. Look at the mess in here."

Lapin had moved from the counter by the time the man finished his sentence. Impolite, perhaps . . . insensitive, probably . . . impatient, always. Time

3

was a precious, valuable commodity. He knew he could have been helping someone in that ninety minutes, perhaps performing an operation that other surgeons considered impossible. Lapin got all the rejects, cases that other cutters of note viewed as hopeless. *So now what?* he asked himself as he walked away. He looked at his watch, studying the second hand. *Maybe a meal. That would be different. An uninterrupted meal without the constant "Dr. Lapin. . . ." being announced throughout the corridors. A whole hour and a half alone.* He smiled, nearly laughing at the prospect, as he made his way toward the nearest telephone. Ah yes, the ever present telephone. If he wasn't at an operating table with the electric knife in his hand, he was usually on a telephone, talking and consulting with doctors, patients, or lost, lonely, frightened people from all over the world.

Dirty, rotten air traffic controllers . . . I should have called. . . . He began to feel uncomfortable, disturbed. It was that gnawing feeling he always contracted in airports. The feeling had festered, grown, and then manifested itself over several years of waiting in airports . . . waiting just like today for Ari, his son, his only offspring, his legacy. It was the same feeling he got when taking Ari to the airport and having to watch him leave. Dying inside a little after each fleeting visit, Lapin held back the words that hurt too much to even mutter aloud. *Maybe this time*, he thought, *maybe this time we'll be able to get all the words out*. He hoped so. He had seventeen years of pent-up feelings to express to his son; he would never give up hope that one day the words could flow freely.

He remembered all the emotions that wrenched inside him each time he waited for Ari's flight to arrive, wondering if his son would really step off the plane or not be there at all, as had sometimes been the case. Oh, how he remembered and relived those moments. But this was 1981, and Ari was finally moving to California for good.

***

Ari was nearly four. He was the pride and joy of his father's life. Lapin remembered how his son would wear the white doctor's lab coat he had especially made for him--the one with "Ari Lapin" embroidered

4

over the left breast pocket. Lapin remembered how the boy wore it all the time, playing with his father's stethoscope, listening to anyone's and everyone's heartbeat, and shaking his tiny index finger at make-believe patients and prescribing seriously, "Now you take two aspirins and call me in the morning." The boy's future was locked in--that's what the old friends seemed to think as they laughed at the all-too-serious youngster.

The laughter and togetherness had become less frequent, slowly eroding as the accelerated quest for a successful surgical practice captured Lapin and absorbed more and more of his time.

***

He spent four demanding years at Indiana University and received his medical degree. It had been a lifetime goal--a dream he'd nurtured as an abandoned child in Israel. Now, in part, the dream had become a reality.

The first floor corridor in Ortman Hall was jammed with med students. They were all graduating seniors who would soon be full-fledged doctors. Electricity charged through the misty hallway. The fervor and excitement could be felt throughout the main building of the school complex. It was an unparalleled moment--both joyous and fearful. The ritualistic procedure of publicly posting the internship assignments was to begin any second now as the main office door would open and a postgraduate teaching assistant would walk to the bulletin board. Then, with one single thumb tack, he would post a typewritten list which would determine the future of every young man who waited impatiently in the hall. It wasn't as if they didn't know; every student had applied, in his specialty, to the hospital of his choice months ago. The list no doubt had been prepared and typed weeks ahead. It seemed perhaps that the instructors and professors enjoyed watching the prospective doctors squirm, as if somehow initiating them to a lifetime of anticipation. It was tradition, yet, in a profession that special-izes in treating and perpetuating humanity, it somehow appeared grossly inhumane--almost barbaric.

The door opened to reveal a tall, thin man whose sandy hair crept over the back of his white lab coat collar. He smiled confidently at the men he had trained and worked with for four years. Holding the much wanted list playfully behind his back, he taunted, "Let's make a deal. . . ."

"C'mon, Watson," one of the students called, "post the damn thing." The comment was echoed by several others as Watson walked to the board and ceremoniously positioned the thumb tack. His modest congratulations to the group were drowned out as they jockeyed for a first-hand position to read their fate.

"Boston General," a student shouted. "John Hopkins," screamed another, throwing his arms into the air. "UC in San Francisco . . . California, here I come." Comments and congratulations flowed freely as each student read the next point of arrival in his career. For most of the young doctors it was a time for celebration, but for those who only received their third choice, it was unquestionably a time of deep disappointment. But that disappointment was soothed by the inevitable fact that someday they'd be wealthy and respected in a community of their choice.

Ron Lapin stood in the back of the crowd. There was a strange, eerie sense of confidence about him. He knew where he was going. He just knew.

He stood apart from the group, a loner of sorts. Some days this could be blamed on his heritage and others on his unwillingness to participate in social functions and parties. Medical school was difficult and draining. The time not spent in classes, lab, or study was usually spent earning money for the family, for Rowena and Ari. *After all*, he thought, *that's who it's for*. They had struggled together, sacrificed, done without. The schooling would continue, but now as an intern, he'd get paid. Paid!

The crowd thinned, going various ways to continue celebrating. Ron Lapin, M.D., moved to the bulletin board. He flipped through several pages and located his name, followed by "straight surgical internship-- Maimonides Medical Center, Brooklyn, New York." It was his first choice. A smile would normally have been appropriate, but he saved it, knowing the real work was just beginning.

A surgeon. He was actually going to become a surgeon. It was more than becoming a doctor. It was more than diagnosing or dispensing prescriptions. It was more than delivering babies or setting broken bones. He would hold a life in his hands alone, and have the knowledge and talent to save it.

6

Historically, great surgeons are born with steady, sure hands that perform instinctively as they flirt and dance with disaster inside a patient's body. Lapin had such hands.

Rowena was thrilled. Now they could go back to the East Coast. Ari, too young to understand what was going on, donned his lab coat and joined in the party. It was such a happy time.

After the move and a few days to settle in, the hospital came first. Rowena found herself alone more and more. The days in the hospital drifted into nights and days. The complexities of surgery were more than fascinating; they became a magnetic, magical siren song beckoning Dr. Lapin closer and closer. The endless days wore on as his knowledge and skills became more proficient.

It had been one of those thirty-six hour days. How do the body and mind survive such punishment, case after case, body after body? Day and night, night and day, there's an endless stream of blood and scrubbing until your skin is raw.

Finished for a little while, Lapin half closed his eyes, dazed from pure physical exhaustion. Everything he did now seemed difficult, and much slower than usual.

"Sleep," he whispered to himself, "just a little sleep and then, finally, some time to play with Ari. Maybe we could go out somewhere and. . . ." His words trailed off as he realized he was at his apartment building. He could already feel the warmth and safety of his own bed--no food, no conversation, just sleep. Afterwards, they could catch up on all the other things . . . it'd been so long since they were out anywhere, seen a movie or anything . . . *can't think about it now . . . sleep first . . . then we'll fix everything . . . everything is going to be fine, just fine.*

But everything wasn't fine. The sign on the elevator read, "Out of Order." *I really don't believe this.* Lapin shrugged in acknowledgement of his fate and began to climb the four torturous flights to his apartment. *How does an exhausted body go on?* Having reached the fourth floor, he just wanted to collapse and let Rowena drag him inside and put him to bed. But he was too close now to give up.

He turned his key in the lock and opened the door. He took a few steps into the foyer and stopped. *Wrong apartment*, he thought. *No harm, nobody's here. The place is empty.* He backed into the hallway and pulled the door shut. He stopped again. His tired, weary eyes opened a little wider. He looked at the door. Apartment 4-B. "That's my apartment. What the hell's going on?"

The daze was rapidly clearing as he reopened the door and walked back into the living room. "Rowena!" "Ari!" Nothing. Silence, room-to-room, wall-to-wall silence. The entire apartment was bare. There was nothing left except an air conditioner and an eight-by-ten picture of Ari in a cheap frame. No note. Nothing.

He shook his head remembering that their car, which was usually parked in front of the building, was also gone. They were gone. Everything was gone. Lapin was alone . . . again . . . exactly the way he had been left alone by his mother when he was only a one-year-old.

"Ari?" he whispered, knowing no sound would return. There was only the echo of his own deserted and pain-filled voice. "Ari?"

He sat down on the cold floor in the middle of the empty living room, held his son's picture, and cried.

***

The following week Rowena called. For Lapin, it had been a sleepless, agonizing week. She'd taken Ari and moved to Philadelphia. Lapin was crushed, stripped, nearly destroyed. His relationship with Rowena had dissipated to polite amenities, hello's, and goodbye's; but not, in his mind, to the point of desertion. It wasn't until later that he realized it was he who had deserted her for his career and the hospital. "Weren't they part of his career?" he asked himself so many times. "Wasn't it for all of them?"

Repeated attempts to reconcile were fruitless. She was gone . . . gone with his only son.

The five-thousand-dollar-a-year salary for interns was quickly appropriated for child support and rent. Little was left over for the luxuries of life, like visitation with Ari. So Lapin expanded his already overcrowded schedule by making house calls for other physicians at night. He borrowed friends' cars and rode into the bowels of Brooklyn, the Bedford-Stuyvesant region.

8

Each night that he ventured into this no man's land, he sharply increased his potential of becoming one of its countless statistics--the victim of a mugging, or worse. He was a marked man as he traveled their streets conspicuously carrying his black physician's bag filled with narcotics.

He'd seen two people stabbed on the subway and had done everything possible to stop their bleeding, but death was inevitable. Their lives were wasted on the floor of an underground train which seemed to carry these poor souls on an endless, frightful ride going nowhere.

He had seen psychotics die a slow, wretching death from injections of powdered milk rather than the life-supporting heroin their bodies craved. He had seen the self-induced, blood-letting, coat-hanger abortions in dimly lit hallways where no one cared about the mother, let alone the child.

It was a concurrent, all too realistic secondary education for the first-year surgical intern. It was the slice of life that few men view firsthand at ground level. It was a box seat to reality in its most despicable form.

Lapin had been a student of loneliness all his life--though not always by choice. Now circumstances forced him to learn life through the despairing, apathetic, dreamless eyes of these debased souls.

Seeing life from that barren perspective only burned Lapin's goal more deeply into his heart: to be a surgeon and to return hope to people when theirs had run out.

He hadn't bartered months of housecalls, along with their insightful realities, to gain a new perspective of man's existence. They were the dues Ron Lapin paid to finance his two-hundred-fifty-mile round trip to visit Ari in Philadelphia.

Month after month, he made the trip on alternate weekends. The money he made going in and out of that hellhole was never enough to stay overnight, just enough to rent a car to make the trip, spend a few precious, fleeting hours with Ari, and then make the lonely drive home--to the hospital.

Every other weekend he was on forty-eight-hour call. It wasn't worth the effort to try spending some time at home. The apartment was filled with memories that still cut too deeply. Instead, he slept during those few rare hours in the surgeons' lounge, only to be

9

constantly awakened by dreams, and more often by nightmares of reliving the emergency surgeries he'd performed on the gunshot victims, the people laid open by moving cars, and the attempted suicides.

He was constantly learning about his trade, his craft, his art. It was the kind of knowledge that only comes from the experience of laying a cold steel scalpel on a living person's skin, making an incision, separating the tissue, and actually going inside.

The educational experience didn't go unnoticed by Lapin's superiors. At the end of his first full year at Maimonides, he was appointed assistant resident of surgery--a critical moment in his medical career that confirmed his credibility and right to continue traveling down the road he selected.

Lapin was good with his hands and he knew it, but he now proved to have an equally important and necessary attribute--he had the heart.

Having the heart, the will, the determination, and the perseverance would all be critical in enduring the four grueling years. As a resident, he would have to withstand endless nights of work, few vacations, and seeing Ari only every other weekend.

The desire to succeed and the drive to be the best were compelling. The light at the end of the tunnel was like an intense magnet drawing him toward his goal. The perpetual challenge of being both innovative and creative in his field enticed Lapin to work night and day.

His salary increased to eighty-five hundred dollars a year, and the child support payments went up accordingly. Rowena moved to Cherry Hill, New Jersey, and married a school teacher. The constant threat of adoption was wielded as an incentive to increase the amount of his support. Weekend visits grew more strained with a step-father in the picture. Lapin found the man to be cold and dogmatic rather than the loving father figure he felt Ari needed. Ari was now exposed to a man named Norman, who was prone to chest pains and generally not very healthy.

Through four bone-chilling New York winters, Lapin rose from assistant, to senior assistant, to resident, and finally to chief resident of surgery. The years were demanding, arduous, perplexing.

It was during this time while working in the research laboratory that Lapin encountered an instrument that would change the future of his surgical career.

He was doing cardiovascular research on dogs when he first used the electrocautery instrument. Simplistically, the knife was a five-inch-long electric scalpel. As he used the knife on the animals, Lapin found the benefits to be nothing less than remarkable.

He could cut quickly and cleanly through the tissue, and, as he cut, stop and cauterize any and all bleeding vessels. This made surgery considerably easier since his view wasn't obstructed by unconfined blood. Lapin was fascinated with the instrument. He began using it for all research-related operations. He became proficient with it. The more he used it, the more he wondered why the electric knife wasn't being used regularly on people. After all, eliminating the pooling of blood in the surgical field allows you to see one hundred percent better. It made sense to him. It made a lot of sense.

"I'm sorry, Dr. Lapin," Reinhardt said. "It's just too impractical; dogs are one thing, but you're talking about human beings."

"I can appreciate that, doctor," Lapin countered, "I truly can appreciate what you're saying. But the benefit of seeing so much more clearly what we're cutting . . . and not having to transfuse. . . ."

"Ron. . . ." The interruption was expressed in a somewhat compassionate, somewhat condescending tone. "You're a surgeon . . . a good surgeon . . . but listen to me and forget the electric knife." Reinhardt might as well have said forget your birthright, forget your roots, forget who you are. The instrument was not to be forgotten . . . it was to be used.

Lapin did use it, over and over, until he handled it with expertise. It had a feel, a touch if you will, that could only be developed and perfected through use.

He rotated through Coney Island General and operated on countless emergency room cases--trauma patients, critical patients. He continued his heart research by using the electric knife on animals, but his arguments for its beneficial use on humans remained unsuccessful.

He kept making house calls at night, seeing Ari every other weekend . . . and wondering why Rowena had taken his son and left him. His only recurrent answer was that she had married an idea, the American dream, and not the man. It wasn't a conclusive deduction, but it was something.

The days melted into nights, and the winters into spring. The constant desire for more knowledge continued to motivate Ron Lapin, even though the answers he found were inconclusive.

***

Maureen worked the night shift in the intensive care unit of Maimonides. She was short, with dark hair, and quite attractive. She at first stayed away from Lapin because of somewhat seriously dating a doctor from Rochester. Then, too, thinking Lapin was a resident rather than an intern made a big difference to her.

"I'm involved," she'd tell him when he asked her to dinner.

"Great, let's just have lunch then," he'd reply, with a smile.

She ignored Lapin for over two months--actually avoiding him. During a chance meeting in the hospital hallway, Lapin charged, "You treat men like commodities . . . we're not just notches on your belt, you know."

Maureen was silent for a second, stunned. "I'm not like that." She was hurt.

"Prove it."

The lunch turned into dinner, then dancing, and then a full-scale romance. Maureen ended her relationship with the doctor from Rochester. She and Lapin fell in love. He was happy, almost content, for the first time in a very long while.

Maureen had a daughter from a previous marriage and had long since decided against having any more children. It was a painful decision for Lapin to accept because he hoped to have another son, but he yielded to her wishes. He thought he could live with it since he still had Ari, in a remote manner of speaking.

The hospital had an apartment house on 49th Street in Brooklyn which they ran for the staff and some personnel. Ron and Maureen lived there two years while he finished training and she continued working in the emergency room. His salary the last year of school increased to twelve thousand dollars. With Maureen's income, they lived comfortably--not well--

but comfortably.

It was late fall. The leaves were turning color as New York began to button up for the winter.

"You off tonight?" She was surprised to see him.

Lapin closed the apartment door behind him. He rubbed his beard. "They rotated some new guys into the emergency room . . . told me I should go home and get some sleep. That's different, huh?"

"Drink?"

Lapin nodded slowly. He was tired. He collapsed into a chair and began to sift through the mail lying on an end table while Maureen fixed the martini.

"Anything new at work today?" she inquired with notable hesitancy and caution in her voice.

He continued to shuffle the mail. He knew what she was asking, but chose to ignore it. "Same old stuff: appendectomy, two D and C's, bowel resection, couple biopsies . . . you know. . . ." There was a pause as he found a letter from The Good Samaritan Hospital in Miami. "Sorry I missed you for lunch. Got tied up with Reinhardt arguing about the electric knife again."

Maureen handed him the drink and noticed the letter in his hand.

"*L'chaim*," Lapin said, lifting his glass in her direction.

She sat on the couch facing him and watched with concern as he read the entire letter. His expression never changed. He laid the letter back down on the end table, took another sip of his drink, and gave her a weak smile.

"So?" There was impatience in her voice; she hated to be put off.

"So . . . it's the same as the rest of them, so what?" he answered matter-of-factly.

"So what?" she repeated, getting a little louder. "So what is that you get out of school in about eight months and it'd be nice if you had a place to work . . . a job."

"I'll find a place."

"What'd Good Samaritan say?"

He handed her the letter. "Same as the rest. They're over staffed with general surgeons . . . thanks for my interest . . . they'll get back to me if they have an opening. I love it when they put the emphasis on the 'if' rather than the 'when.'"

"Forgive me, but I don't think sarcasm is particu-

larly beneficial when you're looking for a job."
Maureen got up to fix herself a drink.

"Look, if the hospital says they're full, they're
full." Lapin wasn't enjoying the conversation; they'd
been having the same one too many times lately. "I
don't want to talk about it. I'll find a place."

"Has Peterson found a place yet? Or Schwartz?" She
already knew the answer, but she wouldn't relent. "Of
course they found a place . . . and you know why they
found a place?"

Lapin gave her an icy stare, shook his head in
dismay, and opened the newspaper. He tuned her out
completely and reverted to his own private channel.

"I'll tell you why they found a place. They play
the game," she continued. "They do what they're told
to do and they don't make waves."

Lapin turned a page. She hated it when he avoided
her. With each rejection letter he received from
hospitals along the East Coast, their verbal exchange
fell more and more into this set pattern.

"But not you," she persisted. "You have to be a
rebel. Isn't that what your instructors call you?
You always have to find new ways to operate, even if
it means overriding your superiors and taking charge
of other doctors' patients." She lowered her voice,
almost pleading, "Why can't you be like everybody else
and just listen to what they say and do what they tell
you?"

Lapin folded the newspaper slowly and laid it down.
He took a long, deep breath--just as he'd been doing
since the rejection letters started coming in six
months ago.

"Maureen," he passively replied in a soft voice,
"I'm not like everybody else. I'm different. I can't
explain it, but I'm different. Surgery isn't a game
you play. . . ."

"I know that. . . ."

"Let me finish," he said, stopping her. "It's
somebody's life you're dealing with every time you
stand over them with a scalpel in your hand." It was
evident in Lapin's voice that the only thing he
enjoyed more than surgery itself was talking about it.
There was an undisputed reverence in the tone. It was
respect. "There are better ways to do things, to
perform procedures, to save lives. I'm looking for
those ways and I'm going to find them."

"Can't those things wait until you're on a hospital

staff somewhere?"

"Operations can be performed cleaner, faster, more efficiently . . . and safer."

"You can't operate if you don't have a hospital."

Why, he asked himself, *did it seem that more and more they never heard each other when they talked.* He picked up the newspaper and reopened it.

"And what's the big deal about staying on the East Coast?" she asked. "Why don't you send out your resume and apply to some hospitals in the Mid-West, or even the West Coast?"

"How many letters did we get back?" he said. "Dozen? Dozen and a half? That's how many times I've told you why I'm going to stay on the East Coast--so I can be close to Ari." Then his voice became very soft. "Ari."

Three more months passed, but it felt more like a lifetime filled with rejection letters from Maine to Florida. Lapin knew that when these hospitals contacted Maimonides they were told that he was an excellent surgeon and that he had a gifted career in front of him. He also knew that Maimonides' response would focus on the fact that he didn't join the team, but, as a loner, followed his inherent tendency to do things his own way and not always by the book.

Research is research; surgery is surgery. That seemed to be the common viewpoint. Surgery is an overcrowded field, for all the obvious reasons, but most hospitals would still appreciate adding a talented team member to their staff.

His lack of participation as a team member seemed to be the recurrent stumbling block. Because of the influx of more compliant surgeons, most hospitals could be overly selective in filling positions while avoiding unnecessary risks. They sent Lapin polite rejection letters, an additional three months' worth.

***

"I'm going to California next week."

Maureen's eyes opened wide. She spun away from the stove. "When? Why?" There was an excitement in her voice. They were words she'd been hoping to hear.

"Got an interview." Lapin was cool and unemotional, despite knowing she'd be thrilled.

"Ron, that's great." She practically dragged him into the living room, talking a mile a minute. "When

do you leave? Tell me about it. What hospital?"
Then, in a seductive yet ridiculing tone, she asked,
"Why didn't you tell me?"

"I didn't want you to get too excited. It's just an
interview."

"So, tell me about it," she pleaded. "What hospital? Where is it?"

"It's not a hospital. It's a doctor's private
surgical practice in Orange County. . . ."

"Where's. . . ."

"Just outside of L.A. Guy's got a big practice. He
needs an associate to help him with his case load.
Sounds like he's doing well . . . real well."

"But how. . . ."

"The guy ran an ad in a medical journal looking for
a surgeon. I called him. We talked. Sent him my
resume. He liked it and called me back. And I'm
going to meet him next week. That's it."

Lapin's intuition was correct. Maureen was indeed
overly excited. She could hardly contain herself.
The initial magazine advertisement mentioned thirty-
five thousand dollars a year--more money than Lapin
could really imagine. Anticipation grew the entire
week before he left. The trip was a complete success.

Lapin returned and told Maureen the amount of money
advertised was the figure that could eventually be
earned. The actual starting salary was eighteen
thousand plus malpractice insurance. It was still
fifty percent more than he was earning now, plus the
bonus of being out from under the thumb of his
instructors. California had always offered vast,
unlimited opportunities.

Doctor Korn had told Lapin in no uncertain terms
that he wasn't interested in having a partner. A
piece of the action was never considered. He simply
wanted a qualified, talented surgeon to assist him
with his abundant, growing practice. In Korn's mind,
he found that man and offered Lapin the job.

The trip, the weather, the conversation . . . it was
all wonderful. He told Maureen that he accepted the
position and that they'd be moving as soon as his
residency was completed. She was thrilled. His
eighteen month search for a place to work had finally
resolved itself. The security afforded the wife of a
surgeon would soon be hers. *Ron will be happy too*,
she thought. *He'll finally have the freedom he wants
and so desperately needs in the operating room.*

16

The last weekend visit to Cherry Hill was riddled with emotion. Lapin kept trying to make small jokes in an attempt to lighten the mood and make Ari laugh. As they walked through a deserted playground that last Sunday afternoon, he had to keep looking away from his son to conceal the tears he wiped from his eyes.

"California sounds great, dad. . . ."

"Yeah, it's great. It's warm there . . . almost all the time."

The two walked in silence for awhile, holding hands, avoiding the eventual goodbye that would have to be said. Lapin had hated their previous goodbyes when they'd be separated for only two weeks . . . now, there was this goodbye. They both started to speak at the same time, looked at each other, and laughed.

"You go ahead," Lapin said.

The youngster hesitated for a second. There was an innocence about him--a purity. He stared straight ahead as they walked, avoiding eye contact. "How long will it be, dad . . . till I get to see you?"

Lapin took a few more steps in silence to mentally compose himself in an attempt to make sure his voice wouldn't crack when he answered.

"Well, we have to get a place to live and get all set up. It won't be too long, son. . . ." His voice started to break, but he caught himself and cleared his throat. "I haven't spoken with your mother about it yet . . . but it won't be too long . . . I promise."

The boy nodded. He knew it was a noncommittal answer and yet he understood. Finally he spoke. "Dad?"

"Yes, son?"

"What were you gonna say . . . before . . . when we both started talkin' at once?"

Lapin sniffed and pursed his lips tightly together. He knelt down so he could face his son eye to eye. "Just that . . . I'm going to miss you, Ari . . . and I love you."

The tears flowed freely now. Unashamed of showing their deepest emotions, the two embraced tightly for a long time. Not knowing when they'd see each other again, they just held on and on. Then, through his own little boy tears, Ari whispered, "I love you, too, daddy. . . ."

***

The trip to the West Coast was pleasant, even fun. The outdated, broken-down Camaro did all that was asked of it and more. Maureen had started two small grapefruit trees from seeds and refused to leave them behind.

"You don't seem to understand," Lapin kidded, "there's a rumor going around that California has a grapefruit tree or two already."

"I don't care," she said. "I started these and I'm going to see them grow."

They looked at each other and laughed like children going on a new adventure. They spent hours talking of the future. Maureen had been a head nurse in an intensive care unit and in an emergency room. As generally happens in the position of head nurse, Maureen lost all patient contact. Dealing with patients had been one of her strong points. Then, too, she had experienced what's commonly referred to in the nursing profession as "burn out." Together they decided that she would not return to the nursing profession.

Entering into private practice meant developing referrals from other doctors. The importance of this point was hammered home with great clarity by Dr. Korn during the initial interview. The selective process of entertaining, wooing, and seducing other doctors' patients was absolutely one of the most critical factors in creating a successful surgical practice.

Maureen's role would be to plan and execute the necessary functions to promote her husband and act as a business manager of sorts by keeping track of all the records and doing the accounting. She would also entertain his associates by giving gourmet dinner parties. She had always loved doing that.

It was a warm, crystal clear day in June, 1973, with unlimited visibility across the desert and mountains. They hid the two grapefruit trees under a blanket in the trunk and innocently shook their heads "no" at the state line inspection station. The uniformed officer waved them through, and they entered the Golden State laughing.

Santa Ana was a peaceful, sleepy community, and the townhouse on Sunflower Avenue was exactly what they needed. It had a large open dining area with lots of space for entertaining. The apartment was close to Korn's office and Hope Hospital.

Immediately upon their arrival, Lapin went to work while Maureen started to set up housekeeping.

Hope was a small, private facility with several investor owners. But Lapin didn't care about any of that. The business side of things was of little importance; he was there to be a good surgeon.

The first day there he met with some of the other doctors, surgical assistants, and scrub nurses who'd be working with him. They would become his team when, as a single entity, they stood together around the operating table. Lapin was basically satisfied with their competence, but felt there was room for improvement. He'd seen better and felt that excellence in the operating room was a necessity. He had long been dedicated to the philosophy of doing your best, knowing that marginal room for anything less just didn't exist when a life was involved.

One of the first things that bothered him was that Korn wasn't that good of a surgeon. Oh, he was competent, but certainly nothing exceptional. He went to the table, did a mediocre textbook cutting job, and then went back to the golf course or investment office as soon as possible.

He had a constant influx of new patients, no question about that. Lapin felt from the very beginning that Korn was essentially buying a lot of them by involving them in business deals, land speculations, and even investments in his own medical clinic. But, that's just the way it was. Korn was business oriented, profit oriented, money oriented. Lapin had no problem with that, but he was certainly bothered by Korn not using his full potential as a surgeon.

Their relationship started the way they had agreed it would during the initial interview. The two doctors would rotate responsibilities: every other day in the operating room, and alternate days making rounds and being in the office for patients.

It worked that way for awhile. Maureen gave delightful dinner parties for other doctors, and they started to refer more and more patients to the partnership. Korn was the chief of surgery and began to spend more of his time and energy with hospital politics than with operating, rounds, or patient care.

In time, Lapin began to feel that he was being used. Day after day would pass with one reason or another preventing Korn from performing his scheduled surgeries. Soon his follow-up with patients and hospital rounds became increasingly rare. Lapin shouldered the added responsibility and spent whatever hours were necessary in the operating room, the hospital, and the office.

"Sometimes," he told Maureen, "I feel like a slave."

"You're doing good work, the experience is wonderful, and you've finally got the freedom you've been wanting. . . ."

Lapin turned slowly and looked at her without a smile. They didn't laugh much these days. "That doesn't hardly work, does it?"

"What?"

"Being a slave--with freedom--that just doesn't hardly work."

Lapin's reputation for quality and excellence was spreading quickly. His skills and talents were highly respected. More doctors began to refer patients. Patients began to refer patients, sometimes to the chagrin of their former physicians.

Surgery is a very personal thing because a patient wants to have complete confidence in the man cutting him open as he lies, unconscious, on that table. There's not much margin at all for error on an operating table, nor is there room for someone who is unfamiliar with a procedure, or who is going to quit in the middle of it.

A strange thing happened about six months into the partnership--the camaraderie that existed at the outset was dissipating. Korn and some other doctors at Hope became less polite and less cordial toward Lapin. A coolness permeated the facility.

The daily surgical schedule, probably the most widely read bulletin in any hospital, generated constant questions from doctors as to why this doctor sent that patient to that surgeon. It certainly annoyed those surgeons who discovered publicly that physicians were now referring their patients to another surgeon.

What might have been considered a very complex problem actually becomes quite simply a matter of economics, pure dollars and cents. If a physician no longer refers his patients, it could result in a loss of tens of thousands of dollars in income over a period of time for the surgeon. It's a very expensive proposition to lose a doctor who's been sending business your way.

20

Additionally, a surgeon's large ego can be devastated when a physician sends patients elsewhere; it's difficult to explain away a peer's lack of confidence in your professional abilities.

Lapin, whose name appeared more than any other on the surgical schedule, was taking business from other surgeons in the hospital as he received more and more cases. He wasn't well liked, but he was protected. Working for the chief of surgery gave him a buffer, a safety zone, that other surgeons couldn't penetrate for whatever reason, without going through Korn. No other surgeon was going to challenge the top man in the department and risk putting his staff position and privileges on the line.

Rumors were started . . . locker room conversations at the golf course . . . talking behind his back . . . nothing specific, just innuendos about Lapin's abnormally busy surgical schedule. It had caused some doctors to lose money and to lose face, so professional jealousy was certain to follow.

Korn, for awhile, was amused. He actually seemed to enjoy the agony of others. It certainly didn't bother him that Lapin now carried the major load. It didn't bother him at all since he could spend the extra time putting together business deals and financing his own clinic.

Then, the worst possible thing happened. Doctors who had been referring their patients to Korn began to specifically request Dr. Lapin for surgery. Improved patient care was obviously their motivation. Korn was incensed when this news slapped him in the face publicly. It was a direct personal insult and a bitter pill to swallow. After all, he was the chief of surgery--supposedly the best.

Lapin's hands did most of his talking. Doctors sent patients to him as a direct result of his skill and competence in the operating room. It was a thunderous vote of confidence from his peers--with the exception of Korn.

Korn began criticizing Lapin's work, scrutinizing his patients' charts for any minor infraction or error in an entry, and seizing the slightest discrepancy in hospital policy so he could blow it completely out of proportion.

Lapin began to learn that physicians, and more specifically surgeons, are carnivorous animals. When one becomes too successful, another's personal esteem is challenged. Anonymous requests began to surface asking that patients' charts be reviewed just in case something a little out of the ordinary could be picked apart and made into an issue.

Lapin found himself standing alone in the middle of it all, in much the same sense that he stood alone at an operating table. The outcome was completely in his hands. A surgeon always has the option of terminating the procedure and closing the patient, or of staying until he resolves the problem.

In the operating room, Lapin always chose to stay. He'd continue to work on patients that most surgeons would have closed much sooner. He'd refuse to give up and back away from the table.

This time, his competence was not only questioned, but challenged by jealous peers who were losing patients. It bothered him a lot. After all, Ron Lapin wasn't the God-like figure that surgeons are thought to be. He was human.

The man had feelings, deep feelings, and his deepest feelings were for the patients. So, he lived with the insults and the subtle, snide remarks. He tried his best to tune out the back-stabbing, jealous comments that steadily increased in the doctors' lunch room. His intrinsic loyalty was focused on the perpetuation of human existence to the best of his God-given ability.

Maureen was remarkably supportive by handling the books and arranging some fine dinner parties. But the increased time Ron spent at the hospital caused her loneliness to grow like a cancer. It was evident that their time together had reached an unacceptably low ebb. Neither of them liked the fact that they were together only when entertaining, but they were forced to accept the situation for awhile.

The townhouse was too empty most of the time so Maureen acquired a companion and called him Ethan. He was a thoroughbred German Pointer, a fine house pet, and good company. The first thing Ethan did was eat the two grapefruit trees that Maureen had so carefully nurtured and trekked across the country. She was upset, but it was the kind of thing a person could get over--after all, California did still have a grapefruit tree or two.

Maureen was bright, creative, intelligent, and talented. She understood the importance of what she was doing to help her husband. That had been their decision together, but it wasn't enough. Maureen began to seriously question her own existence, wondering daily about her own identity--who she was and what she was doing with her life. It wasn't an overnight revelation; it happened over a period of time.

Those questions weren't answered by giving successful dinner parties, keeping accurate records, or even training Ethan. She'd had more in her life before and had somehow let it slip away like a fading mirage in the desert.

Without diminishing any household responsibilities, Maureen set out in search of that self. She began at the University of California's Irvine Branch, starting with courses in philosophy and psychology in a search for "truth." She later studied biology and interior decorating.

***

The confrontations continued at the hospital. More surgeons became upset over Lapin's increasingly heavy surgical schedule and posed more questions about his competency. Lapin had less backup from Korn, more time in surgery, and less time at home. He grew tired from the hours . . . and the pressure . . . and from constantly looking over his shoulder to see who was coming after him next.

Maureen redecorated the apartment. Their guests loved it. Lapin hardly noticed. She took horseback riding lessons and later began entering shows with hunters and jumpers.

Christmas time of '73 dealt another traumatic blow when Ari was supposed to visit during his school vacation. It was something Lapin had looked forward to since they left the East Coast. Rowena had initially approved of it, so plans were made. Everything was set. Then she changed her mind and wasn't going to let Ari make the trip.

Their long-distance arguments only made Rowena grow more adamant. Her primary concern, she said, was that Ron wouldn't let him return to her. Lapin argued in vain, trying to convince her otherwise. Then she suggested a bond--a cash performance bond--that she somehow thought was supposed to guarantee their son's return to New Jersey.

After hundreds of dollars on long distance phone

calls, she finally conceded and returned to their original agreement.

The trip and the visit were fabulous. Ari loved California and had a fantastic time. The two got along famously. It was a warm, pleasant reuniting for both of them. On the day of Ari's scheduled departure, Lapin took him to Los Angeles International and waited as the plane filled with people. Ari was the last to board. His dad wanted them to spend every possible moment together.

Their goodbye, like the others, was emotional. It would be four, five, maybe six months before they'd see each other again. That's a long, long time. The airport was packed with people, but through the mist that covered his eyes, Lapin didn't see a single one of them. He only saw his son's large, innocent, loving black eyes as they waved goodbye to one another.

Maureen began to spend time with realtors looking for a house. Lapin explained that they couldn't afford one yet, but she insisted that, for entertainment purposes, they needed more room. Plus, she pleaded convincingly, it wasn't fair for Ethan to be kept inside all the time. "The dog's growing and needs some freedom, some space." Lapin really thought she was only concerned about Ethan's growing space.

He shrugged and told her to do whatever she thought best. He had the battles at the hospital to fight. He wasn't going to argue with her, too. It took too much time and energy that was better spent elsewhere.

Korn began to experience some difficulties with the medical clinic he'd funded. The authorities discovered that he had it staffed with medical students from the University of California at Irvine and eagerly investigated. The clinic was in jeopardy. Although the investigators showed signs of nervousness, Korn held his own. He was a powerful entity in both the medical and political communities.

He had refused to stand up for Lapin, and Lapin, in turn, had wisely refused to work in his clinic. The pressures continued to mount, growing to the point where, from Lapin's perspective, it just wasn't worth it anymore. He requested a meeting with Korn to either straighten out their differences or terminate their relationship.

He had earned his money, Lapin pointed out. He'd paid his own way. Sure, he was paid forty thousand

dollars for the year's work, but he had both attracted
and performed surgery that billed out at over a
quarter of a million dollars. Somehow, parity didn't
exist. A sense of fairness had long since been abandoned. Lapin began the fragile conversation with
logic, but that didn't work. He tried compassion and
understanding; that didn't work. Finally, he tried
emotion. Nothing worked.

Korn's mind was set. They had made their deal, he
felt, and nothing was going to change. Lapin hadn't
really prepared to deal with that unexpected
ultimatum. Korn's rigidity left him with only one
choice: to make an on-the-spot decision that he would
rather have avoided.

"Doctor," Lapin said with diplomacy, "I think that
what we have here is an inability to communicate."

"I disagree, Ron. You just do the job you were
hired to do and everything will be fine."

Lapin stayed calm. "I'm doing my job . . . and
yours. I don't mind that so much, but I do mind
having to do it without any support from you."

"I have other interests," Korn said, "things that
need my attention."

"This partnership . . . this practice . . . needs
your attention." Lapin's voice was getting a little
louder.

"The practice is doing fine," he shrugged. There
was irony tinged with sarcasm in his voice. "Haven't
you seen the billings for the year?"

Lapin knew at this point that his plea had fallen on
deaf ears and that any further conversation on the
matter would be fruitless. Korn had exhibited the
compassion of a brick wall. Lapin wasn't quite sure
what he was going to do, but he knew that he wasn't
going to continue on this way.

"Dr. Korn, I'm sorry to have to say this, but I'm
afraid it's impossible for me to continue working for
you under these conditions." Lapin took a deep breath
and studied the man's unyielding eyes. "I'm giving
you my resignation."

Korn was unmoved and retorted, "And just what do you
think you'll do then . . . without me?"

"Go into private practice, I suppose," Lapin
answered.

"Uh huh," Korn mused as he shuffled some paperwork
on his desk. He seemed to be taking the news well.
"Let me tell you something, Dr. Lapin." He continued

in a calloused, dead-serious affront. "Nobody quits on me; nobody ever has, and nobody ever will. If you resign, you might as well pack up your little black bag and move back to the East Coast because you will never work out here again. Oh, you can try . . . but I'll bury you every time you do." Korn hesitated long enough to look Lapin squarely in the eyes. "Are we clear on that, doctor?"

Lapin had never been a man to be threatened. The chronic pressures he had endured, both as the surgeon and as the man, created a cellular structure that could only be second to steel. Returning the stare, he accepted the direct challenge. "I'm resigning, Dr. Korn, effective immediately. And I'm going to stay here and practice--right here in Orange County."

***

"I can't believe you resigned." Maureen was distraught. "How could you possibly do such a stupid thing?"

"I didn't have a choice. I had to."

"And now what do you propose we do?"

"Work that much harder--we'll make it. I have to go to the office tonight."

"But I finally found a house for us. It's perfect. It's exactly what we need."

With a heavy sigh, Ron concluded, "We can't afford it . . . please, can we talk about it later?"

"That referral business we've worked so hard to build up . . . what about that?"

That referral business was exactly what was on Lapin's mind as he closed the door behind him and terminated the second turbulent conversation of the day. Korn had made it explicitly clear that any and all new referral business enticed into their practice by Lapin was going to stay there. Korn suggested the possibility of legal action if Lapin should contact any of those doctors or patients.

Another challenge? Another threat? Most certainly. Still, Lapin was the wrong man to threaten.

***

It was a moonless, pitch black night. Lapin turned off his headlights before entering the deserted parking lot. Jodie was understandably scared, and it

26

showed. She worked as Korn's receptionist for what, one year now? She never really liked him, but she still questioned what she was about to do. Lapin compassionately sensed the inner conflict she was experiencing.

They parked a safe distance from the office building and quietly closed the car doors behind them. Once inside the building, Lapin broke the silence with a hushed whisper, "How much is Korn paying you?"

"About four hundred a month," she whispered back.

"How do you get by on that?"

"You just do, I guess."

"Amazing." He sighed as he continued, "Well . . . I'm not exactly sure how we're going to do it . . . but somehow we will." Then he smiled at her, "Okay?"

"Okay," Jodie said, and smiled back.

They made their way to the patient files and each carried an armload of folders to the copy machine. Korn's threatening challenge was going to be clearly answered. They turned the machine on so that they could copy every file pertaining to Lapin's personal patients. But the light on the machine didn't flash. The machine didn't respond. Jodie pressed the start button over and over. Nothing.

"What's wrong?" he whispered.

"I don't know." Frustration and fear were conspicuous in her voice. "The damn thing just won't work."

There was a moment of strained silence, a what-do-we-do-now kind of hesitation. Lapin grabbed a nearby legal pad, and they began hand copying every single file. They sat on the floor, writing information from midnight until five-thirty a.m., just before the morning janitorial staff arrived.

Needless to say, they were dead tired and had to drag themselves to his car. But in retrospect, their overnight venture proved to be a wise move. Jodie resigned immediately and Korn had the office door locks changed that same day. Consequently, they would have had no possible mode of entry in the future.

Three days later Lapin received a letter from the hospital notifying him that his privileges had been summarily removed, which meant he could no longer practice at Hope. He knew Korn was acutely upset, but never imagined that he could be vindictive enough to try to destroy his career by having him thrown out of the hospital or by prevailing upon staff doctors to back him.

The battle lines were clearly defined and Lapin had little choice but to fight for his very existence. Of course his request for a hearing was granted so as not to deny him his "due process." Although it's a mandatory step, it is on occasion a successful vehicle for justice.

Two things were established at the hearing. First of all, the clearly defined charges--although contrived--primarily accused Dr. Lapin of unnecessary surgery. In due time, counteraction could be presented so that the charges would be reversed and dismissed case by case. The second point was that to properly present his case--his defense, if you will-- Lapin should prepare for a long, drawn-out series of hearings and should be represented by top legal counsel.

Good attorneys come complete with exorbitant fees, and Lapin explained that his financial position would not allow for costly legal representation.

The board sympathetically acknowledged his disclosure and huddled for a meeting. When they settled back in their chairs, the chairman cleared his throat. "Dr. Lapin," he began reflectively, "the board recognizes that you find yourself in a delicate and most unfortunate situation. . . ." He hesitated, as if seeking support from the other members. "Based on these circumstances, we've decided to allow you to resign rather than have your privileges removed."

There was wall-to-wall silence. Thirty . . . sixty . . . ninety seconds of deafening void. Finally Lapin cut through the hovering stillness with his distinct Israeli accent as he clipped off each word at its root. "Let me see if I understand this correctly . . . if I don't defend myself, which I can't afford to do, I'm going to be removed from the staff." Lapin had purposely, yet cautiously, approached sarcasm in his tone of voice. Several board members caught the inflection and expressed facial displeasure.

The chairman added, "I'm afraid that's correct . . . unless of course, as we mentioned, you choose instead to resign."

Great options, he thought to himself. He would now have to make another on-the-spot decision, knowing that his permanent record hung in the balance. If it showed that he'd been removed from a hospital, his chances for a staff position or for operating privileges would be greatly impaired, if not totally destroyed. This would be the first of many unforeseen career decisions to face him in the not too distant future.

"Gentlemen," he began confidently, "I seem to be in a position without alternatives. . . ." Then he added with razor-sharp directness, ". . . as I'm sure you're all quite aware."

The chairman abruptly cut him off, "Dr. Lapin. . . ."

"If I may finish," Lapin interrupted, "I'd like to present my resignation . . . effective immediately.

The board visually tallied one another, turning their heads from side to side, making casual eye contact with their peers, and then nodding. The chairman spoke for the group, "Your resignation is accepted, doctor."

And so began a long uphill climb, challenge after challenge, battle after battle.

Lapin retained privileges at Skyline Hospital, the only facility which had not followed in Hope's unwarranted footsteps. He applied for privileges with other local hospitals, but each time the story was quite the same.

"Why were you dismissed from Hope? Who were you affiliated with at Hope?"

"Dr. Korn," he'd respond.

"Dr. Korn is not held in very high esteem at this hospital. We're afraid your application will have to be denied. And since you have apparently falsified information on your application--about the matter at Hope--we have to report you to the California Board of Medical Quality Assurance."

Several interviews ended there with the worst possible news a doctor could hear: being reported to the California Board of Medical Quality Assurance. The BMQA was the political and medical KGB of the State of California.

The BMQA--the policing arm of the medical community--was not the best group of people with whom to become involved. The consensus of informed individuals was that the board occasionally conducts what could best be described as witch hunts. Usually after no one in particular, they wield their eminent power just to remind practicing physicians that they are still in existence, still omnipotent, and still have the absolute authority to revoke a physician's

29

license--and all without accountability for their actions.

"It's not right," Lapin contended with a raised voice. "It just isn't fair," he emphasized with clenched fists.

Maureen remained passive, trying dispassionately to induce a calming effect.

"Ron, fair and right have nothing to do with it. That's just the way it is."

"Then the way it is is wrong." He slammed his fist on the kitchen counter. Ethan jumped up and scurried into the living room.

"It's wrong to go to school for fourteen years--fourteen long, hard years of busting your butt days, nights, and weekends just to keep getting better . . . finally getting out and having one good year . . . one great year. . . ." He hesitated for a second. The possibility of having only one great year was painfully disquieting. He slowly started to speak again, his words weighted with anger and bitterness. "Then . . . one person . . . one person . . . can finish you for good."

The room was silent.

Skyline was the only hospital in which Lapin could work. He found an office nearby and began his private practice. Oddly enough, he shared office space with a long-time Korn associate who viewed the entire situation impartially. "Business is business," he'd say. "If you can bring patients in here, you can help pay the rent. That's all I care about. Case closed."

***

Together Lapin and Jodie contacted every person he'd treated while working with Korn and informed them of the recent change and his new address. They cautiously worded their letter to avoid saying anything detrimental about Korn, just stating that they'd dissolved their "partnership" and that Lapin was now on his own.

It was a tough month, but what else was new! Lapin couldn't remember the last time he'd had an easy one. He just kept going . . . not giving up . . . not letting down . . . just working and working . . . harder, longer.

A general surgeon's private practice usually takes eight to ten years to develop--eight to ten years of

30

entertaining with those all-important dinner and social functions to painstakingly amass a patient referral list. Lapin didn't have eight to ten years; he had to create a successful practice immediately. The best way to do that is to be where the patients are, in the hospital emergency room. He practically moved in, doing emergency surgery on trauma patients who had no attending physician of their own.

To build his practice with that kind of intensity, Lapin would have to spend more time away from home and Maureen. She was still in school, taking riding lessons, and looking for a house that Lapin was convinced he couldn't afford.

Finally, she found it. It was on top of a mountain in Tustin. She was thrilled with the large, old, stately Spanish motif.

There's no way, Lapin thought, *that we can possibly afford this house. No way.*

The realtor just stood by and watched. There wasn't a reason in the world for him to do any more selling. Maureen was doing it all.

"Look at the size of the dining room," she bubbled. "We can have twice as many people for sit-down dinners."

"Doesn't matter how many people can sit down if you can't afford it," Lapin affirmed in a kind manner. But, it was as if she didn't even hear him.

"Look at this back bedroom. I'm going to convert this into my office. We can put files here and. . . ."

"Maureen," he interrupted, "we don't even have enough for the down payment. I've had my own practice for the sum total of thirty days. Some time . . . that's all I'm asking for . . . some time to get the business going."

"Ron," she whispered, equally firm, "I do the books, remember? We've done fantastically well for the first month of a private surgical practice. It's going to be fine."

"The down payment?" he asked.

She lowered her voice so the realtor wouldn't hear. "We can borrow it. . . ."

Lapin shook his head and shrugged with a heavy sigh. "I've got to get back to the hospital."

The realtor smiled.

Maureen was right. They could have twice as many people for sit-down dinners. And they did--three times a week. Other doctors loved the house, her gourmet cooking, and the witty, stimulating conversations around the massive fireplace in the high-ceilinged living room.

Lapin usually made it to the dinner parties, but sometimes Maureen willingly gave them by herself. She began to utilize her interior decorating classes, and couldn't understand why Lapin refused to help her re-brick the kitchen when he got home from work at ten or ten-thirty at night.

"You don't care about the house," she would accuse.

"I care about paying for the house," he'd answer.

Their communication had dwindled into rare conversations. Ron and Maureen were the perfect couple only when entertaining. They were slowly drifting apart, and neither one was quite sure what to do about it.

Lapin was married to the hospital, and his practice grew rapidly as a result. Maureen continued searching to find herself.

At first, the other surgeons at Skyline respected Lapin. They admired his abilities and skills. Most, in fact, observed him in the operating room and were astounded by his speed and clarity of purpose. They marveled at the remarkable, almost psychic insight he showed in pinpointing internal problems and correcting them without undue loss of time. They knew he was a special man and a gifted surgeon. Some even went so far as to publicly announce him as their first choice if they themselves ever needed a surgeon. That was a high compliment indeed.

The same thing that happened at Hope began to recur. Rumors started to surface. "Unnecessary surgery," they whispered behind his back. In spite of the fact that Lapin exhausted every effort to treat his patients without surgery, other surgeons soon felt he was taking business away from them, too.

Lapin's practice skyrocketed. The simple truth was that he was better than his jealous peers and was always available. The Spring Medical Group, a team of doctors who'd been taking care of nearly all of the surgery and medicine at Skyline, resented Lapin's intrusive practice and aggressively went after him.

The same surgeons who had praised Lapin's abilities and had personally chosen to go under his knife if the need arose, now began to look more closely at his daily surgical schedule. Realizing that Lapin per-formed more surgery than all six of them combined made

32

them resentful of his talents and success.

They questioned his charts unreasonably. "Why did you do this, that, or the other?" They were after-the-fact questions. They were minor, picky, insignificant questions without relevance or substance. It was "Monday morning quarterbacking" at its finest. Nevertheless, they were questions that had to be answered as a matter of hospital policy. The pretext of patient care is always a respectable way to curtail a doctor and is indeed a formidable weapon.

The more time Lapin spent answering their questions, the less time he could spend in the operating room. "Something" was found wrong with nearly every one of his charts. By using this ploy, the other surgeons felt that cases normally going to Lapin would now go to them.

They were wrong. Lapin's reputation had preceded him. He was not only personally requested, but actually waited for whenever possible.

Resentments grew, and the list of patients' charts that were unjustly challenged grew proportionately. Working relationships were undeniably strained.

Over the next three months, Lapin found himself spending more time playing politics and defending his charts and procedures than he spent operating. And the man never was much of a politician.

He was disillusioned, disenchanted, angry, and hurt. Thoughts about leaving California--and even the medical profession--began to creep into his mind.

Why me? he questioned. *Why don't they just leave me alone and take care of themselves and their own patients? I'm just trying to do the best I can at what I know how to do.* The questions of course went unanswered, but his inner tension grew at an accelerated pace.

Summer had nearly ended and Lapin could hardly wait for Ari's visit. They were going to have such fun at this reunion! Anticipating their time together took some of the strain off things at the hospital.

To alleviate the constant petty complaining, Lapin turned more and more to performing operations that other surgeons refused. That way, he reasoned, the other doctors wouldn't be blinded by jealousy or the fear of him taking their patients.

How could they? he logically deduced. *If they're given the opportunity and turn it down, how could they possibly complain when I end up doing it?*

Little did he know!

He was performing exceedingly difficult operations on patients who'd been abandoned and forgotten, and he was doing so with an astonishing degree of success.

Still the senseless complaints were lodged. Still the jealousy grew and festered.

Ron Lapin chose to put it all behind him for a couple of days so he could become completely involved with Ari's visit. Adrenalin surged through his body as the anticipation excited his senses.

***

Lapin looked at his watch and smiled at the realization of missing lunch again. He'd spent the last hour and a half in the phone booth, talking with patients and doctors and attorneys from all over the country. It was time to stop now; it was time just for Ari.

Just as he left the booth and turned toward the huge plate-glass window, the giant TWA airplane rolled to a stop. His heartbeat quickened. He took a deep breath and walked to the deplaning portal.

Anxious people awaiting loved ones surrounded him. The air was charged with electricity. East Coast flights have a way of creating excitement as the passengers begin to exit. Lapin became immersed in a raging sea of emotional reunions that jolted his memory. It brought back to mind the long separation, the pain, the void in his life, and the long legal battles he persistently fought and lost in his quest for more time with Ari.

He remembered initially surrendering to Rowena over the custody issue because he couldn't afford a lawyer to match her New York Fifth Avenue superstar. Lapin got Ari two days a month and one week a year. She got everything else.

Their second legal encounter was in the small county courthouse in Mount Holly, New Jersey. He wanted more time with his son; she wanted more money. She came to court with a flashy, animated Newark attorney dressed in a brown velvet suit. Lapin used a young Mount Holly lawyer who was familiar with local politics. Rowena sat quietly crocheting a small replica of the American flag. She was the perfect picture of motherhood and apple pie all rolled into one, acting so angelic and innocent. He watched as she took the stand and lied to the old judge. *What a charade, what a sick, ugly game she played with Ari's life*, he thought to himself. He lost and she won once again.

Too, he remembered the occasion when Ari never arrived at the Los Angeles Airport at the designated time.

Rowena had promised to let him stay in California for one year, but reneged at the last moment. It was a year later when Lapin finally found out what had really happened. Before leaving for the airport, Rowena had warned Ari that it would be his fault if his stepfather Norman had another heart attack. What a heavy guilt trip to place on such young shoulders. . . .

He remembered and remembered.

Off came the endless chain of passengers: nuns, students, businessmen, families, vacationers. . . .

There was Ari. Lapin studied the youngster for a long moment, a smile of parental satisfaction lighting up his face. He glowed with warm, loving pride. Ari stood on his tiptoes, trying to see over the crowd to spot his father. His eyes swept first left, then right. Then their eyes met.

There was a motionless moment of unspoken communication between father and son. Their eyes expressed the deep love they held for each other.

Slowly, they walked toward one another, never altering the direction or the intensity of their stare. The distractions of a terminal--the P.A. announcements, the crowds, everything--became muffled. Their shared purpose was all that existed for them: to reach one another.

The embrace was so warm, so tender, so very loving.

The words could flow now. The conversation raced non-stop in their effort to catch up on just about everything. "How're you feeling? How are things in school? What've you been doing? Can't believe how much you've grown." And eventually came the elaborate, detailed plans for the visit, from the places they were going to go to the things they were going to see and do. Lapin had the whole itinerary outlined in advance. That kind of preplanning was a habit he'd developed over the years.

His strategy was to envision events before they took place. After foreseeing the desired outcome, he'd plan the course of action necessary to achieve those results. This approach worked particularly well with his surgical cases.

Before each operation, he'd sit alone quietly and visualize the complete procedure. By methodically reviewing the entire process--from the exact location of his incision . . . to what he'd find once inside the body--he could mentally examine all potential problems and conclude with the most appropriate solution. By using this mental checklist to prepare, he knew what to expect and how to deal with it before he ever started.

The proud father waited at the baggage area with his son. There were throngs of people milling around, anxious to be on their way. Ari explained how he'd developed the habit of reading the newspaper each day, the *New York Times*, and asked if he could run to the newsstand to get a paper while they waited for the suitcases. "Of course," the beaming father replied.

Lapin watched as the boy elbowed his way through the crowd. He was proud of his son and thrilled that they were together. He hoped with all his heart that Ari was proud of him, too. It's difficult enough just being a father, but when you try to be one from three thousand miles away, the undertaking assumes new, monumental proportions.

Time, distance, and circumstances tug dispassionately at all relationships. Lapin was grateful for this opportunity to further cement the bond between them. He felt happy and guilt-free.

A few minutes later, the luggage began its slow descent down the conveyor belt. The crowd pushed and shoved as they jockeyed for a position around the carousel. Lapin looked for Ari and could see him coming in the distance. But something was definitely different about the way Ari looked. Something had dramatically changed.

The excitement that filled his face earlier had deteriorated into a troubled face with a distant, questioning expression. Lapin was concerned for his son and wondered what could have possibly happened at the newsstand to create such a severe turnaround in the boy's demeanor.

The youngster walked at a slow determined pace as if on a dubious mission. The questioning look seemed to intensify with each step as he came closer and closer.

Lapin, generally able to read the boy like a book, was now bewildered. He knew that something had happened. *But what? What?* He waited by the carousel until Ari reached him. Neither spoke as they came face to face.

Ari's dark eyes were clouded with an indeterminate fear. Doubt permeated his entire being. The boy was confused--that much was crystal clear. He opened his mouth to speak, but no words came out. He stared at his father as he slowly shook his head from side to side.

"What?" Lapin finally asked. "What?"

The boy hesitated, his disbelieving stare even more pronounced. Then he whispered . . . almost pleaded, "Why?"

Ari handed Lapin the newspaper, but instead of the *New York Times* it was the *Los Angeles Times*. He unfolded it so that his father could clearly see the bold, sweeping headline on the first page. It read, "Well-Known Surgeon Accused of Unnecessary Operations," and the sub-heading in type almost as large read, "Treats Jehovah's Witnesses. . . ."

Lapin stared at the headline, transfixed. He was unable at the moment to respond or think rationally. He looked into Ari's eyes and saw his son's pain--a pain that only Lapin's personal touch could heal completely. He replayed Ari's whispered plea over and over, *Why? Why? Why?*

2

Maria's eyes snapped open. Her pain was greater than any she had ever experienced. The lower left side of her abdomen felt as if a fire of hot coals was burning inside her. It felt like she was being ripped open from repeated stabs with a dull, serrated knife.

She pressed both hands against her side in an unsuccessful attempt to ease the pain. Silent tears fell from her eyes. She was sweating profusely. Her agony intensified as she lay there defenselessly. Shooting pains brought on uncontrollable spasms that shook the bed more violently with each attack. It was as though a ferocious wild animal inside her clawed savagely at her body in an attempt to escape.

"Maria, what is it?" Dennis whispered urgently. She was gasping for air and couldn't answer. Her silent tears gave way to open sobs. The pain was unbelievable--far beyond what she could bear.

"Is it the baby?" Dennis asked, quickly wishing he hadn't. *Stupid, stupid, stupid*, he thought to himself. *Of course it isn't the baby. It can't possibly be the baby. She's only two and a half months pregnant.*

Maria was biting the inside of her mouth, trying to control her suffering. There was another shooting pain. She cried out, but the piercing scream brought no relief. Dennis raced to the other side of the bed to see what was happening. He looked at Maria's face, touched it, and tried to comfort her.

The anguish in her eyes and the strained contortions of her facial muscles convinced him she needed much more than any comforting touch or reassuring words he could possibly offer.

"We're going to the hospital," he said, attempting

to control his tears. His voice was filled with compassion for his wife, but he managed not to show his fear. "Lie still. Everything is going to be just fine."

Maria was moaning as she rocked back and forth. Despite her pain, she responded with a faint smile and weak nod.

Dennis reached for her housecoat and gently wrapped it around her. Then he tried to help her sit up on the edge of the bed, but she doubled over in pain. Even with his help, it was impossible for her to sit up straight.

"You okay?" he inquired hopefully. Dennis changed his clothes as quickly as possible, never taking his eyes off the frail woman he loved so dearly.

He finished dressing, went to her side and asked, "Can you walk?" He put his arm around her to help, but her knees buckled like jelly and she very nearly fainted. Fortunately Dennis had enough of a hold on her to prevent her from falling. There was another pain, another cry of agony.

Dennis lifted her trembling body into his arms. She seemed so weightless. Slowly he carried her through the house, constantly offering words of comfort. She didn't respond.

"Hold on, babe . . . everything's going to be just fine . . . hold on. . . ." With great care he placed her on the front seat of the car and closed the door behind her. She was still bent over and leaned against it for support. He drove cautiously, avoiding major bumps and potholes.

The nearest hospital, he thought frantically, *no time to try and find our doctor. I've just got to get to an emergency room. Just got to.* St. Francis was only ten or twelve blocks away, yet the drive seemed like an eternity. Holding Maria's hand as they drove, he whispered reassuring thoughts and offered prayers.

Dennis burst through the double swinging doors. "My wife's outside!" he shouted. "Please!"

A doctor, nurse, and two aides ran to the waiting car. They carefully placed her on a cart and wheeled her inside.

"What happened?" the doctor asked. He took Maria's pulse as they walked.

"I don't know," Dennis answered, panic consuming his voice. "She was in a cold sweat and doubled over with pain when I woke up."

"Slow down, son," the doctor said. "You did the right thing by getting her here as fast as you did."

"But can you . . . I mean, will you. . . ." Dennis' voice trailed off as he watched Maria being wheeled quickly into another room.

He felt a hand on his shoulder and heard the doctor's voice. "We're going to do everything possible. What we need is for you to calm down and give our admitting nurse some information. Okay?"

Dennis sensed the doctor's compassion and nodded slowly, never looking away from the room down the hall.

"We're going to do a complete examination, find out exactly what the problem is and get it fixed. You go see the admitting nurse and I'll be out as soon as we've finished."

"She's pregnant, doctor," Dennis whispered. With renewed strength, he added, "She wants this baby more than anything."

The doctor acknowledged him with a sympathetic smile and turned toward the room.

"Doctor," Dennis called out to recapture his attention, "I just want her to be all right . . . that's all."

Dennis turned and methodically wove his way to the waiting room and found an empty chair. Even at this hour the hallway was a flurry of activity. Illness has no consideration for the clock; it's timeless, but never timely.

Dennis was distraught and confused. He didn't understand what could possibly have happened to Maria that would bring them to an emergency room at ten-thirty at night. His emotional reactions were quite normal, but were quickly dispelled as he closed his eyes tightly and began to pray.

They weren't the prayers one might expect under such circumstances. Dennis understood that Maria's condition was very serious, but the words he used were not coming as a novice prayer offering to beg some unknown Deity for a break. He wasn't pleading for a second opportunity to put his life in order. He wasn't blindly offering to lead a life of purity and dedication in exchange for some Divine Being sparing the life of a loved one.

Dennis' religious life was in order. His peace had been made with the God he'd known intimately since

41

he was baptized at the age of twelve. His prayers, therefore, were similar to those he had offered to Jehovah for as long as he could remember.

The Scriptures that he mentally quoted gave him strength. He put his complete trust in Jehovah. His heart became fearless, but his knees still shook violently. The belief that replaced his fear was the absolute knowledge that death was not permanent, but rather like falling asleep until awakened by Jehovah in the resurrection.

The nurse's soft, clear voice quietly interrupted Dennis' meditation. He walked to her desk and mechanically answered all the questions about insurance, childhood illnesses, her last visit to a doctor, and the family physician. After every question, he wanted to ask the nurse to check and see if the doctors had made any headway, and to look in on Maria to find out if she was all right or at least in less pain.

He kept his questions to himself, deciding to follow the doctor's advice to the letter. After all, the doctor said he'd talk to him as soon as they finished the examination, so Dennis was determined to wait patiently.

The nurse could sense Dennis' concern. When she finished her paperwork, she promised that if he returned to the waiting room, she'd take a quick look and give him a progress report.

An emergency room is perhaps the most trying place in a hospital. Waiting there for someone to be examined creates more anxiety than nearly anywhere else in the building. The wait invariably seems longer because you have no clear-cut idea of the progress, if any, being made. There's no way of knowing exactly what's going on behind the examining room doors.

There's only the waiting . . . and the anxiety . . . and the perpetual fear of the unknown. It's a room sown with seeds of negative thoughts powerful enough to choke out anything so fragile as hope.

Dennis studied the other faces in the room--faces afraid to make eye contact with one another. He instinctively wanted to help these people cope with their own personal pain. He wanted to talk to them and share the knowledge that, by means of God's Kingdom, all man's problems would be solved.

It was this period in his life more than any other

that really tested Dennis' belief, trust, and faith. Dennis was solid and mature in his faith. There was never one selfish silent scream of *Why me, God? Why have you done this to me? Why am I being punished?*

Instead, there was a calm inner peace of understanding that had taken root and grown as he himself had developed into manhood. He had come to appreciate the meaning of the Scriptures as they were taught at the meetings, Bible study groups, and intense discussions specifically designed to give understanding of the absolute Word of God. He had complete knowledge of a better, timeless existence in paradise--a paradise that he'd talked about and explained to others all his life.

So it was logical that Dennis' thoughts would naturally turn away from himself and focus on the poor lost souls occupying the dimly lit room with him. To any who would listen, he would offer to explain the better way of life that was coming soon.

His concern and deep love were still in the examining room with Maria. But his first and foremost dedication was to his God, the Almighty God who alone provided the strength to sustain him.

The nurse returned and explained that Maria was still being examined and that no conclusive diagnosis had been reached yet. The comforting news was that Maria had been given an injection that was strong enough to diminish her pain, though it wasn't enough to make her unconscious during the preliminary testing.

Each minute seemed like an hour slowly ticking away. He flinched each time the door down the hall opened and a physician in a lab coat came out. *How long?* he thought, looking at his watch. *How long? Only half an hour? Impossible.* He tapped the face of his watch to make sure it was still running. It had seemed like three or four times that long. *Why doesn't someone come out to tell me what's going on?*

Finally, Maria's doctor came through the door and walked purposefully toward Dennis. His face was expressionless and impossible for Dennis to read. The doctor was direct--there wasn't time for small talk. "Your wife has what we call an ectopic pregnancy, sometimes referred to as a tubal pregnancy."

"What does that mean?" Dennis asked. He then

listened intently as the doctor explained.

"It means that the fetus has been improperly implanted in the tube rather than the uterus." The doctor used his right hand to draw diagrams in the air as he spoke. "The fetus has ruptured the tubal wall and your wife is bleeding internally."

Dennis was speechless. He knew that Maria was in trouble. The doctor studied him for a moment to make sure he was all right before he continued. "The primary problem is that she's having massive bleeding from the rupture. We have to go in immediately and stop the bleeding."

"Can you?" Dennis asked. "I mean, can you stop the bleeding?"

"I'm sure we can, but we have to do it right away. Her hemoglobin count, the blood count, is down to six-point-five grams. It's already dangerously low."

"What's it supposed to be?"

"Normal is about fourteen or fifteen. She's probably lost most of the blood in the last twelve hours. She's in real bad shape. We have to operate right now." The doctor hesitated for just a second, then added, "If we don't, she'll die."

"Do whatever you have to do, doctor. She just has to be okay--she has to."

"We'll take care of it. She's in the best of hands." The doctor was warm and understanding. He displayed a real capacity to reach out and care. Dennis could feel his compassion and was appreciative.

"Doctor?" He hesitated, almost afraid to ask. "What about the baby?"

The doctor emitted a low, heavy sigh. *This is the worst part of being a physician*, he thought, *absolutely the worst part*. "The fetus isn't going to live. It's impossible to re-implant it correctly in the uterus . . . I'm sorry . . . right now we have to deal with Maria's life . . . right now."

Dennis understood the urgency and nodded in agreement. The pain of losing the baby would have to wait. Right now Maria was all that mattered. He followed the doctor to the nurses' station and watched as he picked up the medical questionnaire.

"My team is here," the doctor said, "my assistant, the anesthesiologist, and the two scrub nurses. I've called for a specialist to scrub with us . . . just in case things get complicated. He'll be here in about half an hour and we'll start as soon as he arrives.

The nurses are prepping Maria now. I gave her a sedative so she's not having any pain."

"Good. Thank you."

"We have some forms for you to sign."

Dennis nodded again. *Of course*, he thought, *the forms*. "I suppose you have the standard blood forms?" Dennis asked matter-of-factly.

The doctor gave him a blank, quizzical look. He truly didn't understand the question. "What blood forms?"

"The standard release forms saying you agree not to give Maria any blood." Dennis hesitated as he spoke the painful words, "and that we release you from any liability . . . for anything . . . if anything should go wrong."

The doctor shook his head, not quite believing what he had just heard. "Perhaps you didn't understand me. Your wife is dangerously near death. She's lost a tremendous amount of blood."

"I understand what you're saying, doctor." Dennis' voice was totally controlled. "Surely Maria told you while you were examining her."

"Told me what?" Annoyance crept into his voice.

"That she will not allow any blood to be put into her body."

"She has no choice. If we don't transfuse her, she'll die."

Dennis looked at the doctor, wishing that somehow, someway he could make him understand, but inwardly knowing the heavy odds against it. "My wife will not have blood put inside her."

The doctor was stunned. He stared at the young man facing him. His tone was understandably serious. "You're wife is twenty-two years old. The two of you have a two-year-old baby at home who needs a mother. I know that we can save her life. Standing here arguing about a blood transfusion is not only pointless, it's absolutely ridiculous."

"Doctor," Dennis interrupted, "we're not arguing. There never was--nor is there now--any question; because of our respect for the sanctity of blood, Maria will not have a transfusion."

The momentary silence was interrupted only by the normal emergency room sounds. The doctor broke the temporary stalemate with a forced whisper, pushed through his teeth. "Your wife is going to die. . . ."

Dennis enunciated clearly, "Then she'll die."

45

"Why? For what possible reason?"

"Because abstaining from blood is a command from God. It's a direct order written many times in the Bible."

The eyes that moments before had shown such compassion turned swiftly to anger.

He'd taken an oath, the Hippocratic oath, an absolute oath, to preserve life to the best of his ability. The doctor felt he had the ability to prolong the life of this young woman, but only with the precious life-giving substance, blood. He forced one more attempt at logic. "I can accept your religious beliefs," he began, "but we're talking about something greater than that. We're talking life and death, right here and now."

"Actually," Dennis answered, "that's where we don't quite agree. You're talking about life here, right now. However, Maria and I are talking about everlasting life." Dennis could see that the doctor didn't understand, but finished, "We refuse to violate God's Holy Word and risk losing everlasting life under His Kingdom."

Just then a nurse interrupted their conversation. "Excuse me, doctor. There's a gunshot wound in room three. Could you give us a hand until it's time for Maria's surgery?"

The doctor dismissed her with a wave, indicating that he'd be right there. He returned his attention to Dennis. "I'm going back to work now. There's someone down there who's interested in me saving their life, and they're willing to let me do my job the way I was trained to do it."

Dennis started slowly, emotion choking his words, "I want . . . I want you to save Maria's life, too."

The doctor shook his head--not saying no--just not understanding. "What religion are you anyway? What religion would let you stand here and allow your wife to die?"

"We're Jehovah's Witnesses."

"Right." This time the tone was sarcastic, and the head shaking was to express disgust more than anything else.

"Will you help her?"

"Without blood?"

"Yes."

"You're absolute about it?"

"Yes."

46

"Then I want you to find another doctor, and I want you to remove her from this hospital immediately." The doctor grabbed Maria's chart from the counter and began to scribble some notes on it. "I'm noting here that you've refused medical attention and have removed your wife of your own free will. I want you to sign it."

"I want you to do what you can to help her." Dennis was pleading now.

"I'm going to help somebody who'll let me. I'm through talking to you. If you won't let me give her blood, she's going to die . . . and I don't want her dying here." He handed Dennis the chart for his signature.

"What would you suggest I do now?"

"Without a blood transfusion?"

Dennis nodded.

"Might as well take her home and let her die there."

"Isn't there anyone who'll do the operation without giving her blood? Anyone?"

"Not that I know of. Besides, anybody who tries it would have to be crazy. Her blood count's too low."

"Can Maria stay here just a little longer while I try to find someone?"

All compassion, kindness, and understanding were now gone. Doctors don't like to be told what to do, ever. His tone was firm and final, "I'll give you an hour. I want her out of here."

Dennis watched in disbelief as the doctor turned and walked away.

***

The conversation during dinner had been strained, but no more than usual. Tension had become so commonplace that it evolved into an accepted norm. Maureen spent most of the main course complaining about all the improvements the house needed. It wasn't at all what Lapin needed to hear--not today. He nodded politely and gave an occasional grunt of acknowledgement.

"Ron," she said teasingly, "sometimes I honestly think you don't hear a word I say." Her perception seemed to be improving.

Lapin sighed, "I'm just starting to wonder if it's worth it. Any of it."

"What? Worth what?"

"I'm a good surgeon. I do my job well. I don't bother anybody . . . I just don't know why they keep coming after me."

Maureen smiled. "Because you annoy people. You can't make pleasant small talk with other doctors. You demand perfection from the staff at all times. You do more surgery than the rest of them and it's threatening. Certainly you can see that."

Lapin could see it, but he didn't understand it. It made no sense at all.

"We had another committee meeting today," he said. "Almost the entire two hours were spent going over my patients' charts."

"It'll be all right."

"I'm the one who examined the patients. I know what's wrong with them and what they need. I had a second opinion confirming mine in almost every case. Then after the fact, they take my charts apart, point by point, looking for anything that might possibly be out of order. Any chart can be taken apart. Hell, I don't have picture perfect charts, just people who walk out of the hospital alive." Lapin, angry and irritated, continued, "The worst thing was that Doctor Abrams told one of my patients she didn't need the operation I've got scheduled for tomorrow." His voice level had raised to the point where several people from surrounding tables were now privy to their conversation. "Can you believe that? I mean, can you actually imagine that?"

Maureen pressed her index finger to her lips. "It'll be all right. Just relax."

"I just don't know if it's worth it any more."

"Everything's going to be fine. Don't worry about it." The waiter stopped and refilled their coffee cups. Lapin withdrew back into his private world and continued to worry silently.

"I have some good news," Maureen added. "I've been talking with several people about it. . . ."

"About what?" he asked.

"I'm coming to that. I've been doing some reading lately and looking into it, and I've decided that I'm going to take acting classes."

"Acting classes," he repeated. His expression didn't change. "Acting classes?"

Maureen nodded. It was an energetic response. She was excited that she'd told him.

"Why?"

48

"Why? Because I'm going to be an actress, that's why."

Her enthusiasm was unshared. "Who's going to take care of the house, and the books, and the business while you're taking . . . acting classes?"

"I am," she said. "It's only one night a week, and it's something I've wanted to do for a long time."

"Since when?"

"A long time. I know I can be a good actress. It's important to me."

Lapin was silent for a moment, sipping his coffee. This wasn't exactly the conversation he'd planned on having. "I don't think it's a good time. Not right now."

"The classes start next week."

He knew that she'd made up her mind and that any argument against it, or even a continued discussion, would be fruitless. "So," he said with resolve, "where are these classes?"

"Los Angeles."

"L.A.!" he exclaimed. He just sat and shook his head.

The silence was interrupted by the beeper on his belt. Since the conversation seemed to be over, he pushed his chair back and stood looking down at Maureen.

"Ron," she said, eyes sparkling and alive, "it's an acting workshop at CBS. It's a great opportunity for me. Nothing else is going to change."

He stared at the floor several moments before replying. "I don't know why, but I have a strange feeling that if you start this acting thing . . . our marriage will fall apart."

Maureen was speechless, unable at the moment to defend her plans. She watched as her husband turned and walked toward the bank of telephones in the lobby.

The answering service told Lapin about the emergency call they'd just received. He knew the number was for St. Francis before the girl had a chance to tell him. After waiting several rings, the receptionist answered and had Dennis take the call.

"This is Doctor Lapin," he responded in a monotone.

"Thank you for returning my call, doctor." Dennis was a man running out of time and spoke quickly. Lapin could sense the desperation in his voice.

"What can I do for you?"

"It's my wife . . . they say she has a tubal

pregnancy and she's going to die . . . unless someone operates on her right away."

"Why won't they do it there?"

"They refuse to do it without giving her blood."

That was news to Lapin. He'd never heard anything like that before. "I don't get it. Why can't she have blood?"

"It's against our religious beliefs and convictions. We're Jehovah's Witnesses and we believe that it's against God's will to put blood into our bodies. Can you do the operation without giving her blood?"

Ron Lapin's first concern was the patient's safety, and his second thought was the challenge of doing something no one else would do. He looked into the dining room toward Maureen. "Jehovah's Witnesses, huh?"

"Yes, sir." There was a long silent pause, then Dennis explained, "Dr. Lapin, they're making us leave here soon. We don't have much time. I've already called seventeen surgeons and they've all turned us down. Could you help us? Please?"

Not getting involved would have been the easy, safe thing to do, but Lapin reacted to the urgency on the other end of the phone. "I'll call you back in five minutes and let you know if I can help. Ten at the most."

"Thank you. I'll be waiting."

As the line went dead, Lapin looked toward the ceiling. "Why me?" he thought out loud, but he wasn't surprised that he didn't get an answer. He smiled to himself, then quickly dialed another number.

A sleepy voice answered, "Hello. . . ."

"George, it's me, Ron."

Doctor Gordon wasn't very happy. "Do you know what time it is?"

"I'll explain tomorrow. I've got a question. It's important."

Gordon sat up in bed, turned on the light, and reached for his reading glasses. "Shoot."

"What do you know about the Jehovah's Witnesses?"

The man took the phone away from his ear and stared at it. Then he asked in dismay, "What did you say?"

"Jehovah's Witnesses. What do you know about them?"

"Are you out of your mind?"

"I got a call from a guy who says his wife is dying over at St. Francis. They won't operate because she refuses to take blood or something like that. Anyway,

50

he wants me to do the surgery. What do you think?"

"Go home and go to bed."

"And let her die?"

"It's not your problem." Lapin didn't say anything. "But it's going to be if you get involved."

The words "get involved" flashed through Lapin's mind. Somehow, he liked the sound of it; it had a nice ring. Involvement . . . complete involvement . . . what a fascinating challenge.

"Why shouldn't I get involved?"

"Look, Ron, those people are nothing but trouble." Gordon sounded sincere, like he was really trying to help.

"The Witnesses?"

"Right. They're all crazy. This blood thing is just too much. Some of them actually believe that stuff. I mean, they'd die before they'd take blood. They're nuts. Suicidal."

"Sounds to me like they've got a lot of faith."

Gordon could detect a sense of involvement in Lapin's voice. "C'mon, Ron, I'm telling you. It's not something you want to play with. You already have enough doctors wanting to shoot you out of the saddle and a case like this could finish you . . . especially in a conservative community like Orange County. Listen to me, Ron, and forget about it. Out here, the John Birch Society is on the left . . . don't be a hero."

Lapin smiled at the phone. "Thanks for your help, George."

"Wait a minute before you jump into this," Gordon said. "What's her blood count?"

"Didn't ask."

"Didn't ask. That's great. She might be too far gone already to even help. Have you thought about that?"

"Gotta' run, George. Thanks again."

"Call me. . . ." But Doctor Gordon's last words were spoken to a dial tone.

Another dime, seven more digits, and Dennis was back on the phone. "This is Doctor Lapin," he said again in the same monotone. "Do you know your wife's blood count?"

"Five and a half."

"Not good. Not good at all. That's less than half of what it should be."

"I know." There was an uncomfortable, long pause.

51

"Will you do it, doctor?"

There was no hesitation. "Transport your wife to Skyline Hospital. It'll take you about twenty minutes to make it. I'll meet both of you there and have everything arranged."

Again the silence. Then Dennis spoke. "Thank you, Doctor Lapin. You're the only one who. . . ."

"Save it," Lapin interrupted. "You can tell me how great I am later. First let's take care of your wife."

They hung up. Lapin made the necessary arrangements with his people at the hospital and then informed Maureen he was going to work that night--that's all, just that he was going to work. The drive from the restaurant to the hospital was quiet. They were each lost in their own thoughts--their own separate and private worlds.

Lapin went through a series of mental checklists. He was trying to imagine all the things he could conceivably find when he opened the abdomen. He was trying to imagine why he even said he'd do it in the first place. He opened the car door.

"Will you be late?"

He didn't respond. He was still lost in deep thought.

So she said it louder. "Will you be late?"

"I don't know." He was totally preoccupied. "I'll call you." After a moment, he remarked, "By the way, I've got a feeling you don't really want to be an actress at all. You want to be a star." He slammed the car door behind him and walked into the emergency room.

The ambulance hadn't arrived yet. He decided to wait downstairs so he could meet Dennis and Maria there before he scrubbed. His first major obstacle was the anesthesiologist whom he ran into as he walked through the swinging doors.

"We're pretty much set," the man said. "Isn't it kinda' shaky goin' in when she's lost half her blood? Shouldn't we build her count back up a couple of grams?"

"We'll be fine," Lapin said. "Everybody else ready?"

The other doctor nodded. "I forgot to ask, what's her blood type so I can have a good supply in the room? We're sure going to need it."

"I've already phoned it in. It's a rare type, but

we'll have all we need in plenty of time." Lapin had lied intentionally.

The answer seemed to satisfy the other doctor, and Lapin left for the operating room. Silently, he stood staring through the pane glass windows into the still darkness of the night. He could feel small beads of perspiration begin to form in the palms of his hands. He could feel the self-induced pressure and wondered for just an instant if he'd done the right thing.

It didn't take a genius to figure out that if he lost this patient it could signal the end of his career. All the years, all the study, all the learning--all riding on a patient that he'd never even seen.

So nobody else will do it, huh? he thought to himself. *Nobody else will respect their religious beliefs? Who knows, or right now even cares, if what they believe is right or wrong. Right now what matters is that a young woman is dying and no one else will help her.* Lapin respected other people's beliefs. He admired integrity. He was in awe of people who were willing to put their life on the line for a cause that they honored. *To be willing to actually die for something they believed in . . . those are rare individuals*, he thought. *Not many of them left.* The esteem he held for people with this degree of commitment had developed as a child in his native Israel where dedicated people are the norm and not the exception.

The ambulance arrived in a flurry of lights and sirens. Maria was taken directly to the operating room--it would be just as easy to examine her there. Lapin had already changed into his surgical greens and was ready to work, but he waited for Dennis to get out of the ambulance. Their warm handshake was more than sincere; the appreciation it showed transcended the flesh.

"Come upstairs with me," Lapin said. "We can talk on the way."

Dennis nodded. "What about checking her in?"

"You can do that while we're getting her ready. It'll save us some valuable time." A split-second thought flashed through their minds as they realized that the operation must be conducted with complete perfection--or they'd be checking a dead woman into the hospital.

No one ever likes thinking about a patient having

trouble on the table or possibly dying. And that was certainly true in this case.

"How far along is she?" Lapin asked on the elevator.

Dennis liked the man instantly. He liked the striking self-confidence he displayed in his own abilities. "Two and a half months," he answered.

The door opened and they walked in silence for a few steps. Dennis' voice was a little shaky as he posed a thought he didn't really want to accept. "They told me the fetus won't survive." He blinked several times and looked straight ahead.

Lapin had never been one to mince words--never. He'd learned that people generally wanted to hear the the truth straight out, not sugar-coated with false hope. Honesty, complete honesty, like commitment and integrity, is an uncommonly rare, precious human quality.

Dr. Lapin spoke slowly and carefully, making sure there could be no question about what he was saying. "If their diagnosis was correct, it probably will not survive." He waited for a second in case Dennis was going to say anything else. Lapin continued, "Our primary concern is Maria . . . okay?"

He put his hand on Dennis' shoulder and smiled. It was the first smile Dennis had seen from the man. And, actually, it was Lapin's first real smile in three days. That simple little gesture conveyed the warmth and concern he felt inside.

"Okay, doc," Dennis answered.

The doctor who was assisting Lapin came out of the operating room. "Ron . . . the blood count's down to four-point-eight."

Lapin nodded and turned back to Dennis. "Everything's going to be fine."

Dennis watched him disappear around the corner and, for some reason, felt a real confidence in the man. Then his thoughts returned to Jehovah and he asked for His guidance over the work Lapin was about to do, knowing that Maria's life was now in both their hands.

While Lapin was scrubbing, the anesthesiologist walked over to the sink. "Ron, that blood still hasn't come."

"It'll be here. We'll just start without it. She's losing a lot of blood. Run the saline solution in faster."

"I don't like it."

"We'll be fine. No problem. It'll be here."
Lapin's confidence was difficult to question. The
doctor then shrugged and returned to the room. Lapin
disliked any form of deception, but he knew this was
the only way he could keep his commitment to Dennis.
If he were to suggest performing surgery without
blood, the team might all walk out. Then the hospital
administration would become involved in a meeting to
discuss the issue, and probably would even call in
experts. None of this was going to help that girl or
stop her from bleeding to death. Her problem was
immediate. It required attention right now. He had
promised to respect their religious beliefs. He was
scared, but there was no way he could admit it.

Lapin scrubbed quickly and walked into the room. He
stared at the body on the table as one of the scrub
nurses helped him with his surgical gown and gloves.
Maria was nearly as white as the walls surrounding
her. It was frightening.

"Everybody ready?"

They all nodded, but the serious concern they felt
registered on their faces. This was an unusual case--
very unusual. Normally a patient with a hemoglobin
count this low would be given transfusions until the
blood count had reached the safe, acceptable level for
anesthesia: ten, eleven, or probably more. There
would also be ample blood in the room, just in case.

"Let's do it." Lapin walked to the table and picked
up the steel scalpel. It would be the only time he'd
hold it that night. A thick cloud of tension hovered
about the room. One of the nurses tried to lighten
the mood. "Anybody got a good prayer?"

"Somebody's already taking care of that," Lapin
replied.

He laid the steel blade on Maria's stomach and made
the initial incision. He felt his knees buckle
slightly as if brushed by a small charge of electricity. He was scared, but his deft, experienced
right hand didn't waver one centimeter. The six-inch
cut was straight and clean.

The assistant began to dab the bleeding skin with
lap sponges to improve the visibility. Then, without
being asked, he handed Lapin the electric knife. It's
an instrument, controlled by a foot pedal, that
requires considerable coordination.

The knife had been mastered by Lapin. He began to
deepen the incision with the five-inch-long blue

plastic scalpel.   It made a low-toned hum as it cut
through the fat, fascia, and muscle.   Each time a vein
was severed,   he laid   the   steel tip of the knife
against it to instantly cauterize the area and stop
the bleeding. It worked.

Clear plastic tubing from the suction device snaked
its way into a container, clearly measuring the blood
loss from the body. Lapin briefly glanced at it.
There were only a few drops so far, but he knew that
would change once he was through the peritoneum, the
thin membrane that lines the walls of the abdomen.

There was always the stark moment of anticipation--
just before actually opening a patient's abdomen--when
Lapin contemplated the unknown and prayed to God that
he might have the ability to correct whatever was
wrong.

"Suction. . . ." Lapin's voice was calm and in
total control. Maria's blood was drawn out of sight.
The knife broke through the peritoneum, the last
layer, exposing the inside of the pelvic area and
abdominal organs.

"Oh, no!" one of the nurses whispered. The abdomen
was filled with an estimated five units of blood--
clots as well as fresh blood. The team looked at one
another; a sight like this was rare.

"We're going to need that blood real bad," the
anesthesiologist said, pointing at the stomach area.

Lapin waved him off. "It's coming," he said. "More
suction." His voice was still the calm monotone they
had grown accustomed to hearing. The assistant rapidly filled the container with the siphoned blood. It
was impossible to see how bad the problem was until
the liquid had been drained away.

Lapin had been seeking a challenge, but he questioned if this was the right one. *Is it possible,* he
thought, *that this time I've bitten off too much?* It
was risky. It was an operation deemed unsafe by his
medical peers only hours before.

Sure, it was exciting and different! Adrenalin
pumped to his brain. He knew the procedure had to be
done hurriedly. He also knew he had absolutely no
margin for error.

The abdomen was clear enough to see now, though
blood still filled the area. There were several large
clots and a large, severed artery behind them pumping
blood out rapidly. It was blood that couldn't be
replaced--no matter what. That had been his promise.

56

He bent over the body and looked closer. The fetus had ruptured the left tube, which was now a large black mass. He reached inside and held it in his hand, then rapidly clamped the spurting artery.

Emotion must be non-existent in an operating room. All available time, effort, and energy must be directed to the task at hand. Emotional outpouring comes later, when you're alone. That's when you try to figure out what could have been done differently, perhaps better.

The assistant surgeon looked at Lapin. It was in his hands now. The support was there, but for all practical purposes, Lapin was alone--alone like never before. He looked around the room and realized that this truly was his solo flight. Without blood as a back-up, he was sixty feet in the air doing tricks never before performed, and all without a net.

Masterfully he used the knife and sutures to stop the bleeding. Ever so carefully he then removed the ovary and the left tube, which still held the fetus. Each blood clot was then taken out. He made a rapid yet thorough check to make sure everything else was all right.

"Start waking her up," he told the anesthesiologist, "I'm closing." There was a ring of deserved satisfaction in his voice.

"I just can't believe that damn blood didn't get up here," the anesthesiologist said, irritated. "Too damn risky. We were lucky."

"We're not out of the woods yet," Lapin replied.

"I know we're not. You still better give her at least four bags of blood in the intensive care unit."

"Right," Lapin agreed, knowing full well that he wouldn't.

Then both doctors quickly worked in tandem to close the three abdominal wall layers.

The assistant looked at the clock on the far side of the room. "Skin to skin . . . fifteen minutes!" That's the normal amount of time used from an initial incision to the final suture, with another fifteen minutes allotted to complete the procedure--that is, without any of Maria's complications. To Lapin, those fifteen minutes had seemed like an eternity.

"Congratulations, doctor." The comment came from one of the scrub nurses but was resounded by everyone in the room. They had just seen surgery at its finest, and they each recognized that fact.

Acknowledging their compliments with a nod, he suppressed a slight smile. *I did it,* he thought to himself. *I did it.*

Dennis sprang instantly from his chair the second Lapin appeared at the door. *Funny, Lapin thought, I know the anxiety is there, but somehow Dennis doesn't show it the way most people normally would. That's odd.*

Lapin motioned for Dennis to sit back down and he joined him. "There was no way we could save the baby," he said. "I'm sorry." He never pulled punches with a patient's family. Experience had taught him that being up-front and totally honest was the easiest way to deal with his own conscience.

Dennis nodded a painful acceptance. "Maria?" he quietly asked.

"We've stopped the bleeding . . . and I think she's going to be okay . . . but it's early and we're just going to have to wait and see. She's lost a lot of blood."

"Can I see her?"

"She's in the recovery room. As soon as she wakes up, we'll move her into intensive care. It'll be just as well if you go home and come back in the morning. It looks like you've had a rough night, too."

"I'd rather stay with her."

"I can understand that, but it'll get rather crowded." Dennis looked puzzled, until Lapin explained, "I'm going to stay with her myself."

"Oh," Dennis said. "Is that normal?"

"Normal is a blood count of fourteen, with a minimum of five units of blood in the operating room." Lapin seemed to be smiling. "That's normal."

"No blood, huh?"

"That's what I promised."

There was a look of resolve in Dennis' eyes that Lapin wanted somehow to know more about. It was a peaceful, serene kind of look that perhaps reflected the inner feeling Lapin personally searched for without success.

"Stop at admitting and give them whatever information they need," Lapin instructed. "I'll go down later this morning and finish the report."

Dennis nodded. He stood and started to leave, then stopped at the door and turned back toward the young surgeon. "You're a good person, doctor. Jehovah watches over you."

58

Lapin, momentarily speechless, stared straight at the man. What do you say to a comment like that? Words wouldn't come.

"One more question," Dennis said.

"Shoot."

"Well, first . . . thank you." Lapin just shrugged. "No, I really mean it. Thank you, not only for doing what you did for Maria, but also for doing what nobody else would do."

There was a hushed moment, then Lapin replied, "That's your question?"

"No, this is. . . ." The room became blatantly still. "Would you have let her die . . . rather than give her blood?"

"Yes." Lapin was undauntly concise and direct.

"Thank you." Dennis turned and walked away. Lapin listened to the footsteps as they echoed down the hall. *What kind of a man is that?* he wondered. *What kind of people are these--these Jehovah's Witnesses?* He was lost in thought with a hundred unanswered questions formulating in his mind.

A scrub nurse walked to the door. "Doctor Lapin, Maria's waking up and wants something for pain."

"Wait till her vital signs stabilize, then give her some Demerol." He untied the surgical mask from around his neck as he walked down the hallway. *Maybe I'll find out,* he thought. Then looking through the door of the recovery room at the young, stark white body lying on the gurney, he reflected, *Maybe I'll just find out.*

He stayed with Maria all that night, checking her vital signs and giving her massive amounts of intravenous iron to increase her blood count. She was stable, but remained in critical condition. Lapin slept in a chair outside her cubicle, nodding and dozing. Over the years, he'd acquired the ability to sleep in five and ten minute stretches.

A hand gently shook his shoulder. "Doctor, you're due in surgery in fifteen minutes."

He looked at his watch. It was six-fifteen. He checked the cardiac monitor hooked to Maria's frail body. It indicated the stability that he'd hoped for, although she was still as white as the hospital sheets around her. Things looked as good as could be expected. Only time would tell.

The next operation was routine, simple by comparison. Dr. Lapin's new group of assistants had of course heard the news of Maria's operation. It had spread quickly throughout the surgical staff. Their consensus of opinion deemed the operation too risky. They said he shouldn't have operated on a patient with a hemoglobin count below ten. Some suggested he should have obtained a court order to transfuse Maria . . . to protect her child at home . . . to guarantee the little girl a mother. They were filled with conflicting sentiments: admiring his courage; questioning his judgment.

Lapin didn't respond to their thoughts, feelings, or innuendos. He went about the business at hand and removed the patient's gall bladder while the the team continued to chatter away.

Then another thought occurred to him about what had been different in Maria's case. Physicians are notorious for operating room chitchat during surgery . . . which was exactly what they all were doing right that minute. But earlier that morning, when Maria was lying on that table, it was different. The room had been totally silent then.

From the first moment he touched Maria with the scalpel until the final suture, there had been no idle chatter. The only words spoken were the ones relevant to the procedure. Isn't that interesting? The seriousness of the case and the intensity of the attending team had been unlike anything they'd ever experienced before.

Lapin asked his assistant to finish closing the patient's skin and left the room. He had about a half hour before his next case and he wanted to look in on Maria and check her blood count.

Dennis was waiting outside the ICU. Lapin was fascinated by the aura of confidence in the young man. It was indeed a rarity to see that in someone waiting outside this room.

"Good morning," Lapin said. "Looks like you got some sleep."

Dennis nodded and smiled. "A little; how 'bout yourself?"

"Enough."

The two men studied each other for an instant before Dennis spoke. "How's our patient?"

Lapin smiled, "Let's go see."

During the confusion of the emergency, Dennis hadn't noticed that Maria's skin was actually bone white. Now he was clearly shaken. Lapin understood Dennis' shock and explained that the color would return as her blood count increased.

Her vital signs were good. She was stable and had had a restful night. She was conscious but still weak. Conversation was difficult through the oxygen mask she wore. Dennis held her hand as Lapin explained the details of the operation. He intention-ally omitted an important detail. Maria, fading in and out of a light sleep, was too fatigued to question it herself.

Dennis looked at Lapin, then Maria, then back. "I have to tell her."

Lapin gave no indication of his support or opposition to what he'd just interpreted as a request for his opinion. Dennis' love was apparent as he looked deeply into Maria's eyes. He spoke slowly, hoping that she'd understand.

"Maria . . . honey . . . we lost the baby." The room was silent for what felt like a long time as they waited for her reaction. But Maria was too physically spent to show the emotion she felt inside. A single tear slid across her cheek and dropped to the sheet as she stared at the ceiling. Even though her eyes were dull, her pain was clearly evident.

Dennis was strong. His eyes, too, swelled with tears. His voice remained steady so that his words might strengthen her, "Right now, babe, the important thing is you . . . just you. Doctor Lapin says you're gonna be all right. You just have to hold on."

She rolled her head slightly to the right, giving her an extended view of her doctor, the man who'd just saved her life. "Thank you," she whispered, then lapsed back into sleep.

"Can I stay here?" Dennis asked. "I'd like to pray with her."

Lapin nodded approval, impressed with the honesty of his patient's husband. Dennis seemed to possess an inbred serenity that captured the surgeon's attention. "I want to talk with you later," he said as he left them with their prayers.

Hospital coffee has a distinctive flavor--a sterilized taste in every hot, steaming cup. It isn't necessarily bad, just different. Lapin joined Dennis as he started his second cup. The cafeteria looked nearly empty as it serviced only a few nurses and the families of one or two patients.

"So, doctor," Dennis started, "how's your morning?"

"Normal," Lapin replied, sitting down. "I'm not going to kid you. It'll be two or three days until we can really determine how she's going to do."

"It's out of our hands now."

The doctor smiled, thinking that he understood what Dennis was talking about. They both sipped. "The most important thing," Lapin continued, "the most critical thing is to get her blood count built back up. Once that happens, we'll be okay."

There was another moment of reflective silence, then Dennis threw him a curve. "Do you believe in God?"

"Of course I do. But I have a strange feeling our beliefs are a little different."

"Undoubtedly," Dennis confirmed. "Is this the first operation you've performed without a blood transfusion?"

"I've had many cases where blood wasn't needed. This is the first one I've ever done where it was and I promised that I wouldn't use it."

"Maria's going to be all right, isn't she?"

"Based on the way she looks now, I'd say so. Yes."

"Then she didn't really need the blood, did she?"

"Hindsight's always twenty-twenty."

"Did she?"

"I didn't come here to argue," Lapin responded firmly. His time was much too valuable. He'd made the pilgrimage with a specific purpose in mind. "I did the operation. I did what was necessary."

"Why?" Dennis asked.

"Why did I do it?"

Dennis nodded.

"I'm not sure. I just knew someone had to. You sounded desperate. Seemed rather unfair to me that no one would help you out. I don't know."

Dennis just listened. He made no attempt to interrupt. Lapin continued, "I want to know about this thing that you have. This refusal to accept blood transfusions."

"This thing, as you call it, is an absolute belief in the Scriptures as God's Holy Word."

Lapin raised a thick black eyebrow as he inquired, "God says you're not supposed to have blood transfusions?"

"Absolutely. On several occasions."

"Oh?" Lapin's subtle double-take went unnoticed. "I guess I missed that."

"Not if you read the Bible," Dennis said.

"Leviticus 17:11 says, '. . . the soul of the flesh is in the blood, and I myself have put it upon the altar for you to make the atonement for your souls, because it is the blood that makes atonement by the soul in it.'"

Lapin didn't say anything for a couple of seconds, then replied, "Sorry, I didn't get anything in there about blood transfusions."

"Let me go on," Dennis said. Lapin's tone of voice fell somewhere between mild understanding and guarded pessimism. The tone was one Dennis had heard thousands of times, to the point where it didn't bother him in the least. "It continues in Leviticus 17:14, '. . . you must not eat the blood of any sort of flesh, because the soul of every sort of flesh is its blood. Anyone eating it will be cut off.'"

"I'm impressed," Lapin said. "Those sounded like direct quotes."

"They were."

"Then I'm more impressed."

"With the Scripture?"

"More with your memory."

"Being cut off," Dennis explained, "means exclusion from eternal life."

"Eternal life. . . ." Lapin pondered with the same raised eyebrow. "What does that have to do with accepting a blood transfusion?"

"Everything," Dennis answered, "absolutely everything! If a man, any man, eats the blood of any sort of flesh," Dennis smiled and added with emphasis, ". . . any flesh . . . he'll be cut off . . . and out. That's what it says."

A confidence swept through Lapin. He loved to win. He was nearly smug with his reply, "'Eats the blood.' You said, 'eats the blood.' I'm sorry, but I still don't get what that has to do with blood transfusions. Being brought up as an orthodox Jew, I've read Leviticus and I used to salt all my meat for forty-eight hours before I'd eat it. That would draw out all the blood. But I'd still take a blood transfusion if my life depended on it and I'd still remain a good Jew."

Dennis was unshaken by Lapin's alleged profoundness, "Let's look at it this way," he resumed. "If a man was an alcoholic, a confirmed alcoholic, and he went to his doctor for help . . . treatment . . . and his doctor told him that he was absolutely going to die if he didn't stop drinking . . . you with me?"

"So far," Lapin answered attentively.

"And the man stopped drinking . . . and for all practical purposes the man's life was saved . . . does it seem logical that the man's life would once again be placed in jeopardy if his doctor or anyone else for that matter gave him alcohol intravenously? By transfusion? In his veins?"

"Yes, but. . . ."

"And the man would probably die?" Dennis interrupted.

"Yes, but. . . ."

"It's the same thing. The Bible says . . . God says . . . don't take blood. If you do, you will not attain everlasting life. It's just that simple."

Lapin was momentarily speechless, almost thankful when he heard his name announced over the P.A. *Saved by the bell* was his uncontrollable thought as he excused himself and walked toward the wall phone. A gnawing feeling erupted inside him. It wasn't so much that he'd lost a confrontation, it was just that Dennis made sense. It was difficult to absolutely pin down, and he was sure that at that moment he couldn't convey the same controlled rationale Dennis had just expressed, but he knew it sure made sense.

Lapin had trouble getting the analogy out of his mind as he spoke to the operator on the phone. It was the recovery room calling. A patient was coming out from under the anesthetic and a nurse needed some further orders. He gave complete instructions and informed the nurse that he was on his way.

Medically, Lapin was sound. But emotionally . . . emotionally, it was an altogether different thing for him. He returned the phone to its cradle and looked at Dennis, not knowing how to respond. What could he say?

He stopped at the table on his way out of the cafeteria. When their eyes met, Lapin knew he was looking at a man whose beliefs came from deep within his heart. The aura about Dennis transcended belief in mere theories; it gave evidence of his absolute knowledge. Dennis knew deep within him--without reservation, without question--that what he said was the truth. Lapin could feel that conviction also.

Lapin's question of how to respond resolved itself. He didn't understand exactly where the answer came

64

from, or why, or the logic behind it, but nevertheless
the answer was there. He chose acceptance, at least
for the time being. "You know what, Dennis?" Lapin
finally concluded. "You're right." And then he left.

3

It was business as usual: operating, consulting, making rounds, and hearing the continual corridor chit-chat about his successful but allegedly dangerous operation. None of this really bothered Lapin. He'd been through wars before--Israel, Indiana, Brooklyn, and Santa Ana. All this had developed a sense of character that Lapin found increasingly rare in his colleagues. They seemed more interested in talking about their financial interests than their patients, and more inclined to find fault with their new associates than to help or encourage them.

Maureen was less than happy whenever he called in the middle of the night to tell her he wouldn't be home. She'd be even less happy tonight when he called and repeated that message. Lapin thought that by being a nurse, Maureen would realize that patient care had to come before anything else . . . but she didn't. He was perplexed by her lack of understanding when he called. Didn't she realize this patient was special, that her blood count was half of what it should have been, that he operated successfully without transfusing any blood, and that he. . . . The only thing she understood was that he wasn't going to be home, again.

Lapin spent a second night in the ICU monitoring his special patient. Maria's blood count rose half a point. The doctor actually slept an hour--a full, uninterrupted hour.

There were more conversations with Dennis as the days wore on, and of course with Maria as she grew stronger.

Lapin learned that Maria's mother had been a battered child. She had been beaten incessantly by an

overachieving father who demanded perfection. At
fourteen, she escaped his constant abuse by running
away from home and surviving in the streets. There
she eventually became a prostitute to support herself.

From that point on, the road to heroin was a short
one. The magic liquid she injected into her arms was
the only pleasure she attained from this existence.
Her world was gray and empty, lacking cause or
purpose. Her life was dismal at best.

This was the life Maria was born into, out of
wedlock. It was a life of moving from place to place
and town to town because there wasn't enough money to
pay the rent. Sometimes there wasn't even enough to
buy food. Maria had watched her mother, her only real
contact with the world, commit suicide in daily
increments.

Maria explained to Lapin that she'd been alone at
home one Saturday morning when she first met the
Witnesses. Two very nice ladies came to her door and
wanted to speak with her about the Bible. Naturally,
she sent them away after she told them straight out,
"What the hell good's the Bible," and refused to
discuss it any further.

She smiled as she told Lapin how intrigued she was
with their sincerity. As they left, one of the ladies
had actually told Maria that she'd pray for her. *So
what?* was her first thought. Maria had lived her
sixteen and a half years in a cruel and heartless
world. Prayer and religion were totally nonexistent
for her; she didn't believe in any of it.

The following week, as she was helping her
unconscious, strung-out mother into bed, she remembered the previous Saturday's visit. *How nice it'd
be,* she thought, *to actually have the peace in my life
that those two ladies seemed to possess.*

Saturday came again and so did the two women. This
time Maria sat and talked with them for about twenty
minutes on the front porch steps. Because she'd
learned all too well never to trust anyone or anything, Maria carefully guarded everything she said or
asked.

She was impressed not only with their concern, but
also with their knowledge of the Bible. Each time
Maria asked a direct question, she was answered with a
quote from the Scriptures. The women seemed so
content with their lives. It was something Maria had
seldom seen, but she certainly liked it.

68

They offered to study the Bible with her, but Maria refused. *Don't trust anybody,* she thought to herself as she wondered what these people really wanted. The ladies smiled at the young woman, somehow understanding her unwillingness to accept their offer.

As they prepared to leave, one of the ladies handed Maria a publication called *The Watchtower* and asked her to read it. Maria was noncommittal and said she might, if she got a chance.

She avoided the thirty-two page magazine at first, not wanting to get involved. She invented several excuses for not even looking at it. Finally, late on Friday, she picked the thing up and devoured it, word for word, cover to cover.

There was much that she didn't understand, yet she read *The Watchtower* over and over. It told her about things like earthly blessings under the Kingdom. It talked about a life filled with peace and serenity. These were things Maria had never been exposed to before. She longed for explanations, but still wouldn't commit herself. *Nothing that good could ever be easy. Nothing could really be that good. Don't trust anybody.*

The following morning she waited impatiently for the two ladies to return. She felt a curious glow in her heart as she saw them turn the corner and start down the street. She met them on the steps, *Watchtower* in hand, and they talked at length. She seemed to question them about nearly every statement in the magazine. What about this? And that? The ladies answered first with Scriptures and then explained in laymen's language so that Maria would understand more clearly.

She understood the concepts, but had trouble believing them. Her whole life had been so diametrically opposed to what she was hearing. *But, dear God,* she thought, *how very much I want to understand and believe.*

Once again, the ladies offered to study the Bible with her, and once again she refused. They smiled and left other copies of *The Watchtower* and the *Awake!* magazines. Maria watched them walk down the street. She wasn't exactly sure of what they had--but she knew that she wanted it.

Three more weeks passed by, she told Lapin, and each Saturday the ladies would stop and talk. Maria was filled with questions about life, suffering, and rejection.   Each time, the ladies seemed to have a quote from the Scriptures and an answer that made sense.   It was uncanny.   She tried, from her misguided perspective, to challenge them.   Every single time she did, they had an answer.

Somewhere in this time frame, she said, she actually started to feel good about herself.   It was the first time in her life that she could remember feeling that way, and she liked it.   She liked it a lot.

Then one day, the ladies invited her to a meeting at a place called a Kingdom Hall.   She recalled laughing at the name, not knowing that much about the Witnesses.   Up to this point, her exposure to Jehovah's Witnesses had been through the two ladies who had become her friends, and through the literature they'd left with her.   The literature was something she'd grown to respect.   For the first time in her life, she belonged somewhere and she loved the feeling.

She was hesitant at first about the meeting, but anxious to meet people who shared the same beliefs. She honestly thought that the feelings she'd come to develop were just too good to be true.   Maria wanted to trust others, but she would first have to combat a lifetime of contradictory teachings.

The meeting turned out to be an absolute blessing. Her two friends introduced her to everyone there, and she was overwhelmed with how sincerely they accepted her.   They all made her feel more welcomed and comfortable than she'd ever felt in her life.   She sensed a true feeling of belonging--unnatural for her, but wonderful.

Maria took a Bible home with her that night and started to read.   The only Bibles she'd ever really seen before were the Gideon Bibles in hotel rooms. But now each time she opened her Bible, it reminded her of the meetings and all the people. *The Witnesses . . . so warm, so friendly . . . so willing to help.* She wanted to be more like them.   She wanted to know what they knew, and feel what they felt.

Maria's guilt surfaced and she wanted to confess to them what she was really about.   She wanted to tell them about her mother and the wretched life they shared.   She wept as she read the Bible, feeling unworthy of the Witnesses' attention and care.   On Saturday morning, she greeted her two friends with tears in her eyes and deep-seated pain in her heart.

In an emotional outpouring, she explained her guilt. She begged their forgiveness for not telling them the truth about herself. Expecting the rejection and condemnation that she'd grown to accept, she was astonished with their response.

One of the women asked Maria to join them in prayer. Maria couldn't believe what was happening. They told her that God would forgive her and used Bible Scriptures to support their words. Her emotions turned instantly from misery to joy. Her tears of depression and guilt now radiated with gratitude and praise.

She hugged each of the women and the three of them cried together. Maria had found the way to have peace in her life.

Her mother, however, was quite a different story. She was critical of Maria for reading all the time and for going to all those meetings. Of course, she didn't understand what was happening in Maria's life-- how could she? Her God was a needle in her arm, a quick fix.

Maria loved going to the meetings at the Kingdom Hall. The Witnesses had taken her in and accepted her. They had become her new family. She began attending Bible study groups and learning truths from God's Holy Word. A sense of worth and purpose became hers. At each meeting, she'd include her mother in her prayer.

Her mother didn't respond. She continued to go downhill, further and further, faster and faster, until the night Maria returned home from a meeting and found her dead on the living room floor. As she stood looking at her mother's body, she felt none of the expected emotions. Instead, the sadness was replaced with the confident knowledge that her mother was finally at peace and her future now rested in the hands of Jehovah.

Three months later at the Kingdom Hall, Maria met Dennis. They prayed together and went door-to-door together to spread the Truth, the absolute Word of God. Maria was content with the peace she'd finally found. She was baptized, and she and Dennis became man and wife.

Maria's story came to Lapin in bits and pieces over the two weeks it took for her to fully recover. Her sincerity and her undying faith left an indelible imprint on Lapin; to him, the woman was truly remarkable.

The fact that the surgery was performed without a blood transfusion was lost in the shuffle of a busy hospital's paper work. No one ever said much more about it. It was business as usual.

Lapin walked beside the wheelchair as the nurse pushed it through the swinging doors leading outside. He had spent considerable time with Maria and Dennis and was going to miss them. They, too, would miss him. They had each become more knowledgeable from their shared experiences, but more importantly, they had each grown into better people from their encounter. Lapin held Maria's hand. "I'm going to miss you," he said.

Maria smiled and nodded. She understood the sum and substance of those simple words.

"You take care of her," he continued, shaking Dennis' hand warmly.

"Doctor," Dennis started, with emotion filling his voice.

"I know," Lapin said. "I know."

They were all silent for a moment, basking in the affection they felt for one another. Maria sensed something unspoken within Lapin and said, "Doctor Lapin, I want you to know something." Lapin looked down. "It's all right about our baby," she said. "I know you did everything possible."

Lapin's eyes began to fill with tears. Maria continued, "I thank you for what you've done. We both do." Her eyes, too, were tearful. "You're a good person and someday I hope to be able to repay you. . . ."

"You already have," he whispered.

Maria stood and hugged the man who had saved her life and given her more time on earth to spread the Truth that could save other souls. She smiled and whispered in his ear, "We'll see, Doctor Lapin . . . we'll see."

***

The weeks that followed were routine as far as Lapin was concerned. He hadn't heard from Maria or Dennis; but each time he entered the Intensive Care Unit, he could feel their presence, especially hers.

Jan Jordan, the ICU head nurse, could see it in his eyes each time he entered the room. She had asked him about it several times, but each time he refused to discuss it. The experience with Maria had been too personal. Jan liked Lapin and respected him as a surgeon. She'd seen what other doctors could do and knew Lapin was one of the best. It bothered her deeply that he wouldn't talk about what had happened on the case. What he had accomplished was much too important not to share with others.

Jan was also in charge of in-service education, which included setting up classes for the nurses. Surgeons and physicians were invited to discuss their unusual patient cases.

She asked Lapin several times to talk with her nurses about Maria, and he finally accepted.

The nurses were completely spellbound. What he had done was hard to believe. According to medical books, an operation like that on a person with such a low blood count was nearly impossible. Despite this fact, Lapin delivered the dissertation so matter-of-factly that it came off as "no big deal."

The nurses were impressed, and Jan was especially pleased that he finally got the story out. It was therapeutic: "physician, heal thyself."

Maureen started her acting classes. Eventually that meant less entertaining at home, and that was all right. A shrug of acceptance and a wait-and-see attitude was all Lapin could muster. He was busy attending to his patients.

***

"Doctor Lapin . . . call the operator . . . Doctor Lapin. . . ." The P.A. announcement in the background caught his attention as it did forty or fifty times a day. He excused himself in the midst of prescribing medication for a patient and walked to the nurses' station across the hall.

"This is Doctor Lapin," he said into the receiver.

"Doctor, you have an emergency call."

"I'll take it. This is Doctor Lapin. May I help you?"

"Doctor . . . I've been told that I need an operation." The man hesitated for a second. "And . . . and I was wondering if you'd do it."

There was static on the line. "Where are you calling from?" Lapin asked.

"Arizona," came the reply.

"Arizona?" Lapin repeated. "Why are you calling me way out here? Don't they have doctors in Arizona?"

Another second of silence passed. "I talked with Maria Joseph. She told me you'd respect the blood issue. I'm one of Jehovah's Witnesses."

A hundred thoughts raced through Lapin's mind: Dennis, Maria, their story. He couldn't forget her overwhelming faith and her last smiling whisper, "We'll see, doctor . . . we'll see."

"Doctor, are you there?" the man questioned.

"I'm here. You say nobody there will do the operation?"

"Not without blood."

"What's the problem?"

"I have cancer . . . of the rectum."

Lapin closed his eyes momentarily. He knew from experience that the blood count itself wouldn't be a problem, but the procedure was very bloody and sometimes a risky operation. "I think you should take the blood and have the operation there," he said.

"Doctor. . . ." The voice was fading, pleading. "You know I can't take blood. No one here will respect my religious beliefs. You're the last hope I have, Dr. Lapin. Maria said. . . ."

"When was it diagnosed?" Lapin interrupted.

"I've been going to Mexico for two years for treatment."

"Mexico?" Lapin asked incredulously. "What's in Mexico?"

"A cancer clinic."

Dear God, Lapin thought to himself. *This poor man . . . these poor people.* "What did they do for you in Mexico?"

"Diet mostly. They gave me a lot of herbs to take. They said that would put the cancer in remission." Lapin shook his head in disbelief.

"Doctor . . . will you help me? I can't go to the bathroom anymore without a lot of pain."

There was a moment's hesitation, a flurry of thoughts, and then the words, "How soon can you get out here?"

"Will you do it?" the man asked hopefully.

"Come . . . and we'll talk . . . we'll see."

They finished the conversation and hung up. *Now what have I done*, Lapin thought. *Do I really want to get involved . . . with these people . . . with their problems . . . with the whole thing?*

Maureen lent an unsympathetic ear. "Look," she analyzed, "I know you're good, as good as there is--but you were lucky, too. You shouldn't have done the first one--let alone consider a second. Don't get involved, Ron. These people will only be trouble. They'll start coming out of the woodwork. Don't do it. You don't need the hassle."

"And they don't need to die either," he replied. That ended the conversation. She knew that he was going to do it.

Maureen's feelings and comments were echoed by everyone Lapin approached on the subject. "Leave them alone." "Don't get involved." "They're only trouble." She was right about one thing: he didn't need the hassle. His self-supporting practice was growing. He had twenty-one physicians sending him patients. He was busy and successful, very successful. Why would--or should--he risk all that for something he absolutely didn't need.

Lapin searched for a logical answer, but none came. He only knew in his heart that he was going to do it. *These people have a right not only to their religious beliefs, whatever they are, but also to proper medical care. Isn't that what the Hippocratic oath is all about? Isn't it?*

"They're suicidal," some of the other doctors said. "They want to die." But Lapin didn't buy that theory for one second. He'd seen a will to live in Maria that was totally unique. He'd also seen a degree of courage that was rare. Her courage and strength came from an unquestionable faith in an everlasting life . . . by means of a resurrection after death. She was completely unafraid and prepared to die. But suicidal? Not for one second.

Lapin believed he could do the operation. He knew he could. His biggest obstacle was finding an anesthesiologist who'd go along with the procedure. Afraid that the one who had worked with him on Maria would insist on using blood this time, he began to ask other members of the staff to assist him.

After several refusals, complete with snide remarks, he spoke with Fred Garcia. Garcia had finished his residency at Long Beach Hospital and was now dividing his time between working at Huntington Community, at Newport General, and on a trauma team at Skyline. Garcia was busy.

When Lapin finally caught up with him, Garcia was

intrigued at the prospect. He, like Lapin, looked for challenges--that's why he joined the trauma team. Interestingly, he'd had a rare experience with one of Jehovah's Witnesses during a rotation round at the medical college of UCLA.

An emergency patient was admitted to the hospital with a vascular malformation in his brain that continued to grow. If the aneurysm ruptured before being removed, it would cause his death instantly. The patient somehow convinced the attending surgeons that he'd rather die than take blood. Having no time to transfer him anywhere else, they agreed to his demands.

Forms and agreements were signed at the patient's insistence, but the doctors were cautious enough to obtain a court order to use blood . . . just in case.

Garcia, perplexed by the case, consulted his professors for advice. They agreed that a man's conscience must be his guide. If Garcia, as the anesthesiologist, were to promise the patient not to administer blood, his word as a man and as a doctor must be given seriously and truthfully.

He agreed, and the operation began. Garcia had the patient enclosed in a G-suit, a total body suit that's used to put pressure on the blood vessels and centralize the blood. He gave the patient a volume expanding fluid called Dextran to keep the blood pressure as low as possible. It was a successful nine-hour operation. When it was over, the patient was as white as a sheet despite having had only minimal blood loss.

Blood had been available in the room, but Garcia vowed in his own mind not to use it--no matter what. In a short period of time, the patient completely recovered.

So when questioned by Lapin about the operation, Garcia wasn't possessed by the fear that obviously held back most of his colleagues. He said yes, Lapin smiled, and the operation was scheduled. Nevertheless, Garcia, like the others, left Lapin with the unanswered question, "Why?"

Why, Lapin thought, *why?* How he longed for an answer. Why was he so willing to go out on a limb all alone again? He already answered the challenge of being able to do it--in Maria's case. Now what? Was it the challenge of doing it again, better and faster? Even that wasn't enough of an answer. There were other reasons locked deep inside.

As Lapin searched for the elusive key, he remembered something from his childhood. It was a quote that he'd learned while growing up on the Kibbutz at Nahalal, an agricultural school in the valley of Israel, just a few miles from Nazareth. He remembered and spoke the words aloud. "First the Nazis went after the Jews, but I was not a Jew, so I did not object. Then they went after the Catholics, but I was not a Catholic, so I did not object. Then they went after the trade-unionists, but I was not a trade-unionist, so I did not object. Then they came after me, and there was no one left to object." The quote was from Martin Niemoller, a German theologian.

He stopped for a second, stunned. He was fascinated that he'd remembered the exact quote, word for word, after all these years. He reflected on the meaning of the words as he repeated the quote again. *Is that the key? Is that it? That sooner or later you have to stand up, fight, and defend other people's rights-- even if they're not your own--because eventually someone's going to attack you and try to take away your rights. Is that it?*

I don't know, Lapin thought, *I don't know. I only know that I'm a surgeon, a damned good surgeon. This man and these people, especially in this country for God's sake, deserve better. At least they deserve decent medical care. And if nobody else will do it, then let them come to me. I'll do it--before there's no one left to object.*

No one can ever run away from their heritage--it's much too far a journey to accomplish in one short lifetime. Lapin faced his own heritage head-on as he examined sickly Mr. Nathan from Arizona. Was it his Israeli background, he wondered, that spawned the empathy in his heart? It was a partial answer, he concluded, but there's far more to it than that. Much more.

"How was your trip?" Lapin asked.

"A little uncomfortable, but I'm here and that's what matters." Lapin grunted and continued his probing. Nathan went on, "Brother Devlin picked me up at the airport and brought me on over here. . . ."

Lapin raised an eyebrow.

"Brother," Nathan said, "that's what we call other people in the Truth, other Witnesses."

"Oh," Lapin responded. "How are you feeling?"

"Well, I'm hurting a little now, but I know I'm going to be just fine soon."

Lapin looked at the man seriously. "And just how do you know that?"

"Because Maria says you're a good man and I believe her. We Witnesses trust each other."

"Doesn't that get you into trouble sometimes?"

"Not really," Nathan said smiling. "We're all in Jehovah's hands anyway."

Lapin nodded. "I suppose you are. So tell me about this Mexico thing."

"The clinic?"

"If that's what they call it."

"Well, the doctors at home said they couldn't do anything for me because I wouldn't accept a blood transfusion, so I had to go down to Tijuana. That was the only place I could go and get any treatment . . . of course, that was before you."

"Uh huh," Lapin muttered. "Did they give you Laetril?"

"No. It's a different treatment than that."

Great, Lapin thought. "Who diagnosed the cancer initially?"

"Doctors at home."

"Then what did they do?"

"Biopsy . . . it was malignant. They told me I'd have to have surgery right away."

Lapin was shocked. "Two years ago they told you that?"

"Just under."

Lapin could feel his anger growing. "And you've been going to Mexico for . . . treatments?"

"Well, I've also been looking the whole time for someone to operate on me."

"And in two years, you couldn't find anyone who would do something?"

"Well," Nathan said, "we came close one time. I found a doctor who said he'd take three or four units of my own blood, over a period of a month or two, and use that during the operation."

"That makes sense. Why didn't you do that?"

Nathan looked at Lapin and smiled again. "The Bible specifies that you shouldn't take blood. It doesn't say whose blood, just that you're not supposed to take it. Using my own blood after it was taken out of my body would be just as wrong as taking somebody else's blood."

Lapin just shook his head and continued the examination. "Has the pain been getting worse?"

"Yeah. I realized that my rectum was closing off on me. It's been real painful. I can't go to the bathroom. I decided to call the Cancer Hot Line over in L.A."

"What'd they tell you?"

"They told me to call USC and UCLA, so I talked to both of them. . . ."

"And?"

"They both said they wouldn't operate on me unless they had a free hand and could do whatever they wanted."

"And then you called me," Lapin guessed, expecting that Nathan's story of frustration would finally be over.

"No," he answered slowly. "I called the Cancer Hot Line again and they recommended that I check with the research center out in Loma Linda. They have some strong religious beliefs, the man said. They're Seventh Day Adventists."

"Did you go and see them?"

"A doctor over there examined me and said I was going to die if I didn't have surgery. He also said I wasn't going to die on his table."

Lapin continued his examination, angered by the horror story he was hearing. He was angry with the physicians he was hearing about. He was angry at the hypocrisy of the medical profession in general. He clenched his teeth and asked, "Did they give you any indication of how long you had before you were going to die?"

"No. It wasn't a very thorough examination. They just said that I was going to, so I went back home to Arizona to die." Both men were struck by the profound reality of Nathan's statement. Then he continued, "I went to a meeting at the Kingdom Hall and one of the sisters was talking about Maria, a friend of hers out here, and how you took care of her. So, I gave her a call. I'd given up till I talked to her. Anyway, here I am . . . finally."

Nathan smiled. You could see in his eyes the faith he had in this special doctor. Lapin put his hand on Nathan's shoulder and returned the smile. "And so you are, Mr. Nathan, so you are."

***

Two doctors who referred their patients to Lapin brought their wives to Lapin's house for dinner that night. As usual, Maureen was the consummate hostess. The women talked about the acting classes Maureen was taking. When she told them how excited she was to finally find something fulfilling in her life, she managed to raise an eyebrow or two.

The men retired to the living room with brandy. Via an unofficial physicians' grapevine, both doctors had heard about the bloodless procedure that Lapin scheduled for early the next morning. With logic and much professional dignity, they explained why they felt the operation was dangerous and shouldn't be attempted . . . unless he used blood after the unsuspecting patient was asleep.

Lapin was growing less and less surprised at the attitudes of his contemporaries. He told the men about Nathan's two-year quest to find someone who'd help him, and of how he held fast to his integrity even though he knew all along that he was dying. The doctors were unsympathetic. They simply said the operation was too risky.

So Lapin told them about the clinic in Tijuana, a place where people went for treatment when they couldn't find any here in the States. To Lapin's surprise, they were aware of the clinic and even supplied him with more information about it.

The place didn't use cobalt, radiation, chemotherapy, or any of those kinds of treatments. They never actually performed surgery. The entire process consisted of diet, vitamins A, E, and C, and a mysterious dark liquid tonic that you drank twice a day. Some patients swore that it cured all their problems.

Sugar was taboo, as were tomatoes. They couldn't eat anything that had been stored in a metal container. To the doctors' knowledge, no medication or prescribed drugs of any kind were ever given. They preferred to treat undiagnosed patients. Sometimes patients were told that once a biopsy was performed by an American doctor, the chances for a cure were considerably diminished.

Lapin's empathy for the plight of the patient ran deep. He became increasingly perturbed at the blasé attitude shown by his dinner guests.

"When was the last time you saw any cancer healed by

abstaining from tomatoes?" he asked sarcastically.

The doctors patiently explained that the clinic--good, bad or indifferent--at least offered these people some hope. They hadn't been able to find that anywhere else. That hope, they concluded, was better than nothing at all.

"There's no reason for that kind of desperation," Lapin countered. "We can treat those people here."

"Not without blood," one of them said.

"Yes . . . without blood," Lapin insisted. Both guests knew that he was absolutely serious.

***

The operating room was so steeped in tension that it put everyone on edge. Garcia had Mr. Nathan safely under the anesthetic, and they were about to begin. The hospital administration wasn't enthusiastic about Lapin's plan, but politely chose to look the other way this time only because Garcia had agreed to assist.

Just prior to surgery, Nathan found out that his insurance wouldn't cover the entire surgical bill. Nervous and reticent, he made a completely honest disclosure of that information. It was almost as if he expected Lapin to put the operation on hold till he could raise the rest of the money.

Suppressing a smile at the man's innocence and naiveté, Lapin assured him that everything was going to be fine and said not to worry. They'd work something out later.

The faces of everyone in the operating room expressed concern, but that was normal before any major surgery. Garcia gave Lapin a thumbs-up signal. "He's all yours, doc".

The young surgeon stepped to the table and positioned his foot on the metal floor pedal that powered the electrocautery knife. Lapin could sense that all eyes in the room were transfixed on the knife; he knew, too, that eyes far beyond the walls of that sterile cubicle were watching him as well.

Speed and accuracy were Lapin's watchwords. Having envisioned all possibilities before he cut, he showed no hesitancy with the knife. There was no time for delay; even the pathologist stood by to do an immediate biopsy.

Once inside the body, his worst expectations were realized. Cancerous tissue had wound its way through

Nathan's entire pelvic area.

The gray, slimy mass had completely encircled the colon and had caused intense discomfort to the patient. The area, without question, had the single worst concentration of this dull, pitted, deadly substance.

The vile-looking mass appeared to be flaunting its ability to defy all medical treatment. The severity of the cancer would have signaled most surgeons to close immediately and start radiation or chemotherapy. They would have estimated the patient's remaining life expectancy and hoped that drugs would control the pain for that duration.

Lapin didn't have that option. "This guy owes me money. Got to keep him alive so he can pay me." His light treatment of the crisis immediately eased the tension in the room. Like a general on a battlefield, he outmaneuvered the enemy. He attacked the major blood vessel leading to the tumor and completely devascularized it prior to attempting its removal. He then carefully separated the tumor from both ureters.

He gave a small sample of the grotesque tissue to the pathologist and then continued with impeccable precision, making each cut only a sixteenth of an inch deep. He cauterized at each interval, regularly checking the blood loss, and constantly consulting with Garcia on the blood pressure and pulse. With painstaking labor, he raced against both the insidious disease and the clock. Nathan's vital signs were holding, the urine output was adequate, and his color was good. He was stable.

Lapin's soaring confidence lifted the team's morale. He knew he could do it, and now so did they. No doubt lingered in their minds once his expertise was thrust into action.

Doctors and nurses would stop outside the door and gaze through the glass pane just to view Lapin for one fleeting second, unsure as to whether they were observing medical history or insanity.

One hour and ten minutes later, he was through. Having removed the rectum and part of the colon, Lapin carefully ran a final check to make sure that all visible cancer was gone. Thanks to Dr. Lapin, Nathan had only lost a half pint of blood--two hundred and fifty c.c.s. Success was his. He'd done it again-- faster, better. Mr. Nathan would go back to Arizona and spread the word of Jehovah's blessings.

They closed the patient, left the room, and walked down the hall.

"Thanks, Fred," Lapin said in sincere appreciation.

"Brilliant, Ron," Garcia replied. "Best I've ever seen."

They stopped at the nurses' station since he still had his post-op report to complete. This would be a long one. Lapin humbly acknowledged some congratulations from a few surgical nurses, and finally took a tension-releaving deep breath.

Lapin looked up at the surgical board where patient information is listed along with the procedure and names of the admitting doctor, the anesthesiologist, and the surgeon. His face went blank and the room became abnormally quiet. Never taking his eyes from the board, Lapin broke the silence. "Why has my name been erased and replaced with Doctor Williams?"

The nurses shuffled a bit and looked at each other for support. Then one said, "Doctor Fletcher was just here. He said that it was his patient and he wanted to make the change."

"Did he say why?" Lapin asked calmly.

The nurses all shook their heads. It didn't matter; Lapin knew why. Fletcher, one of his dinner guests last night, had been more adamant about his stand than Lapin realized. Fletcher was convinced that this bloodless surgery thing was not only dangerous, but politically risky. Last night he had said that any surgeon who would risk it must, in turn, be dangerous and careless. In retrospect, Lapin realized that Dr. Fletcher intended to refer his patients to another surgeon and thereby be no part of the blood issue.

Figuratively and literally, the scorecard tally showed the effects of Dr. Fletcher's decision. As the physicians from both Skyline and the surrounding area became aware of Fletcher's stand, Lapin once again fell victim to ice-cold, questioning stares as he went about his daily business.

One quiet afternoon, Mr. Nathan was reading the Bible and had a current issue of *The Watchtower* lying beside him on the bed.

"You look healthy," Lapin said as he entered the room during rounds.

"Never felt better," Nathan replied, smiling. Lapin studied his chart. His progress had been better than expected.

"Doctor," Nathan said, "I think it's time we talked

about the balance of my bill--the half I still owe you."

"Don't worry about it," Lapin answered. "You just get better. We'll take care of it later."

"No, now's a good time. I've been thinking about it."

Lapin shrugged. "Whatever."

"I figure we've got two options. One, I'm a wholesaler in the lobster business, so I could give you free lobster till the bill was paid. I know that'd be an awful lot of lobster, but. . . ."

Seeing Lapin grin so widely that it almost looked unnatural, Nathan stopped in mid-sentence.

"Mr. Nathan," Lapin finally said. "That's an interesting proposal, but I'm Jewish. You know how you're not allowed to take blood?" Nathan nodded, not fully understanding the doctor's point. "Well," Lapin continued, "Jews aren't allowed to eat shellfish. . . ."

The two men managed to share a whimsical glance before breaking into uncontrollable laughter. It was loud enough to make a nurse poke her head inside the door to see if anything was wrong--making them laugh just that much harder! Things finally quieted down, but Lapin's uncharacteristic smile remained as he added, "And what's the second option?"

Nathan became serious and answered, "I could teach you the Bible. I could help you learn the Truth."

Lapin had heard a variety of things from his patients, but this one floored him. "Interesting concept," he finally replied. "You figure that's worth half my fee, huh?"

"I figure that's worth everything there is."

Lapin contemplated the proposal. He was Jewish and not about to alter his religious beliefs, but the offer fascinated him. "We'll talk about it," he said as he started to leave.

"Doctor. . . ."

"Yes?"

"Some of the Witness friends have started an insurance company. I wonder if you'd mind talking with them. It might do countless people a lot of good. . . ."

"I'm all for that."

"They'll be in touch."

"You take care. See you later."

There was an eerie, unexplainable feeling as he re-entered the hallway, almost like entering a war zone.

Battle lines were being drawn again as other doctors, without discussion or provocation, were following Fletcher's lead and referring their patients to different surgeons.

Lapin was obviously being shunned because he dared to be different. Although the other physicians respected and, in most cases, admired his talent and ability, they still chose to leave him. They chose to put their patients in the hands of a team player-- someone who was an integral part of the system, who blended in without making waves, and who avoided the spotlight of public controversy.

A status quo exists within the standard practices of any group of physicians. Because Dr. Lapin functioned outside that framework, other doctors became uncooperative. Ron Lapin's methods weren't wrong, just different.

Were their concerns and actions in the best interests of their patients? Lapin didn't think so, but there was nothing he could do about it. His patient load abruptly decreased.

He listened attentively as Mr. Nathan quoted from the Scriptures, ". . . that in the last days critical times hard to deal with will be here. For men will be lovers of themselves, lovers of money, self-assuming, haughty, blasphemers, disobedient to parents, unthankful, disloyal, having no natural affection, not open to any agreement, slanderers, without self-control, fierce, without love of goodness , betrayers, headstrong, puffed up with pride, lovers of pleasures rather than lovers of God, having a form of godly devotion but proving false to its power; and from these turn away."

"Makes sense to me," Lapin said.

"Good. That's good," Nathan replied. "By the way, my friends from the insurance company said they'd be calling you this week."

Men will be lovers of money, Lapin thought, *self-assuming, unthankful, disloyal, betrayers, slanderers . . . yeah, it sure makes sense. . . .*

***

Three men from the insurance company arrived for their appointment with Dr. Lapin. As Lapin's secretary, Jodi, greeted the staunch visitors, she observed how much they looked like elders from some sort of church. Interestingly enough, she was right.

After introductory handshakes, the men settled down in comfortable chairs to discuss business. The company they represented served only families in which both spouses were baptized as Jehovah's Witnesses.

A little extreme, Lapin thought, *but then, it's their business.*

The men had heard about Lapin through Mr. Nathan, Maria, and other Witnesses who had called Lapin and received free consultations and advice. They were there to inspect him, determine his motives, and discern his reason for operating on Witnesses while respecting their religious convictions.

Lapin leaned back in his chair and calmly expressed his belief in the Witnesses' right to concordantly exercise their faith while having the best medical care available. He became louder and noticeably irritated as he spoke of the indifference exhibited by his peers toward the JWs. He was upset by the fact that many Witnesses waited too long to get help and that a number of others had come to completely distrust physicians in general.

They appreciated Lapin's directness. He supported and defended the rights of the Witnesses and emphasized that all people are entitled to their chosen beliefs.

When the elders finished, Lapin had a question of his own. He wondered what the real purpose was behind their visit and questioning.

One of the men, Herk Hutchins, explained that their company received countless calls from Witness policyholders in desperate need of either medical treatment or advice. Whenever they sought medical assistance directly, they encountered frustration, futility, and dead ends. Most doctors refused to treat them.

Lapin probed deeper. "What do you want of me? How can I help?"

Hutchins was given the look of approval from his colleagues before he continued. "If we can find a physician with the proper qualifications, we want to discuss the possibility of installing a hot line in his office."

He explained that the telephone number of the hot line would be widely distributed among the Witnesses throughout the country. They could call for medical attention or advice if they weren't able to get assistance in their own area.

86

Lapin liked the men, especially Hutchins. He found him to be a fascinating study in human behavior. In the course of the conversation, Lapin discovered that Herk was actually a retired surgeon. Lapin's interest peaked when Hutchins spoke of how he himself had never given a blood transfusion, and even more remarkably, never lost a patient because of it during his thirty-five-year career.

Lapin knew that bloodless surgery had been done in great numbers. After all, he concluded, operations were certainly performed with success long before the Red Cross was ever formed. But this was the first man he'd met who, by choice, refused to use blood.

Herk had retired from surgery over four years ago. He'd settled into a peaceful, quiet, comfortable way of life and was rapidly boring himself to death. Lapin, though impressed with Herk's credentials, found him to be overweight, disinterested, and complacent. Until recently, Herk had allotted too much of his retirement to television and candy bars.

All that changed when Herk became the medical advisor of the insurance company. Now his responsiveness to humanity was being rekindled.

Lapin could see that Herk was searching for a purpose. He saw a spark of mischievous behavior, a flickering glimpse of desire. He couldn't for the life of him understand why Herk wasn't still practicing. The inner core of emptiness had certainly left its mark on a man no longer part of the surgical theater. Still, Lapin sensed a tremendous worth in the man. There was a great unused human resource within Herk almost begging to be released and put to use.

Lapin viewed his fellow surgeon as a challenge. Little did he know that, in time, this man would become his personal mentor.

Satisfied with Lapin's sincerity and willingness to help, the three men proposed that they install a special hot line in Lapin's office and pay all the expenses it incurred. Lapin agreed to answer the phone and provide his medical expertise to the callers without charge. Although they agreed it would only be done on a trial basis, an important alliance had been struck.

As the men prepared to leave, Herk turned and asked Lapin a question, "Why are you undertaking a cause like this . . . for a group of people that nobody cares about?"

Lapin viewed Herk much like an opponent in a mental chess game, a game of who could out-psych whom. Lapin didn't want to beat him, but rather wanted to win him over to his side so he chose his words carefully. "A man needs a purpose to exist. Although it's difficult to understand the relationship between intangible ideas and the results they produce, it's still important to create the kind of ideas that can be useful, beneficial, and life-giving. That's what I'm going to do."

"What about money?" one of the men asked with reserve.

"You do your job well and the money will always take care of itself."

They shook hands and stood at the office door. Lapin looked at Herk. "Want to do some surgery?" It was a throw-away line.

As Herk considered the offer, Lapin saw that spark of interest reappear. "No, but I'll come and observe."

Lapin nodded and smiled to himself. He knew he had him! Herk had recently adopted the Witnesses' way of life and, as such, was spirtually young, in contrast to being surgically well-seasoned. Herk's mother had been a Witness and he'd grown up in the faith. During college, he drifted away from the Truth, got married, divorced, and led an unfulfilled life.

When he remarried, he followed his wife--a practicing Witness--to meetings and Bible study groups. He grasped the good news of the Bible and was finally baptized.

Herk was the only Jehovah's Witness surgeon that Lapin knew. As he watched him walk toward the elevator, he realized how important Herk's role would be on the journey they were about to undertake. Hutchins could provide practical as well as spiritual aid to their patients. His assistance could be invaluable.

***

Calls from Witnesses began to come in, first from around the state, then from surrounding states, and finally from the entire country. By serving the needs of the Witnesses, Lapin was simultaneously ruffling some feathers at the hospital. Harassment from

Skyline's administration increased. Committees and other doctors were constantly reviewing more and more charts behind his back, always on the lookout for some minor infraction of outdated regulations. Increasing numbers of physicians transferred their referral business from Lapin to other surgeons. Lapin's practice was being damaged and his finances reduced proportionately. Principles can be very expensive indeed.

Emotionally and psychologically, the wounds were equally deep. Unfounded innuendoes that Lapin practiced outside the limits of standard medical care became more and more pronounced. Despite the unpleasantness and the accusations from fellow surgeons, Lapin continued saving lives and performing the kind of complex surgeries his accusers wouldn't so much as consider doing themselves.

After presenting a paper at a scientific surgical meeting in San Francisco, he returned to the hospital later that evening to see a patient he'd operated on the previous day. Lapin had checked on him before leaving that morning, but the case was complicated and he was thorough in his work. It was a difficult situation because the man was extremely overweight, and, to Lapin, that meant the case would have to be followed very closely. The patient had a perforated colon with an abdominal abcess. A second operation would be necessary to rehook the bowel after all the infection had disappeared from the abdomen.

When Lapin left the patient earlier that morning, everything was in order; the man felt good and his vital signs were progressing nicely. Now, less than twelve hours later, Lapin found him in near hysterics--half screaming and nearly frightened out of his mind.

After Lapin left town, a staff physician had visited the man and told him that his surgery had been unnecessary. It was unthinkable that this doctor would review the patient's chart without permission from Lapin, or for that matter, from anyone else. Even more unprofessional was the fact that he had spread his misguided opinions among the nursing staff. Even more unethical was the fact that he'd had the audacity to present his moralistic judgment to the patient himself. That was truly unpardonable!

Lapin worked long into the night to reassure the patient and to counteract the damage done purely out of malicious jealousy.   He showed him X-rays and photographs that were taken during the surgery, explaining in simple terms exactly what had been done and why.   The ordeal ended with a calm, appreciative patient reassuring Dr. Lapin that he would be the one to rehook his bowel when the time came.

   Lapin was gratified that he was able to regain the patient's confidence.   However, the backstabbing and the destructive acts prompted by professional jealousy had to stop.   A patient being tormented like this was the last straw.

4

Bristol Hospital was considered quite small with only forty-four beds. After forty years of service, the facility had become antiquated, run down, and in need of extensive repair. It was owned, like most private hospitals, by a corporation with an apparent attitude of "take all the money out and put as little as possible back in."

The roof leaked. Half the time the operating room air conditioner didn't work, making it very hot, uncomfortable, and sometimes actually unsafe. Lapin learned from several patients that the food was generally bad from poor preparation and usually cold from being delivered late. Most of the equipment was outdated enough to suggest a sense of historical significance.

As Lapin walked through the halls, he noticed the unmistakable musty smell of mortality lingering everywhere. Drab colors throughout emphasized the lack of energy and vitality which should dominate a hospital's atmosphere.

The operating room stood vacant most of the time. The hospital administrators eagerly pointed out that they'd have no qualms about the patients Lapin chose to serve. If he could fill up the rooms on a regular basis, the operating room was his. The administration's only concern was filling the beds and updating the facility.

Lapin's primary concern was taking care of people whose needs went far beyond the standards of medical care. He needed a base of operation where he could prove that, in the long run, bloodless surgery was not only safer, but medically better for the patient. Bristol Hospital provided that arena. It afforded Lapin an opportunity to protect people's civil rights, not only verbally, but surgically. The administration's willingness to offer Lapin that opportunity afforded him the time and space to prove scientifically that discrimination is and always has been just that: discrimination.

In the beginning, Lapin set his talented and able sights on upgrading and streamlining the hospital's operations. He settled for nothing less than one hundred percent effort from everyone around him.

Calls on the hot line were increasing almost daily. And, interestingly enough, they were often calls from other physicians, lawyers, and judges. These professionals were seeking advice about both the complexities of treating patients without blood and the legal problem of obtaining court orders in critical cases regarding the Witnesses. Countless hours were spent on the telephone counseling and explaining the rights of these people. He listened attentively to other doctors' diagnoses and helped administer treatment via long distance. All this was done by Lapin without charge.

The remaining patients at Skyline were all gradually transferred to Bristol. So was Jan Jordan. She had an undying faith in Lapin's work and wished to remain with him. New patients that came from all over the country shared her sentiments. Word-of-mouth communication among Jehovah's Witnesses was far-reaching indeed, as evidenced by Lapin's reputation being spread throughout the country. The hospital began to do as many operations in one day as they had formerly done in an entire week. The place was busy and that made the administration happy.

Lapin once again invited Herk to assist him in some operations. Herk politely refused, but expressed interest in coming to observe.

Lapin felt a sense of satisfaction as he watched Herk don the green surgical uniform and slip the disposable coverings over his shoes prior to observing that first surgical procedure. There was a mutual sharing of ideas between them, but Lapin always felt that he had benefited most from their exchange.

Hutchins came only once that first week. The second week he came back twice and scrubbed on that third visit. The following week, he stood at the table and assisted Lapin by holding a retractor in a patient's abdomen. It was only a matter of days before he helped suture patients after Lapin finished operating.

92

From that time on, he was Lapin's full-time assistant in the operating room. In addition to filling an invaluable role in the surgical arena, Herk became Lapin's mentor regarding Jehovah's Witnesses' philosophy.

The tiny spark that Lapin recognized within Herk several weeks prior had ignited and was now a raging fire. Hutchins' life started anew as he redefined its purpose and developed an intense desire to assist his spiritual brothers and sisters. An affinity was struck between Hutchins and Lapin, and it made them an inseparable pair.

***

When the Witnesses refer to each other as brother or sister, it's considerably more than religious lip service. It was commonplace for an out-of-town patient to be picked up at the airport by a fellow Witness, transported to the hospital, visited during the entire stay, and then taken into a local home and treated as family for the entire recuperation period.

Lapin found their genuine concern and respect for fellow members of the Truth to be a remarkable example of co-existing in peace and harmony. Their willingness to go out of their way to help one another was something Lapin hadn't seen since his formative years in the Kibbutz.

On the home front, entertaining and dinner parties were diminishing. So was Ron and Maureen's relationship. When the situation called for it, Lapin would have recuperating patients without funds stay in his home until they were well enough to travel. It was an idea that Maureen had gone along with initially. After all, she was an experienced nurse who could be helpful to the patients during their recovery.

She began feeling tied down to the patients and the house, however, and subtly expressed resistance to her added responsibilities. She also confronted Ron frequently about never helping out around the house.

"Hi, hon, how are you doing?" Lapin said, entering the kitchen.

Maureen was in the process of remodeling the room and wasn't looking her best. Besides having her hair filled with mortar dust and her fingernails broken and ragged, she was hot, tired, and sweaty. *As if he can't see,* she thought. She just stood there for a moment as she placed her hands on her hips, shifted her weight, and stared him straight in the eye. "How the hell does it look like I'm doing?"

"Looks like we'll be eating out," he said, moving toward the liquor cabinet. She was clearly upset and he didn't want to instigate anything. "There's a new Italian place over in Huntington Beach. Want to give it a try?"

He stood with his back to her as he fixed a drink, but could still feel her icy stare. It was only the tip of the iceberg; Lapin knew there was an underlying tension building up silently. He was on a collision course headed toward a stormy confrontation and desperately wished he was anywhere else.

"I'll tell you what I'd like to try," she seethed. Her voice was trembling. "I'd like to try having you home on an occasional basis. I'd like to try having a husband, and maybe even a normal life for a change. . . ."

"Maureen, it hasn't been a particularly good day. Could we possibly have this argument later?"

"S-u-r-e. Later!" she snapped in a raised voice. "Everything's l-a-t-e-r! Like digging up the flower garden. Three weeks ago you promised you'd do that. One simple thing around here. But is it done? No . . . no, it's not. The damn place will never be finished. You're too busy. And what am I doing? I'm trying out for construction worker of the year."

She was angry. She clapped her hands together and cement dust flew into the air. Lapin still hadn't turned around. The dust particles drifted past him. He raised his eyes toward the ceiling and slowly shook his head.

"Don't shake your head at me!" she screamed. "This is our home--not just a restaurant, or a place to sleep sometimes, or a motel for your precious patients."

He turned and looked at her. "Be careful," he warned.

"I tried being careful," she persisted. Thrusting out her broken fingernails, she added, "Look what it got me."

"Okay . . . I'll dig up the flower garden. Case closed." He took his drink and started out of the kitchen. But Maureen wasn't finished. She followed him like a shadow.

"Case closed," she said. "That's nice . . . that's

simple. What about the rest of the stuff around here?"

Lapin could sense that there was no escape route. Another encounter was inevitable. They entered the living room. Maureen wouldn't relent.

"I can't be expected to do all this stuff myself . . . plus be your social secretary and hostess . . . plus take care of a houseful of recovering patients who keep trying to convince me I'd be fine if only I were a Jehovah's Witness."

Lapin sat down. "That's just their way. They believe they've found the truth and they want to share it with people they care about."

"All I want is some sharing from you."

Further discussion was improbable, if not impossible. It was happening again. Lapin knew it and decided to ask for a temporary truce.

"Look," he began quietly, "the other surgeons at the hospital are starting to get on my back about too much cutting. I'm dealing with an administration who won't live up to their promises of putting money back into the place. I'm working in an emergency room and ICU that are so antiquated they should be bronzed and put in the Smithsonian Institute. . . ." He hesitate for a second. "Plus . . . I lost another doctor today."

His last sentence would have been better left unsaid.

"Another one," she echoed. There was a sharp tone of sarcasm in her voice. "That makes an even fourteen doctors you've lost, doesn't it?" Lapin didn't reply. Her mathematics were correct. "Two-thirds of the doctors you had referring patients are now sending them somewhere else."

"My patient load is full."

"You haven't even replaced one of the doctors you lost." Her anger increased. "Have you?"

"I'm getting new patients every day--lots of them. You know that."

"And how many of your new Witness patients are you doing for free?"

Lapin sipped his drink. He didn't reply.

"How many?"

"The ones that can't afford the operations still need them."

"What about us? What about the things we need? How do you propose we'll be able to afford them when you do free operations and then care for patients in our home?"

Lapin put down his drink and walked out of the room.
"What about us?" she shouted after him.

He went outside, then into the garage where he found
a shovel. His frustration was vented and his anxiety
relieved as he attacked the flower bed with a
vengeance. He dug like a man possessed, releasing his
pent-up hostility shovelful after shovelful. Faster
and faster. Over and over.

Two hours later when he was done, he felt better
inside and out--all except for his hands. Exhaustion
had brought peace to his mental state, but his hands
were now blistered beyond repair. He couldn't operate
for a week. He had paid a premium price.

The next day he hired a full-time gardener and a
part-time housekeeper. Maureen increased her acting
classes to three nights per week.

***

Lapin walked down the hallway studying some X-rays
and dictating medication orders to a trailing nurse.
As they passed a nurses' station, his attention was
diverted by a flashing red light on the wall panel
that indicated a patient was somehow in need. Two
nurses stood talking at the station, oblivious to the
call request.

"Whose patient?" Lapin asked impatiently.

The nurses turned and glanced at the light. "Mine,
doctor," the younger one said.

The other chimed in with a lackadaisical tone, "It's
the leg amputee. She always wants something."

"Mrs. Turner?" Lapin inquired.

The young nurse nodded. "The diabetic--that's her."

Lapin was irritated at their negligence. "So you
just ignore her?"

"She always wants something," the other nurse said.
"She's a real crank."

It was an attitude Lapin wouldn't tolerate and his
reply was firm. "If you don't want to work with
cranky people, go work for a vet. Now one of you go
see what she wants."

With that Lapin walked away and continued to study
the X-rays.

One nurse whispered cantankerously, "What Mrs.
Turner wants is a new left leg."

The other nurse nodded in agreement. "Lots of

luck."

The public address system droned in the background. "Doctor Lapin, call the operator please. Doctor Lapin. . . ."

"This is Doctor Lapin," he said into the nearest receiver.

"Doctor," the operator replied, "you have an emergency call. Should I put it through?"

Lapin exhaled a deep sigh. "Of course," he said. Two clicks on the phone, then, "This is Doctor Lapin."

"Doctor. . . ." There was hesitancy in her voice, a tone Lapin had become familiar with as callers would try to control their sense of panic. "This is Shannon Stewart. . . ." Then the voice failed. Lapin could sense the urgency and tried to calm her.

"It's okay," he softly reassured her. "What can I do for you?"

Mrs. Stewart explained that her seventeen-year-old son Brian had fallen off a horse. He'd developed severe acidic stomach pains, and she had taken him to Riverside Hospital. The emergency room doctors diagnosed the problem as a ruptured spleen and said it needed to be removed immediately. Brian was in shock from the loss of blood. Lapin could hear the woman softly crying in the background.

"Mrs. Stewart," he said, "are you in the Truth?"

"Yes, doctor . . . we are. Can you help us?"

"Nobody there will do anything?"

"They don't want to get involved." She began to cry again. "All they want to do is give blood to my boy."

"Tell you what you do," Lapin said. "You get your son over here as soon as you can and we'll take care of him."

Lapin called the emergency room and told them to page him as soon as the Stewarts arrived. The anesthesiologist, of course, had to be briefed on the probable procedure. He reached Donnelly in the surgeons' lounge.

Donnelly was elderly in both appearance and behavior, so much so that it seemed like he'd been around forever. He often fell prey to paranoia, hyperactivity, or migraine headaches--perhaps the consequence of two unsuccessful marriages. But the man was persistent: he was working on his third.

Donnelly not only worked on Lapin's first bloodless operation at Bristol, but worked on most of them since. Despite his age and personal problems, he was a capable anesthesiologist who could adapt to critical situations. That was important.

Donnelly experienced serious mood swings due to his home life, but generally speaking his moods were low. The residuals of his problem-filled life surfaced inside the operating room in the form of grumbling and complaining. Then, too, the man had the nastiest habit of downgrading everybody on the team behind their backs. He was crafty! He never soiled his own hands, but always managed to cleverly manipulate others to do his dirty work for him. Lapin certainly didn't like his antics, but realized Donnelly was the best available anesthesiologist at the time.

Donnelly was part of the hospital's status quo, the old guard. He fell into line with fellow staffers who were complacent, lethargic, and old. They were comfortable in their staid and stoic environment. It was safe. Their stale, musty existence had become their haven. Without benefit of hiding behind modern technology, their mediocrity was glaring. Based on their narrow perceptions of their environment, they had no reason to become any better at what they did.

"What's the big deal?" older staff members questioned when Lapin began working there. What they saw was a young, flashy surgeon making waves and challenging them to be better. What they didn't understand was the fact that waves create the necessary motivation to stir up positive, beneficial change in patient care.

Lapin was clearly disliked by those staff members, but he was more than familiar with that kind of situation. He had a propensity to push himself and his people to the limit and beyond. Most people are uncomfortable when their potential is put to the test. They feel threatened that a well-concealed truth may rear its ugly head and expose their shortcomings.

On the other hand, Donnelly grew to like Lapin after working with him for several months. He respected Lapin's talent and abilities. He went so far as to refer some of his own private patients to him. Nonetheless, Donnelly began keeping a notebook of everything he felt might be used against Lapin in the future. Lapin was totally unaware of this unorthodox behavior.

Dr. Lapin had almost singlehandedly provided an economic bonanza to a lame administration. Their only contributing share, however, was to leave him alone to practice good medicine.

This state of affairs severely bothered most of the old-timers. They became unnecessarily critical of Lapin and his work because, by comparison, their own abilities were being tested and questioned.

Still, Donnelly was capable. He felt he had observed Lapin enough to understand both the extent of his capabilities and the limitations of bloodless surgery. The case of the Stewart boy bothered him. A spleen removal could be a bloody, dangerous operation. When Lapin explained the boy's situation, the anesthesiologist grew reluctant. He really didn't want to be involved.

Without cooperation from Donnelly, the operation couldn't be done. He agreed to postpone his final decision until after the boy was at least examined.

Lapin liked Brian instantly. He reminded him of Ari . . . of how much he missed his son . . . and of how long it had been since they'd been together. Brian was articulate, intelligent, and very well informed. Lapin asked Mrs. Stewart if he could talk with the boy alone. She agreed.

As the door closed behind them, Brian spoke first. "Doctor, I know what you want to talk to me about and I also want you to know that I understand the situation . . . I really do." His voice was short of breath and very weak.

Lapin was amused at the boy's assertiveness. "You do, huh?" he said, smiling.

"Yes, sir, I do. You want to talk to me about the blood issue."

Lapin smiled again. "I guess you do."

"I want you to know," Brian continued, "that I understand how serious this is, and that I might even die if I don't take blood. . . ."

"That's a possibility," Lapin replied.

"I'm willing to do that--to die, rather than break God's law. I just wanted you to know that so you won't try to talk me into taking blood."

"Feel pretty strongly about it, don't you?" the surgeon asked.

"I feel strongly about God's Word, the Bible, and doing what He tells me to do. It says in Leviticus. . . ."

Lapin waved his hand. Brian stopped. "I know what it says in Leviticus . . . and all the other Scriptures, too." Lapin needed a pause in their conversation at this point to concentrate on the examination. He pressed on Brian's left flank and the boy grimaced with pain.

"Bad?" he asked.

"Real bad," Brian said, catching his breath.

"Relax. Just try to take it easy." Lapin released the pressure. After administering a mild local anesthetic, he inserted a needle into Brian's abdominal cavity. He found blood that he'd hoped wouldn't be there, indicating that the boy was having massive internal bleeding. It was worse than Lapin thought; his face betrayed him.

"Now it's my turn," Brian said. "Bad, isn't it?"

"I'm not going to kid you. It needs to be fixed right away."

"And without blood . . . you promised." It was a statement rather than a question.

Lapin looked at the youngster and thought about Ari again. He took a moment to think, and then he answered, "Without blood."

After X-rays were taken, Lapin ordered large amounts of normal saline and starch solution. These infusions were to build up the body fluid levels by replacing what was lost.

"Prep him for surgery," he told a nurse as he left the room. Once outside, he confronted Mrs. Stewart with the seriousness of the situation. Her son was in bad shape--real bad shape.

But Lapin still exuded confidence. His belief in his own abilities was evidenced not only by words, but by deeds. He emphasized that every operative procedure carries a certain risk factor. The risk in this particular case was abnormally high, he added, but had to be taken or the boy would surely die from the hemorrhaging.

Mrs. Stewart was strong. Lapin was once again overwhelmed by the intrinsic quality of deep faith in the Jehovah's Witnesses he'd come to know.

"You have a fine son," he told her.

"We're very proud of him."

"Where's your husband?" Lapin asked. "Does he know you're here?"

"Yes, I phoned him. He should be on his way, doctor." She guarded her next words as if delivering a great confession. "My husband--I mean my ex-husband--and I are divorced." She seemed embarrassed by the statement.

"I see," Lapin acknowledged.

"Possibly not," Mrs. Stewart replied. "My husband--ex-husband--isn't a Witness. He used to be, but he's not anymore." Lapin sensed that the words caused the woman great pain.

"Everything's going to be just fine," he assured her.

"Thank you, doctor. You're a good person and a brave man."

"If you'll excuse me now."

A nurse showed Mrs. Stewart to a quiet room. She was then joined by several other Witnesses who were very encouraging to her and to Lapin.

I'll take all the help I can get, Lapin thought to himself. *Anytime, anyplace, from anybody.* He stopped to talk with Brian again while the boy was being prepped.

Brian was filled with sincerity. There was still room in his heart to empathize with Lapin and the position in which he had placed himself.

"You don't want to do it, do you, doc?" the boy asked quietly.

"Everything's going to be just fine," Lapin insisted. "You just relax and take it easy. You're in good hands with Lapin."

Brian smiled. "You're Jewish, aren't you?"

Lapin feigned surprise. "You noticed. . . ."

"Have you studied the Bible, doctor?"

"Uh huh," he said, rechecking X-rays and charts.

"Then you really do know what Jehovah says about blood?"

"Pretty much, but the important thing is how you feel about it. If you believe you shouldn't have blood transfusions or blood products, I think your rights should be respected."

"How do you feel . . . I mean, personally?"

"I feel everybody should have the best medical care available when they're sick, regardless of their religious beliefs. It's just that simple. I also think that you're in charge of your own body."

"Wonder why more people don't feel that way?"

"Got me," Lapin hedged. "That's a good question." Lapin didn't feel the youngster needed to hear his truthful answer at that very moment. He held back his philosophy of why other physicians feared facing the unknown--facing something different, something outside the textbook realm, or something undefined in the

standard practice code--but facing something challenging just the same.

"Were you born in the Truth?" Lapin asked.

"Yes," Brian began. "I was baptized when I was
twelve. Next year, when I graduate from high school,
I'm going to pioneer full-time."

"Go door-to-door? Full-time?"

"Yes, sir. Six days a week."

Lapin was a little surprised. "Given any thought
to college?" he prompted.

"I thought about it awhile. But Jehovah's work of
telling people about the Kingdom is our primary
concern. We're looking forward to eternal life--if we
follow Jehovah's guidance. That's worth a lot more
than a college degree or a good job. That's worth
everything!"

Lapin didn't respond.

"Does that bother you?" Brian asked.

"Not if that's really what you want to do. What
does your dad think about it?"

"We don't talk very much. . . ."

"Oh," Lapin grunted.

". . . not since he left the Truth."

"Oh," he repeated insightfully.

"The Bible says we're not supposed to associate much
with worldly people, unless we're spreading the good
news. That's why Witnesses kind of . . . stick together and don't really bother anybody."

"A lot of people might argue with that."

"Because we ring doorbells and things?"

". . . and things."

"To be one of Jehovah's Witnesses means to witness
to all people. It's a biblical requirement that we
preach the good news of the Kingdom and make disciples
of all nations and all people."

"But what about the fact that a lot of people are
perfectly happy with their own religions?"

"Doctor," Brian began slowly. It was almost as if
he were teaching a pre-schooler. "As Witnesses, we're
merely following the example of Jesus Christ. That
can't be bad, can it?"

"Hard to argue with that."

"Christ went to the Jews, and the Jews had their own
religion, but in many ways it contradicted the Word of
God. Also, it was time for some basic changes to be
made."

"Sounds like you've studied."

102

"All my life. I spend about twenty-five hours a week studying the Bible." Lapin was touched by the boy's dedication and sincerity. Brian continued, "All nations and people have religion of one kind or another, either so-called Christian or non-Christian. Churches send out missionaries all the time to convert people from one religion to another. It's important that a person's beliefs conform to the Bible's teachings, but a great deal of the time, they don't."

"Like what?" Lapin asked.

"An example?" Brian said.

"Sure. . . ."

"Like do unto others as you would have them do unto you. . . ." Brian's voice was getting weaker.

But the importance and significance of the youngster's words hit home hard--especially under the circumstances they were both facing. The boy was right. The world basically exists in a do-as-I-say, not-as-I-do state. It's a mentality perpetuated by individuals who feel they're above the law, whether it be man's or God's. It's the feeling of being able to get away with something that seemingly was handed down from generation to generation.

We all inherently know what's right and what's wrong. If we live within an allegedly civilized society, we have little excuse for deviating from those standards. Why, then, do so many violate the principles and the laws that we surely know and accept as right? The wife or child beater commits this atrocity, but so many times hears later from the innocent victim, "It's all right. I understand." A criminal robs a store or an individual on Friday night, only to be exonerated by his confession on Saturday afternoon. "It's all right. Don't worry. Don't do it again."

But they do repeat the act again. We all do. *Why?* Lapin thought, *Why? And why the medical injustice practiced daily on these Jehovah's Witnesses? These people of God--they don't do anything to hurt anyone. Their contact with society and the world at large is solely for the purpose of sharing what they believe to be the truth according to the Bible, God's Holy Word. Why are they so misunderstood and mistreated?*

As an Israeli Jew who'd spent the formative years of his life among survivors of concentration camps, Lapin could relate to their persecution. He couldn't comprehend it, but could relate to it.

"Doctor Lapin," the nurse said, opening the door. "Brian's father is here." The nurse made eye contact with Lapin and continued, "He'd like to speak with you . . . rather badly."

Lapin clearly got her drift. So did Brian. "You promised, doctor, you promised," the youngster invoked.

"I promised," Lapin reassured him. Then he directed the nurse, "You take good care of him. He's a very special young man."

"Anything you say, Doctor Kildare," the nurse confirmed with an exaggerated wink.

Brian laughed and that was good. A healthy attitude was beneficial, especially now.

"You laugh?" Lapin teased, going along with the flow. "That's where I got my license--watching Kildare and Ben Casey on TV." Brian enjoyed the light-hearted diversion. He was more relaxed, and that, too, was important. Lapin continued, "I'm gonna make you a star."

With that he left the room. Then he stood alone in the hallway for a second, basking in a profound thought. *Wouldn't it be nice,* he thought, *to leave them all laughing.* He offered a silent prayer that the laughter would still be going on this time tomorrow. *God's will,* he thought, then corrected himself, *Jehovah's will.*

The seconds spent alone were never long enough. A man from down the hall started to approach him with great determination, almost with a vengeance in his stride. Lapin knew who it was. Introductions weren't necessary, but they took place as usual.

"Doctor Lapin," the man said, nearly out of breath from the walk. "I'm Brian's father. It's rather important that I speak with you."

"Yes, Mr. Stewart, we've been expecting you." He led the troubled father into a deserted waiting room.

"I'm Bill Stewart," the man said, extending his hand.

"I know," Lapin replied, with a firm shake.

"Of course you do . . . of course. . . ." Stewart stammered for words. He was characteristically nervous under the circumstances.

"Mr. Stewart," Lapin said, "your son is in good hands. We're going to do everything humanly possible for him. I want you to be assured of that." Lapin spoke with tranquil confidence. He wanted to induce that feeling in the father, too.

Stewart seemed to react positively to the calming technique. He took a deep breath and rubbed his eyes. He was clearly troubled. He then produced a silver-plated case from his inside coat pocket and placed a cigarette between his lips. After locating the matching lighter, he touched the electronic dot to ignite a spark.

Lapin noticed Stewart's hand shaking as he held the flame to the end of the cigarette. He inhaled deeply and blew the smoke toward the ceiling. Lapin waited patiently.

"How bad is it, doc?" he finally asked.

"The spleen is badly damaged. We have to stop the bleeding immediately."

"Could he die?" The question was delivered with a degree of calm that Lapin hadn't expected.

Without any hesitancy, he answered, "That's a possibility, but as I said, everything that can be done is being done . . . and we all have the greatest faith. . . ."

"Doctor," Stewart interrupted, "we're not talking about faith here. We're talking about facts. We're talking about life and death. Anybody else's life and death doesn't matter to me. This is my only son. Damn it, doctor, can you identify with that?"

"I can appreciate that," Lapin said as Ari's image flashed through his mind.

"I want to be absolutely certain that you do," Stewart replied.

Then he crushed out the half-smoked cigarette and immediately lit another. His mood changed dramatically. His pupils began to dilate and his intensity magnified. "I suppose Shannon told you that we're divorced . . . and that I'm not a 'practicing Witness' any more."

Lapin nodded. "I could tell that from the fact that you were smoking," Lapin answered understandingly.

Stewart paced for a moment, then stood looking out the window with his back to Lapin. He spoke clearly and slowly. "I suppose the question of using blood or not using blood has been discussed."

"Yes. Brian and I talked about it. He brought it up."

"That's why he's here--with you--isn't it?" The tone was crisp, cold, and businesslike.

Lapin felt the attitude change. He chose his words

very carefully. "I'm not exactly sure what you mean."

"Because you're the bloodless surgeon. . . ."

It was coming and Lapin knew it. "I'm a surgeon, yes. I've operated on several hundred Jehovah's Witnesses without using blood. . . ."

Stewart slowly turned and faced the young doctor. His steel gray eyes were piercing, focused, direct. "Now I want to discuss the blood issue."

Lapin knew what was coming. Stewart walked toward him and stopped about three feet away. It was going to be another direct confrontation.

"When Shannon called," he began, "I knew this was going to happen--at least, I was afraid it would. I spoke with my personal physician and he referred me to a surgeon. They confirmed each other's theory."

"And what was that?" Lapin prompted. A degree of defensiveness crept into his voice, which he immediately tried to control.

"That a spleen repair or removal can be tricky, dangerous, and, more often than not, a bloody procedure."

"I could have told you that."

Stewart stared squarely into Lapin's eyes. "I was also advised that it shouldn't be attempted without a transfusion--probably a major transfusion," he confronted.

The man has been coached well, Lapin thought to himself.

Stewart's words turned icy cold. "Understand this," he demanded, "I'm not a Witness any more. What any of them do is none of my concern. I don't care. But I do care about that boy in there. He's my blood." Stewart's voice grew louder as his anger grew more pronounced. "I want blood in that room and I want it in that boy . . . do you understand that?"

Trying to argue would have been fruitless. Lapin stayed calm and continued speaking in a monotone. "Mr. Stewart, I've done several spleen repairs and removals . . . all without transfusions . . . all successful. . . ."

"I don't care what you've done," Stewart interrupted. "That's my son. I'm totally aware of the danger of this operation, and I want you to guarantee me that you'll give him blood."

Now it was Lapin's turn to walk to the window. His posture was erect; his principles, unbending. "I've promised your son that I'd respect his religious beliefs."

"Oh yeah?" Stewart badgered sarcastically. "Well, let me share this with you. That boy's a minor, and you don't have any choice in the matter. I also talked with my lawyer . . . and if that kid needs blood and doesn't get it, I'll finish you. Right now my lawyer is getting a court order to make sure there's blood in that operating room. . . ."

Lapin grimaced. This was the first time he had been faced with this type of dilemma.

The father's wrath became more apparent with each spoken word. "And I'll tell you another thing. If I were you, I sure as hell wouldn't throw away a promising career on a bunch of mindless robots who won't even salute the flag or fight for their country. Someday you're gonna need them and if they won't defend their country, you better believe they won't stand up for you. They don't do anything unless the headquarters in Brooklyn tells them to. You're like me, doctor; you're worldly. You're not in the Truth-- whatever the hell the Truth is."

The two men looked at each other. The thought of having a philosophical discussion at this particular moment never crossed Lapin's mind. His only concern was for Brian. He opened his mouth to reiterate that point, but Stewart spoke. "If that boy needs blood, he's gonna have it." And with that, the father left the room.

Lapin was alone again. The caustic remarks that Stewart spat out didn't bother him. He'd heard them all before. Oh, they used to bother him some, especially in the beginning, but Hutchins had been patient and complete with his teachings and explanations. Now Lapin could quickly dismiss such misguided remarks.

With detailed expertise, Herk had taken the time to carefully outline court cases that the Witnesses had won. During the 1930s and 1940s, hundreds of Witnesses were arrested for doing the work they reverently deemed to be God's. Court cases were fought in the interest of preserving freedom of speech, press, assembly, and worship--constitutional rights that we all expect to be ours. However, in the case of the Witnesses--a small but growing band of people who interpret the Bible accurately--constitutional rights seemed to be viewed differently.

And so, they went to court. In the United States, the land of the free, appeals from lower court

107

decisions resulted in the Witnesses winning forty-three cases before the Supreme Court. Similarly, favorable judgments had been obtained from high courts in countries throughout the world. It had been legally determined that the constitutional rights of Jehovah's Witnesses were to be upheld. They had unfortunately won very few legal victories over the blood transfusion issue, however. The moral casualties were many on those battle grounds.

Herk had told Lapin that Professor C. S. Braden, in his book *These Also Believe,* said of the Witnesses: "They have performed a definite service to democracy by their fight to preserve their civil rights, for in their struggle they have done much to secure those rights for every minority group in America."

On the question of their non-involvement in politics or voting, Herk explained that just as Jesus did not take sides in political matters, so Jehovah's Witnesses remain neutral and are not found to be members of one political party or another. They do not participate in nationalistic movements. They follow God's Word carefully and therefore are a most law-abiding people. They never get involved with subversive acts, sedition, or revolutionary activities; but rather, they put their full trust and hope in God's Kingdom under Christ. By obeying God's laws and living Christian lives, they are an influence for good in every community and contribute to the public order and morality of every country.

Lapin found these principles to be sound and logical. By contrast, other people who were unaware of the Witnesses' beliefs or the motivation behind them were quick to criticize their thoughts, stands, and actions. How clearly the oft-attacked Lapin could relate once again.

Lapin had heard many others before Stewart assault Witness philosophies, but he knew the truth of the matter. He knew, for example, that Witnesses don't fight for or defend their country because Biblical law commands Christians not to kill. The Scriptures instruct them to lay down their lives for their Christian brothers, but certainly not to take their brothers' lives. Obviously then, if they did fight in their countries' wars, Witnesses from one nation would be killing Witnesses from another nation. Jesus, in the book of John, said: "My kingdom is no part of this world. If my kingdom were part of this world, my attendants would have fought. . . ."

The teachings made sense. If the philosophy could be universally accepted, it would totally eliminate the waste of human lives brought about by the idiocy of war.

But for the moment, Lapin was a part of this world-- an important part. Brian Stewart, a minor, needed his spleen fixed. Mrs. Stewart had Lapin paged over the P.A. When he picked up the nearest phone, she explained that she needed to see him right away. The pressure mounted as he waited to meet her.

Her facial expression announced the fact that she was upset. She had just finished talking with her ex-husband, Bill.

"Look," she said, "Bill isn't a Witness any more because he wasn't willing to stifle his personal desires for the sake of the Truth. He began to smoke, drink, run around. . . ." Tears rolled down her cheeks. "He became obsessed with his business. He gave up everything to succeed in that business of his: Brian, me, his faith. And he doesn't have custody of our son. I do."

Lapin listened intently. Time was running out. The operation would begin soon. She continued, "He was disfellowshipped from the congregation."

Lapin was familiar with the phrase, but unfamiliar with its meaning. He thought that one of Jehovah's Witnesses being disfellowshipped was comparable to being stoned to death.

"Now," she said, "he's bitter, antagonistic, and vocal toward all of us--I mean the followers of the Truth."

"Mrs. Stewart," Lapin interrupted politely, "it's about time for us to get started."

After a deep breath, the woman composed herself. "There's one more thing," she said. "Bill told me about the court order and how he insisted that you give Brian blood if it's needed."

"That's what he said."

"Well, if you put blood in that boy--against his wishes and your promise--I guarantee you'll never have another Witness as a patient."

Lapin was stunned, but only momentarily. He was caught between the proverbial rock and a hard place. The factions involved were all pulling him in different directions--his promise to the boy, the father's threat, and now the threat from the mother.

But he had to deal with first things first.

And the very first thing was Donnelly, the anesthesiologist. Lapin ran into him in the hallway leading to the operating room.

"I talked to the boy's father," Donnelly said.

"So did I. . . ."

"I still don't think we should do it without blood. I don't know about you, Ron, but I don't want to risk the repercussions."

"Don't have any choice; the boy's bleeding to death."

Donnelly shot him a look. "You know what I mean."

And Lapin did. They reached the surgeons' sinks and he began to scrub. Brian could be seen in the background through an open door. He was on the table, waiting first for Donnelly and then for Lapin to save his life.

"Did the court order requested by Brian's father arrive yet?" Lapin asked quickly.

Donnelly whispered in a low hissing sound, "No, and I think we should wait till it gets here to start. You know that Mr. Stewart's attorney is out there threatening the hospital administrator."

"Can't worry about that. We've got to start now." Donnelly nervously began to scrub. But then, he was always nervous.

Lapin calmly pointed to the boy and insisted, "We don't have time to stand out here and discuss it . . . we're going to do it without blood in the room."

"If you lose that boy--that minor--you'll lose your license, plain and simple," Donnelly warned. "The kid's father is serious. He'll nail you. It's your license, not mine. You're the surgeon."

Lapin smiled. "How many times have we heard that?" Then he quickly continued before Donnelly could answer, "And how many spleens have we fixed?"

Donnelly interrupted, "Ron, look . . . I know you're good. Hell, you're the best. But you can't spend your entire life on that tight rope. It's not worth it. I don't think these people are worth it."

Neither spoke for a moment. Lapin continued to scrub. He looked straight ahead as he spoke. "That boy believes his eternal life will be jeopardized if we go against the Bible's teachings . . . and they are not 'these people.'"

"I know all about that," Donnelly mumbled. "I'm sorry."

110

"I know you do. And you also know that the only reason we're here is to provide the best medical care that we can without violating their religious beliefs. That's what we set out to do. Witnesses are coming to us from all over the country and from all around the world because they trust us."

"They have good reasons," Donnelly pointed out.

"Yeah . . . like no place else to go. We're their last shot, their last hope. Without us, they go home and die a slow, painful death. Do you want that on your conscience?"

"No, but I don't want the loss of your license bothering my conscience either."

"That's my problem . . . not your's."

The two doctors looked at each other. Lapin put his hand on Donnelly's shoulder. "The Witnesses have made a commitment. And so have we. If we break our promise now and lose their trust, we'll lose everything that we've worked so hard for . . . like integrity . . . and honesty . . . and principles. . . . Those things must be worth something in today's inflationary world."

"And just how do you intend to pull this thing off?" Donnelly asked.

In a quiet, introspective manner, Lapin answered, "I'm a realistic Jew, and, as such, I believe in miracles. If a Jew doesn't believe in miracles, he's not realistic."

Neither man's expression changed. Donnelly turned and walked into the operating room.

A few moments later, everything in the room appeared normal by the team's standards, but the electricity flowing between Lapin and Donnelly was incredible. They were both frightened.

Brian was under, the initial incision was made, and the electric knife was used skillfully. The operation couldn't have been more successful. Skin to skin in twenty minutes. The spleen had to be removed because it was badly torn. The total blood loss during surgery was one hundred c.c.s.

As he left the operating room, a stranger handed Lapin an envelope. He read the contents, smiled, and handed it back to the deliverer. "Don't think we'll be needing this today," he said. It was the court order for blood. He'd won again.

***

Except for Martha, his faithful and trusted house-keeper, the house was empty when he got home late that night. She served the dinner that she'd kept waiting for him and then left for home. Nine empty chairs and him. He still wore his surgical greens. The entertainment that once filled this room on a regular basis was now a thing of the past. It would be no more. The house was quiet.

Because of the ever-increasing time spent at her acting classes, Maureen had taken an apartment in Los Angeles. This was only to change clothes and rest, she explained. He suspected differently. In a few nights, Lapin was supposed to see her in a student production. He didn't really want to go, but he'd promised. Somehow he couldn't forget the words he'd spoken to her when they first discussed her acting classes. "If you start these classes, it'll be the end of our marriage." That now seemed so long ago. *The prophet speaks*, he thought to himself. *How fascinating*.

The scene, she explained, was being directed by Ed Asner. It was the love scene from *Picnic*. Lapin wasn't looking forward to that evening. He'd seen the picture.

He toyed with his food, pushing it from one side of the plate to the other. Ethan walked into the dining room and sat at Lapin's side, not asking for anything. Ethan was just there, the unquestioning and loyal companion. Lapin patted the dog's head and gave him half the steak on his plate.

Reflectively, his mind drifted back to Brian's operation earlier that day. He'd defied the odds and won again, but how long could he continue to beat the odds? He couldn't figure out why the intensity of this particular surgery had been so great. He had successfully completed several hundred operations. He had extended lifetimes. He had received praise and adulation. What more could he want? It must have been that the boy reminded him so much of Ari.

Lapin patted Ethan again and walked across the room to the telephone. He dialed a long distance number and listened to the phone ring ten times before he hung up. *She's probably still in class*, he lied to himself.

Just as he sat back down, the telephone rang.

"This is Doctor Lapin," he said.

112

"Doctor Lapin?" The voice was female, far away, and very frightened. He knew instantly that it was a caller on the hot line. The majority of the calls were routed directly to Lapin. It provided many sleepless nights for him, but most assuredly, some restful nights for others.

"Yes, go ahead," he said.

"This is Carolyn Adams. . . ." There was a long silent pause.

Lapin spoke up, "Are you in the Truth?"

"Yes . . . yes, I am."

"What congregation?" He'd learned the necessity of putting his callers at ease. In most cases, by the time they found out about Lapin and his work on the West Coast, they'd been to several doctors, had possibly been to Mexico, were refused treatment, and were shunned by the medical profession in general. Lapin could appreciate how difficult it was for them to accept that they'd really found someone who would respect their religious beliefs after such a long, arduous, unsuccessful quest.

"I'm in the South Brook Congregation," she said, "in Columbus, Ohio."

Lapin conveyed both confidence and empathy. "How did you get the hot line number?" he asked.

"You operated on Brother Chaplin . . . from Pittsburgh."

"Oh, yes. How is he?"

"He's fine, and he asked me to say hello. He wanted to thank you again."

The woman seemed to have calmed down somewhat.

"What seems to be the problem?"

She answered hesitantly, "It's my heart. Several doctors have told me I need open heart surgery."

"And they won't do it?"

"No."

"What did they say? What do the X-rays show?"

"They said I've got an irregular heartbeat and a blockage in two of the arteries. They also said I might need a replacement for the heart valve that was damaged by rheumatic fever when I was a child."

"Any pain now?"

"On and off. Sometimes it's very painful. They said my condition is serious and that I should have the surgery soon . . . but I'm. . . ." The words trailed off as she began to cry.

"Well then, sister," he said, "I suggest we get it

done real soon. I want you to get all your records and X-rays together. . . ."

"Doctor Lapin," she interrupted, "we don't have much money and I'm afraid my insurance isn't very good." Her muffled sobs grew louder.

"Tell you what," he offered; "let's not worry about money now. Let's take care of you first. Send all your records to my office so I can review them with the two cardiac surgeons who work with us. I'll call you immediately afterwards to arrange for your surgery out here."

"But the. . . ."

"Look . . . if all you can manage is to make small monthly payments to the hospital, I'll talk to the other surgeons and we'll do the surgery for nothing. All you need to do is get out here as soon as you can."

The sobs continued. "Doctor, I can't believe this. What they said about you is true!"

"You just get your records to me as soon as you can. You're going to be fine."

"Thank you, Doctor Lapin. Thank you! I'll have them in the mail tomorrow."

"Okay, dear. Now listen, if you have any trouble at all or want to know anything, you call me, okay?"

"Okay."

"Promise?"

"I promise."

Lapin could practically hear the woman smiling. He had given her comfort where there'd been none in a long time. He felt remarkably good. "Okay. You take care and I'll talk with you soon. Bye-bye."

He slowly returned the receiver to its cradle and seemed to study it for awhile. He thought of all the callers--all the strangers--who somehow found him when they'd run out of hope or places to look for it. How hard it was for some to believe he'd perform major surgery on them without violating their stand on the blood issue--and sometimes without charge.

"How can you charge if they can't afford it?" he'd answer his critics. "And how can you let them die because of a financial condition?" It seemed to go against the basic foundation of the oath physicians take when graduating from med school.

On one hand, Dr. Lapin was criticized by his colleagues for working outside the medical standard of care by refusing to transfuse blood, and on the other

114

hand, for performing so many free operations.

The concept of free surgery upset a lot of people. Lapin felt that his position, though unpopular, was humane. He was not only willing to do what others refused to do, but was willing to do it without charge when the situation warranted that consideration.

He was a capable physician who was willing to negotiate under special circumstances. That differed considerably from the mainstream of medical professionals. To him, it was unconditionally wrong that any human should be denied the best medical care available because of his financial situation or his religious conviction.

Retired physicians joined the ranks of Lapin's critics. His stock answer to their charges was reduced to a single phrase, "If they're right and I'm wrong . . . then I prefer to be wrong." With supreme confidence in his position, he committed himself to that philosophy. But it was just that--those daily challenges that he posed to the medical community-- which persuaded his peers to draw away from him as a friend.

He patted Ethan on the head again and stared into the lonely California night. He looked around as the question crossed his mind of whether or not he was following the right path . . . doing the right thing. He searched for a divine clue.

His life would have most certainly been easier had he not taken the first Witness patient. Sure, he had the material comforts that most people only dream about: the house, the cars, the money, the security. *Security?* He laughed to himself. *Not quite! There's no security when you put your career on the chopping block every time you put a knife to someone's skin, half a dozen times a day.*

Had he followed the normal surgeon's path--followed the rules, played the political games, and not made waves--he would, by now, be spending far less time making far more money. He could have spent more time developing personal relationships with family and friends. Maureen might have been home that very minute, rather than . . . wherever she was.

He would have been respected by his colleagues, rather than accused and avoided by them. The middle-of-the-road existence would certainly have been easier. But to Ron Lapin, that barren, easy road held out a sense of boredom rather than one of purpose and genuine accomplishment.

As he walked through the large, empty house, the thought occurred to him. *What if,* he thought, *what if I didn't choose to follow this path, but was being led down it. . . .* The phone rang. His thought was incomplete, but stirring. *What if I am being led.* An inner peace came over him; he knew he'd never again question what he was doing.

At this time of night, the caller was sure to be a Witness on the hot line--someone who needed him. As he reached for the phone, he now understood for the very first time that he needed them, too.

5

Calls on the hot line increased daily. As time went
by, so did requests from potential patients for
surgical procedures outside Lapin's specialty.
Recognizing a need to provide a full range of surgical
specialties to these "second-class" patients, Lapin
embarked on an intense mission to convince the best
specialists available to work on the Witnesses, the
JWs, without using blood. It made no difference to
him that his action closely paralleled that of the
Witnesses in spreading the Truth as they saw it to a
worldly society.

His first target was Chuck Bonnett, a warm, friendly
individual who had mastered the field of orthopedic
surgery as well as he had the game of golf. At first
Bonnett brushed off Lapin's proposal saying, "Listen,
Ron, I have the most successful orthopedic group in
Southern California. Why should I risk it for people
who are nothing more than a liability?"

Lapin backed off at this point by stressing, "I
asked you to do this, Chuck, not because I want any
old orthopedic surgeon, but because I want the very
best. So just think about it for awhile."

A few weeks later he met Bonnett in the doctors'
dining room and prompted, "Chuck, I have a seventy-
two-year-old man who needs his right hip replaced.
Why don't you do it . . . and I'll take care of the
blood."

Bonnett grinned as he said, "Ron, I probably should
have my head examined, but I'd better just do it
before you get to be any more of a pain in the neck."

The total hip replacement procedure was masterfully
done with minimal blood loss. After they removed the
patient from the operating table, Bonnett shook

117

Lapin's hand and said in a joyous voice, "Anytime you want to put someone on my operating table and assist me, I'll operate. And thanks, Ron. Thank you very much for making me aware that not everything I learned in med school was the last word."

In a low, modest voice, Lapin answered, "Chuck, the secret to my success with these patients is that I seldom allow my schooling to interfere with my education."

"I admire your courage, Ron. Just always be sure to cover your flank."

In a revealing self-analysis, Lapin concluded the conversation by adding, "The first thing I learned at the Kibbutz in Israel where I was raised was 'he who dares, wins.'"

Dr. Mohan Roy, a cardiac surgeon with golden hands and lightning speed, was also an easy recruit. To Lapin's request that he operate without using blood, he merely answered in his typical laconic fashion, "Just bring them in . . . just bring them in."

Ken Neugebauer, a thoracic surgeon, spent twenty years of his life in the United States Navy where he'd acquired a wealth of surgical experience as well as an alcohol problem. After his divorce he joined Alcoholics Anonymous and got the malignancy under control, but his life lacked purpose. He welcomed the opportunity to join the team and remained one of its strongest supporters.

Mahmood Zia, a urologist from Pakistan who did his post-graduate work in England, simply responded to Lapin's request by saying, "Blood? What's that? I never use the stuff. . . ."

In rapid succession, all surgical and medical vacancies were filled more than twice over, giving Lapin the opportunity to cover every medical problem under one roof and without blood. To gather a group of such dedicated physicians--professionals willing to stand up and be counted--was difficult enough, but accomplishing it in conservative Orange County, California, was nothing short of a miracle. But then, Lapin was a "realistic" Jew.

***

"Babcock," Lapin said, indicating a clamp was needed to hold back the stomach wall from obstructing his view.

118

The lady's stomach was laced with cancer. The tumor had grown to the point of penetrating through the stomach walls and into the lower edge of the liver. It looked bad. It had eroded its way into a major blood vessel and was bleeding profusely. They'd been in the operating room too long, over an hour and a half. With the Witnesses, you have to do everything medically possible the first time around because undergoing another procedure could be particularly difficult for them.

"Blood loss?" Lapin asked, never breaking his intense concentration as he looked single-mindedly at the patient.

"Three-fifty c.c.s," Marilyn answered. The loss was not only tolerable, but unbelievably low for a patient who had been open this long.

"Right angle . . . I have to free the common bile duct from this mass," Lapin muttered, requesting another clamp. But this time, the right angle clamp was in his hand before he finished saying the words.

"What are you, psychic or what?" he kidded.

"Just tryin' to pay attention," Smitty kidded back.

"Don't tell me that . . . you want my job."

"You've got a point there. . . ."

The light conversation was all part of the operative procedure. No one's attention ever wandered from the patient or the seriousness of what they were doing. They were all professionals and did their jobs with an unparalleled degree of competence.

Smitty, Marilyn, and Mikie were all OR students on a rotation round through Bristol Hospital. While training them, Lapin pleasantly discovered their ability to both relate and react to the situations he faced daily. They had developed to the point of anticipating the surgeon's needs and that saved precious seconds--seconds that on occasion could mean the difference between life and death.

Finding this core group of surgical technicians was a boon to Lapin, but not merely in terms of support. Their eagerness to learn and their adaptability under fire earned them Lapin's respect. With Hutchins and Donnelly, the six formed a tight-knit team that worked together to perform what professionals later described as surgical miracles. By medical standards, they performed operations that textbooks claimed couldn't be done, and all without transfusions.

They interacted well as a unit, each respecting the

other's position and abilities. It was a working
situation and a feeling that Lapin had never experienced. The operating room had become his haven. It
was here, surprisingly enough, that the man felt
safe. Here he was, far from the maddening crowd. His
performance in the operating room was unquestionably
his spokesman . . . but then his actions had always
spoken louder than mere words. He was a craftsman, a
master, at what he did.

"Looks like that's all of it," Hutchins said.

"Uh huh," Lapin muttered, continuing to probe in
search of anything else that could possibly be wrong
with the woman.

"You want to close, Herk?" Lapin asked. "I've got a
meeting and I really shouldn't be too late."

"Sure, go on ahead." Hutchins had closed thousands
of patients. He could do it in his sleep. Lapin eyed
the man with affection. He felt a real sense of
satisfaction in having drawn his new friend back into
the operating room. It had been a sound decision.
Yet from Herk's teachings and explanations about the
Witnesses, Lapin felt that he himself was getting the
long end of the stick.

He removed his gloves, mask, and shoe coverings
before walking to the surgery nursing station. There
he dictated his detailed surgeon's report--every fact,
every finding, every procedure used on the patient,
including the blood loss and actual time spent in the
room. He hated the paperwork. It took valuable time
away from his patients, time away from doing the
things that were useful and challenging. But he'd
learned the necessity of being meticulous with his
reports. From previous unpleasant experiences, he
knew that people could manipulate your charts any way
they wanted. He hated that vehemently.

His next stop would be a nice one, talking to the
family of the patient. As always, their faces were
filled with anxiety. Three other patients, also
Witnesses, were waiting with them. Lapin's news
brought sighs of relief and gratitude.

As usual, Lapin explained to the families that the
thanks weren't due him--he was only the instrument--
and that the knife was actually in the hands of
Jehovah. When he said this, the Witnesses smiled,
conveying to him that they understood just what he
meant.

120

He was looking forward to his meeting. He hadn't seen Dr. Naito since they'd met quite by accident at a medical conference in Washington, D.C., the year before. They had followed each other's careers and corresponded ever since.

Naito was the president of the Green Cross Pharmaceutical Company of Osaka, Japan. His staff nicknamed him "the steam locomotive," a term befitting his workaholic behavior and uncanny ability to cut through red tape. His company was in the business of developing new medicines and was the eighth largest and fastest growing firm in Japan. The medicine that held Lapin's particular interest was Fluosol-DA, a synthetic blood substitute.

Fluosol-DA 20% is a perfluorocarbon chemical compound derived from the petroleum distillate process and is closely related to Teflon. It has the remarkable ability of transporting oxygen to the body tissues, unlike many of the blood substitutes used by doctors today. This miracle fluid is only one one-thousandth the size of hemoglobin, allowing Fluosol to penetrate into areas where blood cells would be too large to enter. Fluosol also carries three to six times more oxygen than an equivalent amount of red cells.

Fluorocarbons were originally developed during World War II to separate uranium isotopes necessary for atomic bombs. In the mid-60s, American researchers Drs. Clark, Sloviter, and Geyer demonstrated that perfluorochemicals provide sufficient CO_2 to maintain life in animals and that they could be emulsified. This generated the idea that fluorocarbons might be developed as an effective blood substitute due to their superior oxygen-carrying qualities.

In Japan, Dr. Ryoichi Naito and his team of research scientists and clinicians developed Fluosol. Dr. Naito's research began in 1967. Tests on animals were conducted for ten years in both Japan and the United States. In the fall of 1978, German researchers used the red cell replacement to maintain biological function for as long as twenty-four hours in seven brain-dead accident victims.

Dr. Naito, a man in his seventies, was considered the leader in the development of Fluosol. In February, 1979, he and nine associates were injected with Fluosol to prove its human safety. Dr. Naito believed that a medical researcher should demonstrate confidence in his invention by first trying it personally. But without extensive research and testing, the FDA wouldn't authorize the use of Fluosol in the United States. It bothered Lapin considerably that their testing processes were so slow. He, more than most, knew that bureaucratic resistance to change held back progress.

Lapin's interest in Fluosol stemmed from the fact that the Witnesses could accept any type of artificial blood. Fluosol could virtually open the door for good surgeons throughout the country to use a blood substitute and perform procedures on Witnesses without violating their religious beliefs. Lapin was convinced it could save hundreds, if not thousands, of lives each year.

"Doctor Naito," he said warmly, opening the door and extending his hand.

"Jesus Christ, I presume," Naito said, smiling broadly and bowing. The two men laughed openly at their private joke.

The very first time they'd met, Naito used the nickname. He said Lapin bore a resemblance to the picture of Christ that he'd received as a child from his mother. He'd actually gone so far with the joke as to introduce Lapin to colleagues and even once during a meeting as Jesus Christ. Needless to say, when he delivered the line with a hint of seriousness, it instantly captured people's attention.

Naito introduced Lapin to Dr. Tom Drees. Drees was president of the Alpha Corporation, a subsidiary of the Green Cross Company. Lapin and Drees were destined to become good friends while working closely together for the international acceptance of Fluosol.

"Sit, gentlemen, sit," Lapin indicated. "How was your trip?"

Naito smiled. He was a warm, sincere man. His white hair was neatly parted and framed his clear, olive complexion. Despite the fact that he was in his seventies, he had a boyish, mischievous look about him--but his piercing eyes clearly indicated he was all business. "You don't really care about my trip . . . you want to know why I'm here." Both men smiled again. They understood each other well.

"I'd say that was a fair assumption on your part. We can talk about social matters at dinner, if that's okay."

"Okay by me."

"Good. Now, what's up?"

Naito leaned back in his chair and crossed his legs. "We've been keeping up with you, Dr. Lapin, and your remarkable successes with the Witnesses." Lapin shrugged and nodded a modest acknowledgment. Naito continued, "Our board has been continually impressed with the operations you've performed without transfusions."

"You came to give me an award?" Lapin quipped.

"You don't need any more accolades, do you?"

"You know what I need."

And Naito did. "We want to talk to you about the possibility of a cooperative effort with you and your team. We would be honored if you would be the first in the country to actually use Fluosol on one of your patients."

Lapin beamed. "You would be honored . . . I'm the one who'd be honored," he said excitedly.

"You've done what now . . . twenty-eight hundred operations without using blood?"

Lapin was impressed. "You do your homework," he said.

"That's our business, research and development."

"Did you get it approved by the FDA?"

"Not so far, but our sources in Washington tell us they may approve a research protocol for its use only on Jehovah's Witnesses. This is where you and your patients become very important to the project."

Lapin was so pleased with the news he was speechless. Naito continued, "The Witnesses, with their religious conviction against taking blood transfusions, make ideal test subjects."

"Are you concerned about the Red Cross trying to stop this project?" Lapin asked.

"No," replied Naito. "Fluosol is too good a substance to be stopped by them or any other group of narrow-minded people."

Lapin was even more pleased. He smiled broadly. It was almost the boyish grin of a child receiving his first bicycle. "You realize this stuff could put me out of business?"

Naito nodded. "And you don't mind?"

Lapin smiled again. "And I don't mind."

***

It was a dingy, dusty, seldom-used sound stage at the CBS television complex in Hollywood--the kind of place where most acting classes take place.

Not very glamorous, Lapin observed as he entered quietly and found a seat in the back row of the auditorium. Surgery had run late due to another emergency; but that was all right, Maureen wouldn't know. She'd just be pleased that he made it at all.

He quickly discovered he wasn't watching an entire production of the play, *Picnic*. Rather, the students were performing various scenes from different plays to exhibit their acting abilities to an audience composed mostly of agents, managers, and casting directors--all people in a position to launch a successful career.

Fifteen minutes after he arrived, Maureen was introduced along with the scene she'd selected. An athletic, handsome blond was also introduced. He was going to play opposite her in the performance.

At first Lapin was intrigued enough to study what he was watching. Then as the dialogue became more intimate, he found himself sitting on the edge of his chair. His eyes focused intently on the couple on stage. He watched Maureen kiss the blond actor, and blinked. There was an unfamiliar feeling emanating from his chest.

Jealous, he thought. *Can I be that?* He watched as they kissed again and again and again. The audience was captured. The acting was good . . . really quite good. That was also his first impression. But then that strange feeling in his chest erupted again, and he realized . . . as he watched . . . that Maureen wasn't acting.

Is this some sort of punishment, he asked himself. *Is she just afraid to tell me, or what?* There were no answers, just Maureen . . . kissing the stranger.

"How long?" he asked her after the performance. "How long has this been going on?"

Maureen's expression didn't change. She stared straight at him and asked, "Was I good?"

Lapin stared back. He thought of a hundred answers that could have worked--answers that would have provoked a confrontation. He decided against adding to the pain and humiliation. Finally, he just shrugged and said, "I believed it."

Neither spoke. The silence became deafening. Finally Lapin said, "Guess you won't be coming home. . . ."

124

There was another moment of silence, but Maureen never looked away. She openly answered, "No, I don't think so."

Lapin nodded once, twice, three times, then turned without speaking. He walked to the rear of the sound stage and just before he got to the exit, thought to himself, *not very glamorous.*

***

A month passed by . . . a month and eighty-five operations, all bloodless, all successful. The small hospital was kept nearly full with Witnesses who had come to Lapin from around the country. Even with the tremendous influx of new patients and cash flow, the hospital administrators refused to make capital improvements as they'd promised. The roof still leaked and the air conditioner worked sporadically at best. The most intolerable point of contention was their negligence in upgrading the emergency facilities and, more specifically, the intensive care unit.

Almost any condition in itself could be tolerated, but when patients' lives were endangered because of inadequate equipment or poorly trained staff members, Lapin could no longer cope with the situation. At that point, he decided to take matters into his own hands.

After several days of tracking, he finally located Jan Jordan, his friend from his days at Skyline Hospital. She had been in Northern California trying to reconstruct a broken marriage. Her efforts were unsuccessful, and she had returned to the Los Angeles area where she was working as a registered nurse.

When he phoned her he explained, "They're trying to kill my patients over here. I need somebody I can trust . . . start tomorrow . . . please."

Jan, an attractive pixy blonde, was thrilled to hear from him. Without fanfare, her two-word answer echoed pleasantly in his ears. "What time?" Their working relationship was as harmonious as any could be. After her failed attempt at reconciliation, Jan had an unwelcome void in her personal life. She devoted nearly every waking hour to assisting Lapin and the Witnesses.

The rewards for her dedication were an inner peace and understanding she'd never known before. Working closely with the Witnesses each day gave her a firsthand exposure to the kind of faith she'd never had personally. She was pleased with her life and its new direction.

Rana, on the other hand, was not so content. He was an Eastern Indian who had recently finished his internal medicine residency and had started to build a practice in an area overloaded with internists. It was impossible not to be aware of Lapin's level of activity, and Rana envisioned himself as part of the team with a valuable contribution to make as an internist.

Lapin, by this time, had lost most of his referring physicians. Before his first Witness patient, he had been working with twenty-one other doctors who referred their surgical cases to him. Now, they were nearly all gone. That fact alone wasn't earth shattering because word-of-mouth referrals from Witnesses kept him as busy surgically as he could afford to be.

What he desperately did need was an admitting physician, like an internist, to do the admitting, workups, examinations, and things of that nature. The admitting physician would then hold the ultimate responsibility for keeping up with the patients and updating their charts. Rana could fill this need.

With that as a shared responsibility, Lapin could spend more time in consultations, surgery, and post-surgical care. Initially, it appeared to be a bliss-ful meshing of talents.

Lapin saw something in Rana that others seemed to overlook. There was an eagerness about the man, an ambitiousness that was having trouble getting out of the starting gate. He was anxious and willing to learn Lapin's ways. Unknown to Lapin, he was also broke. Recognizing the potential market among Witness patients, Rana emulated everything about Lapin that he could: Lapin's walk, his manner, and his appearance, right down to growing a beard and trimming it the same way Lapin did. *He seems somehow to be too perfect, too willing. But why?* Lapin thought occasionally. *What's his motive?*

Rana wasn't an employee of Lapin's for the simple reason that money was never exchanged between them. All of his service fees were paid directly by the patients. He learned well and he did well. In providing him with this opportunity, Lapin had also provided him with a gold mine. Yet when patients mistook him for Dr. Lapin, Rana seldom bothered to correct them.

The hot line received an average of one hundred calls a day. These calls came in from across the country and around the world. The team was indeed busy. Its fame had spread internationally by word-of-mouth.

***

Lapin turned off his headlights and just sat for awhile. It had been over two months since he'd seen Maureen, and he was understandably filled with anxiety and anticipation.

After all, this was what he wanted: a reconciliation. And what he was about to do would certainly establish the degree of his seriousness.

When Maureen called the other night, he was thrilled to hear her voice. It had been difficult for him to maintain his usual self-control, but he did. He always did. Her request, the reason for the call--strange as it sounded--was worth a shot.

Lapin sat in the parking lot of the studio preparing himself to see his estranged wife and to do what he felt would be best, to give it his best shot.

Maureen had offered several reasons for the seemingly clandestine eight o'clock meeting in Hollywood. It was important to her career, she'd said. Lapin decided to go along with it. She had asked him--begged him--to appear on a new television show being taped that night. It was actually the pilot for the show, that all-important first segment which hopefully would be sold into national syndication.

Maureen explained that the producers had offered her a tape of their segment. This would give her actual film footage of herself to show other producers as she pursued her acting career in both films and television.

More importantly, she would be able to obtain the essential Screen Actors Guild card. The SAG card loomed elusively in the area of a Catch-22 for actors because you had to have a card to get a job . . . and you couldn't get a job unless you had a card. It was a major problem for actors. The exception was unsold pilots. This whole thing was important to Maureen, so Ron said he'd go along with it to resolve one of her problems.

Yet it was her third reason, more than any other, that captured his attention and found him sitting in his car at seven-thirty this muggy California night. The show, *Couples,* dealt openly and honestly with problem relationships. A psychologist interviewed the couple, first individually and then together, and helped them work through and resolve their problems.

Their talking to a shrink, Maureen said, might be the first step in helping them get their thing back together to rebuild their relationship. Lapin wasn't thrilled with the prospect of discussing their private lives in front of a roomful of strangers, but agreed to go along with it. He assured her that he'd give it all he had and do his best.

After a couple of deep breaths, he walked through the side door to the sound stage and saw her talking with one of the producers. When she turned and spotted him, she gave him a greeting much like you'd expect from an old high school friend. There was a warm hug, a theatrical kiss on the cheek, and a whispered "thanks for coming." Lapin instinctively knew something was out of balance.

The producer introduced himself and suggested they start. Maureen quickly asked Lapin for a ride home and said they could talk later. Naturally, he agreed. After all, that's why he was putting himself through this ordeal. Wasn't it?

While having their make-up applied, Maureen again expressed her gratitude to Ron. It meant a lot to her that he had agreed to do this taping. That's what she'd said. Lapin felt hopeful . . . cautiously hopeful. He'd taken the first step, and that was certainly the most important one.

The producer led them to the set. There they were positioned in two comfortable armchairs facing a third empty one. They sat waiting. A considerable part of the show's success would be dependent on its spontaneity, especially since the couples wouldn't so much as meet the psychologist till after the show had started and the tape was rolling.

The waiting was intentionally staged to create an aura of nervous anticipation. That, too, was a component of making the show a success. Lapin didn't need the hype; he was already on edge.

The director gave the command to roll the tape. The show began. Lapin shifted uncomfortably in his chair under the warmth of the arc lights. He could feel the heat intensify as each second stretched unhurriedly into the next.

The psychologist, entering unannounced, took his place in the empty chair. There was no preliminary discussion since it was only a half-hour show. "Maureen," he said, "what do you think the problem is?"

Lapin, quite noticeably, was taken by surprise. He looked off stage, expecting to see the director stop the taping. The word "cut" wasn't heard. He looked around the room for support. There was none. The tape never stopped rolling. Finally he turned and looked at Maureen.

He looked again! He could not comprehend what his eyes were seeing. Tears--big tears--streamed down Maureen's face. Lapin was totally confused. Again he looked around . . . again nothing.

"I don't love him any more," she babbled through her tears. "I haven't for a long time."

Lapin blinked once, twice. *What the hell's going on here?*

"And tomorrow," she continued, sobbing, "tomorrow I have to go into the hospital and have a hysterectomy."

The psychologist interrupted and tried to calm her down.

Lapin was stunned.

"Why is the hysterectomy bothering you so much?" the psychologist asked.

"Because I wanted to have more children." She was still weeping.

Lapin just couldn't believe what he was hearing. He knew about the hysterectomy. Since they were first married, Maureen insisted that she'd welcome that operation when the time came medically. So what was the big deal now about children? It was Ron who wanted to have a family, not her. Unable to contain himself, he asked, "What are you talking about? You never wanted to have any more kids."

"Not with you," she nearly shouted through onrushing tears. "I want to have my lover's children."

Lapin was speechless. Absolutely speechless!

"You're having an affair?" the psychologist asked. She nodded "yes." "And you want to have children with your new lover?" And again she nodded "yes." "What about your husband, Ron, sitting here with you?"

"I want a divorce."

"You want a divorce," the psychologist repeated.

"You want a divorce," Lapin repeated.

"Yes," Maureen concluded.

A hush fell over the studio. The only sound was Maureen's persistent, heavy sobbing. Now the producers had a problem. They were about three minutes into a half-hour show and it had become too quiet.

Maureen seized the opportunity. She explained how miserable her existence with Ron had been. She exhumed, in detail, every dinner he'd canceled, every vacation they had to postpone, and every missed moment of passion.

Then--perhaps to fulfill the equal time requirement from the FCC--she expressed her undying affection for her new lover. She glowed as superlatives poured from her mouth. Lapin sat dumbfounded, near shock. Needless to say, she carried the show. When the director finally said "cut," Lapin had a much clearer interpretation of the word. The red camera light turned off . . . and so did the tears.

The crew remained quiet. There wasn't much to say. It seemed Maureen had said it all.

"How was I?" Maureen whispered to the psychologist.

"I beg your pardon?"

"How was I? Did I do okay?"

The doctor cleared his throat and offered, "Uh, yes . . . yes, you did very well." Then he turned to Lapin and gave him an incredibly sympathetic look.

Lapin couldn't respond. He was too numb.

"You ready to go, hon?" she asked. "Where are you parked?" The change was like night to day, black to white. Lapin couldn't comprehend what was going on now any more than he could comprehend why his wife had just publicly attacked, humiliated, and--for all practical purposes--executed him.

Incoherently he muttered, "I'm in back."

"Great, let's go." And with that she popped up from her chair like nothing had happened.

Once in the car, she readjusted the rear-view mirror to fuss with her hair. The habit irritated Lapin immensely, but now it didn't seem to matter much.

"Didn't I play well to the camera?"

"What?"

"The camera angles . . . didn't I use them well?"

"Did I miss something?"

"Ron, I was acting, that's all."

Lapin sighed, but it wasn't a sigh of relief. "I

believed it." He paused for a second, almost afraid to ask, but he knew he had to. "How much of it was true?"

Maureen didn't hesitate. "All of it."

Lapin leaned back on the headrest and closed his eyes. His own personal pain exceeded the humiliation. It was another sleepless night.

The next day he drove her to the hospital. Maureen seemed unaffected by the previous night's experience. The drive was quiet until she said, "Ron, I want you to assist in my operation . . . you can close when the other surgeon is finished."

"Why?" he asked. The question seemed to come out of nowhere. He was tired. Emotion had been ripped from his soul.

"Because you do that better than anybody else," she answered nonchalantly. "If you close, I know you won't leave any scars. That's important to me . . . in case I have to do a nude scene in a movie."

There was a long, quiet pause, then he mumbled, "Yeah, right." And, of course, he closed. And, of course, he left no scars.

He was later informed by the show's producer that he and Maureen had been single-handedly responsible for the coast-to-coast syndication of the program. The producer sent him a tape of the show, but he never watched it, not ever. He couldn't.

***

Lapin was at home when the phone rang.

"Hello," the voice said. "Is this 714/751-4554?"

Lapin answered. "This is the JW hot line. Doctor Lapin speaking."

"Doctor Lapin, this is Joanna Barnes . . . I was told by a friend that you might be able to help us."

"Are you in the Truth?"

"Yes, doctor."

"Where are you calling from, Joanna?"

"Santa Fe, New Mexico. It's my son. . . ."

Mrs. Barnes explained that her son, Rusty, accidently shot himself in the lower leg while cleaning a rifle. He was released from the hospital after treatment and his wound was healing nicely. But within a week, he was throwing up blood and taking large amounts of aspirin for severe abdominal pain.

Rusty returned to the hospital and was diagnosed as

having multiple stomach ulcers. The ulcerated stomach
walls were eroding away and would ultimately result
in his painful death.

Lapin felt a call to the young man's physician was
in order. It was a Doctor Johnson, a man with a
wispy, wheezy sort of voice that seemed to almost
rattle as he spoke in short bursts of words.

Johnson said that he'd done an endoscopy. The
procedure consists of direct observation of the
stomach by inserting a tube with a light source at the
end.

Rusty was admitted into ICU where the heavy bleeding
persisted. Johnson urged that immediate surgery be
done to control the bleeding. He stipulated that he
wouldn't operate without transfusing blood. Mrs.
Barnes refused. That option was totally out of the
question.

"So what are you going to do about it?" he asked
Lapin in a somewhat hostile tone.

"I'm going to operate on him and stop the bleeding."

"Without transfusing?"

"That's right."

"Well, good luck, doctor. But between us, you're
nuts. In fact . . . you are a criminal. . . ."

Another call, and the plans were quickly made. As
is so often the case with Witness patients, speed was
of the essence. Lapin suggested they rent a Lear jet
to transport him. Joanna said she'd try. Rusty's
blood level had already fallen to a critically low
state, below seven, and was still falling. He'd have
to be moved to California soon.

The team was put on standby for his arrival. They
went back to surgery--business as usual. There were
several more phone calls throughout the day to check
on both Rusty and the flight arrangements.

It was an enormous gamble and Lapin knew it. *Other
than that,* he thought, *the day had been normal.*
"Normal" translated into having eight bloodless
procedures behind him, with an average blood loss of
one hundred and fifty c.c.s. Lapin finished making
rounds and talking with patients' families before
leaving the hospital. He would arrive home later than
planned, and that, too, was normal.

This particular night, however, the housekeeper
wasn't there. Since it was Martha's night off, Lapin
thought it odd to see all the house lights on as he
pulled into the driveway. *Is she home?* he thought. *I*

132

hope so. I really do hope so.

He composed himself and walked into the kitchen. Nothing. Then he passed through the large dining room into the living room . . . and there she was. Damn it, she looked great. She was standing in front of a large oil painting. It was a rendering in rich brown hues of a woman watching waves gently breaking on the shore line. Maureen held a clipboard in one hand and a felt-tipped pen in the other. She turned as he entered, but it was Lapin who broke the silence. "Hello, stranger."

"Hello, Ron." Her tone was far from the one he'd hoped to hear. The distancing coldness was still there.

"Long time no see," he said, testing.

"I thought I'd be finished here before you got home."

He tried not to let his face give him away. "Finished with what?"

"My attorney advised me to take an inventory of all our property."

"Oh. . . ." The word came out slowly. Lapin sat on one of the white couches facing the fireplace. "Want a drink? Still make the best martini in town."

She shook her head "no" and jotted some notes on her clipboard. "When the time comes," she said, "I'd like to have the brown lady."

"When the time comes, we can talk about it."

"For God's sake, Ron, you know you always hated this picture."

He was about to share some long overdue, pent-up feelings when the phone rang and stopped him. It was just as well.

"Hello . . . Joanna . . . tell me what's happening."

He was trying to listen, but Maureen began talking. "A thousand times . . . you told me a thousand times how much you hated it."

Lapin put his hand over the mouthpiece and gestured for her to be quiet, but she continued. "A divorce doesn't have to be bitter, you know. . . . "

"What?" he said into the phone, "It's down to six and a half? You've got to transport him now . . . I mean now."

"But if you're going to start playing games."

"Shut up!" he screamed. Then, he continued his phone conversation. "Okay, I'm leaving now to go back to the hospital. You call me just before you leave.

I'll see you soon."

Maureen was incensed. "How dare you. . . ."

Lapin tore the painting from the wall and threw it to the floor. "Take it! I've got a kid dying and all you want to do is count paintings." He stormed from the room . . . it was over for good and he knew it. There wasn't time to think about his own problems. A patient was facing death. That had to come first. His personal life, as always, would just have to wait.

Rusty was still bleeding when he arrived in the Lear jet later that night. He was quickly stabilized and prepped for surgery. Two hours later Lapin had removed eighty percent of the boy's stomach, stopped the bleeding, and saved his life.

Donnelly, still suffering the effects of an earlier fight with his wife, stood shaking his head in amazement. "Doctor Lapin, that was the finest surgery I've ever seen," he commended. "I just want you to know I'm proud to have been involved with this case."

Lapin smiled. He was proud, too. He took off his gloves and said jubilantly, "Let's do it again! Where's our next patient?" It was one happy operating room, indeed.

Ten days and thirty bloodless operations later, Lapin released Rusty from the hospital. This time, Rusty flew by commercial jet to make the trip home. He didn't know until later that his parents had refinanced their home to cover the air ambulance flight to California.

***

Once again, Lapin found himself on a collision course with the hospital administration. They were thrilled with the abundance of funds being pumped into the hospital, but steadfastly refused to make the promised improvements.

Then, there were the old-timers--the hospital staff members who didn't want to disrupt their precious, stagnant status quo.

It started again, exactly as before. There were the meetings. There were questions about Lapin's charts and the number of surgical procedures performed. Why were there so many patients? Why so many JWs? Why this one . . . or that one? And like before, his time was being spent in politically motivated meetings when it could have been put to much better use in the operating room. By now, the pattern was all too familiar. Monday morning quarterbacking became the favorite pastime of the surgical committee. Second-guessing temporarily substituted for their incompetence in the surgical arena.

Lapin looked to the heavens and asked, "When will it end?" His Jewish heritage provided a possible clue to the answer.

***

Generally, no individual call on the hot line was more significant than another. However, in September, 1979, the impact of an incoming call was destined to change medical history in the United States.

It was from Paul Clark's son. Several things about his particular situation were quite interesting. Paul's son is the secretary for the Jehovah's Witness compound near Wallkill in upstate New York. The complex itself is a combination farm and factory which houses over six hundred volunteer workers. Here the Witnesses handle the printing of the The Watchtower and Awake! magazines for distribution throughout the world. They also produce food for themselves and approximately two thousand volunteers who live and work in the Brooklyn, New York, printing facility.

From one small Bible study group in Pennsylvania in 1870, the Witnesses have grown to over three million members in more than two hundred countries. Originally, their literature was printed by local commercial firms. In 1920, the first of six large buildings in Brooklyn was purchased to accomplish that purpose. Nearby buildings are used to house all the workers needed to operate today's modern printing facilities. These facilities print and distribute tens of millions of pieces of literature in 110 languages yearly. This, combined with similar facilities in other countries, makes the Watchtower Bible and Tract Society of New York the largest printer of religious materials in the world.

Paul was a strong, but gentle, man. His knowledge of Bible Scriptures was no less than amazing, due, no doubt, to a lifetime of study and belief.

One afternoon, Paul suffered from severe abdominal pain. His physician diagnosed diverticulosis and advanced aging of the colon. The doctor said he needed minor surgery and promised to perform the procedure without transfusing blood. Paul agreed. After all, this man had been their family physician for many years and had even delivered Paul's son twenty-six years before. Unlike many physicians who failed to honor the same commitment, this one kept his word; no blood was used. What remained questionable, however, was whether or not Paul actually required surgery for his condition. Lapin has remarked many times since that if Paul had been his patient from the start, surgery might have been ruled out.

The operation seemed to go well, even though there was considerable blood loss. Clark was out of recovery and into ICU before his multiple complications became evident. For one thing, internal bleeding had developed and couldn't be traced back to its source. Peritonitis, the dreaded infection of the lining of the abdominal cavity, had also set in. There had been a breakdown of the sutures holding the severed ends of the colon together. Far too much was going wrong in rapid succession. The bottom line was the absolute necessity of re-entering the patient and correcting the problems.

Both the surgeon and anesthesiologist refused to do the second operation without blood. The loss of blood from the initial surgery had been too extreme. The doctor knew he'd started with a relatively healthy individual, and now, two weeks after surgery, the patient was deteriorating rapidly. Paul's blood count was dropping so dramatically by the hour that you could almost watch his skin pigmentation lose its color.

Pressure was applied to Clark and his family. It's a life-or-death crisis, they were told. But the Witness and his family stood firm. He was willing to die before he'd break his integrity to Jehovah. No blood . . . no man's blood.

Now the surgeon was really frightened. He feared that time would run out before he could obtain a court order to transfuse, but began legal action anyway. It was a surgeon's classic nightmare. He knew that if he refused to finish what he had started, he could be sued by the family for patient abandonment if Clark died.

But Jehovah's Witnesses seldom sue other people, especially doctors, for anything. Never would they sue a doctor for declining to use blood, even if the accepted medical standard dictates its use in their specific case. Their lives are in the almighty and all-knowing hands of Jehovah. The family gathered around Clark's bed, not knowing what should be done medically.

The surgeon had heard of Lapin and endeavored to reach him as a last resort. He tried to remain calm when Lapin came to the phone, but his voice gave him away. Lapin sensed the man was frightened, so he tried to relax him while getting the necessary information.

The surgeon was astounded by Lapin's credentials and experience. Together they decided that Clark was too ill and deteriorating too rapidly to make the trip to Bristol Hospital. They instead made arrangements to transfer him to the Loma Linda University Hospital which was closer.

After they hung up, the doctor immediately called for an ambulance. With post haste, he found the necessary forms for Clark to sign which released him from any further responsibility--in effect, getting him off the hook he'd so unwittingly designed for himself.

Lapin was also busy. His mind raced faster than the proverbial mile a minute. *This is the one,* he thought. *This is the one.* He had waited over two months--waited for just the right patient to be the first to get artificial blood, and this was the one. The patient's blood count was low enough to warrant it and the post-surgical complications necessitated it.

Lapin immediately called the Carter Administration at the White House and, after trying several extensions, got through to the right aides. These aides were in a position to make the final decisions regarding the use of Fluosol. Quickly and concisely, he explained Clark's condition. The call was taped. They said they'd get back to him.

The waiting was agonizing. The minutes dragged by, then several hours passed. Finally, the White House returned the call as promised.

Usage of Fluosol-DA had been authorized as a humanitarian gesture! It would be referred to as a mercy transfusion. Emergency calls were placed to Green Cross in Japan for shipment and to the Alpha Corporation in Los Angeles, a subsidiary of Green Cross, for distribution. The life-sustaining liquid was coming on the next direct flight from the Orient.

Now there was the element of time. Time to wait. Time to think, ponder, consider. Time for Lapin to contemplate and adjust his perspective to the fact that he was about to make United States history by being the person to introduce the use of a milky white liquid substance that experts had predicted for years could never be created. This was more than American history--it was medical history.

Lapin remembered what he had said to Dr. Naito, his friend, "I'd be honored." And, oh, how very much he was.

Clark was transferred and Lapin went to Loma Linda to see him. He explained Fluosol to the dying man and his family. They were relieved that they were finally in the hands of the bloodless surgeon. "Not my hands," Lapin told them, and they understood.

The agony of waiting intensified. An ambulance was at the airport waiting to rush the artificial blood to the patient. Clark was growing severely anemic. His blood count had dropped to three grams and would have to be built back up before he could undergo surgery to reverse the complications.

It was a race against the clock . . . and all they could do was wait.

Clark lost the race. He died just minutes before the wheels of the plane touched down at L.A. International. The Witnesses lost a good man, a good friend.

Never so close and yet so far away, Lapin thought to himself. He felt terrible, but he was resolved to wait for another day.

***

It was Thanksgiving weekend, two months after Clark's death. Lapin was still upset about losing a patient who potentially could have been saved. He was angry that Fluosol-DA hadn't been in close enough proximity to use when the appropriate situation arose.

He had more than one hundred bloodless operations behind him that afforded him ample opportunities to use Fluosol, and he remembered them all. But he had been waiting for a case that fully warranted its use by the strictest standards. As with all of Lapin's decisions, the welfare of the individual had to come first. For that reason, surgical procedures were only considered as the last alternative after other medical treatments proved unsuccessful.

138

Lapin had made the vacation trip to the East Coast alone, with only his thoughts and aspirations for company. Coming to see Ari was more than uplifting; it was the highlight of his travels. The boy was growing, becoming a man. Lapin was so proud of him.

Father and son had Thanksgiving dinner together and were visiting with old friends from the medical school when it happened. They were all sitting in the living room having a drink and talking while the evening network news played softly in the background. At first the show in progress was muffled; then it captured Lapin's full attention.

"Stop," he said. "Quiet for a minute."

The anchorman delivered the news matter-of-factly in crisp cutoff words. "Medical history has taken place today at the University of Minnesota. A member of the Jehovah's Witnesses, a religious faith, has become the first person in the United States to receive artificial blood." The picture changed to that of the hospital where the Fluosol was used. Then the camera tracked slowly down a hallway inside and stopped, showing a picture of an operating room. The voice continued the commentary over the picture, "The medical profession waits anxiously for the results of this FDA-approved endeavor." The picture changed to a patient resting comfortably in a semi-private room, surrounded by happy family members. The announcer went on, "Today, Harold Jacobs was given Fluosol-DA 20, an artificial blood substitute that could revolutionize the field of medicine. . . ."

The voice continued, but Lapin didn't hear it. The anchorman explained vaguely why the Witnesses wouldn't accept transfusions. The man probably explained various other things too, but Lapin just didn't hear it.

Minutes before, Lapin had been telling his friends about the Clark case and how much he hoped to be the first surgeon to use Fluosol. He was quite pleased that the medicine proved useful to a brother in Minnesota, but was understandably crushed when this opportunity to broaden the horizon of bloodless medicine in a scientific fashion slipped through his fingers. Why had he waited? And why didn't he have an answer?

His friends were sympathetic. They really understood how much this meant to him. It had been his avowed contribution to medical science. Although he was not the first to use it, Fluosol-DA 20 would not have been so readily available in Minnesota without his prior efforts. But hearing the news like this--and in front of his son--was shattering. He felt empty and became lost in his thoughts.

Reservations were changed and Lapin returned to the West Coast a day and a half earlier than planned, partially due to a lengthy phone conversation with his friend Tom Drees. Drees is the president of the Alpha Corporation in Pasadena, a subsidiary of the Green Cross Corporation in Japan.

Lapin was honest and open in expressing his feelings to his friend. "Why," he asked, "did you do this to me? For what reason?"

"Ron," Drees said, "you're still first in line. That hasn't changed."

"But what about. . . ."

"The case in Minnesota?" Tom said, finishing the sentence.

"Yes . . . what about that?"

Tom's voice was comforting, reassuring. "The Fluosol used there was used in a post-operative situation to reverse extreme anemia."

"So?" Lapin asked.

"So we're still waiting for it to be used for other purposes . . . primarily as a pre-operative blood substitute. When we can document for the FDA that Fluosol will help build up a patient's blood count to the point where he can successfully undergo surgery, then we'll have a product that's going to save countless lives. That's why you're still so important, Ron."

Lapin let the news sink in. It felt good knowing he was still in the saddle. "What's happening with the Japanese?" he asked.

"They've used it about three hundred times over there with excellent results."

"Well, I think it's time we started using it here in the United States."

"We're ready," Drees said. "Just be patient and let's do it right."

The surgeon was ready. He had gone too far and come too close. He was ready.

Lapin liked Drees. He found him to be a brilliant administrator with innovative ideas. He possessed the uncanny ability to hurdle unyielding obstacles and to navigate an incredibly successful young corporation

140

through the choppy seas of international commerce.

Each phone call on the hot line was carefully scrutinized. Lapin personally listened to nearly every caller explain their symptoms and other doctors' diagnoses. He carefully analyzed the information and was always on the lookout for a viable candidate.

Then a call came from Miami, Florida. It was a sister calling for her husband, Jose Gonzales. He had massive internal bleeding and a duodenal ulcer. His wife had heard about Lapin from someone at her Kingdom Hall.

Lapin wrote down her telephone number, along with that of the physician who refused to operate because of the blood issue. He assured Mrs. Gonzales he'd call her back within ten minutes.

It was evident that the physician was eager to be rid of Gonzales. There wasn't anything he could do, and he certainly didn't want Gonzales dying while under his care. He had more bad news: the patient's blood count was five point five and falling, he was having severe chest pains, and he had a history of angina.

This is it, Lapin thought. *This is the one.* He quickly dialed Mrs. Gonzales' number.

"Hello," she answered quickly.

"This is Dr. Lapin. I just spoke with your doctor, and it's obvious that your husband needs an operation immediately. I feel he should be in the hands of a medical staff willing to take care of him and at a hospital familiar with the necessary procedures."

"Yes, doctor, but. . . ."

"I want you to call your doctor there and have him arrange for an ambulance to transport your husband to the nearest airport. Then. . . ."

"Doctor, I. . . ."

"Then, put him on the first available plane to Los Angeles. We'll pick him up here with an ambulance of our own."

"But, doctor. . . ."

"Time is of the absolute essence. We really don't have the luxury of a lengthy discussion."

The phone was silent. He thought they'd been disconnected. "Mrs. Gonzales?"

There was one more painful moment of silence. Then she spoke. The voice was strained, embarrassed, frightened. "Doctor. . . ." The words were slow, as if being pulled out. "It's about the money. You

141

see. . . ."

"Mrs. Gonzales," Lapin interrupted, "I don't want you to worry about money right now."

"But. . . ."

"Look, your husband needs that operation if he's going to live. Do you understand that?"

"Yes." The hesitancy was still there.

"I'll pay whatever needs to be paid, and you can pay me back whenever you can."

There was more silence.

"Sister?" He could hear soft sobs on the other end of the phone. "Sister, everything's going to be fine. Your husband's going to be all right."

"Thank you, doctor."

"Thank me later. Right now I want you to get on the phone and make a plane reservation. Then call the doctor and make sure the ambulance has been scheduled. Will you do that?"

"Yes."

"Good. As soon as that's done, I want you to call me back with the airline, flight number, and the arrival time."

"Jehovah will bless you, doctor."

"I hope so, but please get those things done and call me back. I'll make all the necessary arrangements at this end. Okay?"

"Okay."

The other team members were coming out of the operating room just then, heading for the physicians' lounge to rest a few minutes before the next patient. Lapin reached out and touched Hutchins on the shoulder.

"Herk. . . ."

The rest of the group walked on.

"I think we've got him," Lapin said.

"Got who?" his friend questioned.

"The Fluosol candidate."

Herk's eyes lit up. He had shared Lapin's disappointment when he heard about the case in Minnesota. "Looks good, huh?" he asked.

"It looks right. They're getting him ready to fly out here from Miami. Keep your fingers crossed."

Herk put his hand affectionately on the young surgeon's shoulder, "Good luck," he said.

"To all of us," Lapin added. "I know everything will go great."

Then the phone calls began--first to the physician

in charge of Fluosol at the FDA, next to the Alpha
Corporation, and then to National Airlines. Then,
just like before, the waiting began.

While he waited, he made the best use of his time by
doing two more operations. But this time, the
discussion held over the patient wasn't light and
offbeat. Instead, he held a meeting to prepare his
team for the arriving Fluosol candidate.

Lapin told them everything that had transpired and
asked that all plans for the evening be cancelled. It
was going to be a long night. The entire team would
have to work in shifts to monitor the patient's progress until the blood count reached an acceptable
level for surgery.

"Reschedule any morning surgery that could last
longer than twenty minutes," he told Mikie.

"Check."

"Herk, can you think of anything else?"

"I think we're covered."

Dixie, a scrub nurse on the team, entered the room.
"Doctor," she said, "Mrs. Gonzales is on the phone."

The hysterectomy was nearly finished. Hutchins
looked at Lapin, "Go talk to her. I'll finish up
here."

They were getting close. This was it. Mrs.
Gonzales had made all the necessary arrangements. Her
husband was being moved into the ambulance as they
spoke.

Lapin got the flight number and all other pertinent
information. Then he spent another minute or two
reassuring the woman that her husband was going to be
fine.

Gonzales was scheduled to arrive in Los Angeles at
seven o'clock that evening. The flight arrangements
had been tight, but now all wheels were in motion.

The FDA called back, and for the second time,
approved the use of Fluosol on the grounds of
humanitarianism. The Alpha Corporation called back.
This time the Fluosol was in the United States, just
across town, and was on its way to the hospital. They
were sending four units as requested, plus two extra
as backup. Naito called and wished the young surgeon
the best of luck.

Surgery was finished for the day. Now, the waiting
began again. They had everything they needed--
everything, that is, except the patient.

Lapin went on rounds to visit his patients. Somehow

the news of the Fluosol had leaked. In each room, the Witnesses greeted him and graciously expressed their appreciation for what he had done for them personally. They told him they prayed that he might be successful in accomplishing this medical feat for their brothers and sisters to come.

He was truly moved by their sincerity. Here he was in this tiny, run-down hospital because this was where he chose to be. This was the only place he could find to treat the Witnesses. This was where he belonged.

Several times as he went room to room, he came close to tears. Their gratitude was overwhelming. Their prayers for the future, as well as for him personally, were uplifting. He couldn't help but notice an analogy between what the Witnesses did and what he was doing at this very moment. They went door-to-door and he went room-to-room. They both shared hope and spread good news about the future. They were both totally devoted to a cause greater than themselves, regardless of the obstacles placed in their paths.

Mrs. Simmons was eighty-three years old and had been a Witness all of her adult life. She was a tiny lady with sparkling eyes and a quick wit. She came to Lapin with a large bleeding breast tumor. When the fungating mass was removed, the biopsy showed that it was malignant. Even so, Lapin had given her at least two extra years of physical comfort.

She was an ideal patient who neither complained nor caused trouble. Lapin was quite fond of her and always looked forward to their visits. Her room was dimly lit and quiet when he entered. Only the light above the bed was on as she enjoyed her favorite pastime, reading the Bible.

"Mrs. Simmons," he said, "how are you feeling this evening?"

"Just had another delicious dinner of gravy and jello, thank you."

It was all she could do to keep from smiling. They'd played the game for the past few days. Lapin was pleased that she was doing so well.

"We'll have you on solids soon. Maybe tomorrow."

"Likely story." They smiled at each other. Then she continued, "Guess it's going to be exciting around here tonight, huh?"

"You heard?"

"You don't think you could slip something like that

past me, do you?"

"How silly of me. . . ."

She liked the young doctor. Her affection was almost maternal. "Ron," she said, "I guess I'm old enough to call you Ron. . . ."

"I guess so."

"May I ask you a question?"

"Sure."

"Do you believe in divine guidance?"

"Yes . . . usually . . . well, sometimes. I'm not quite sure."

The lady gazed compassionately at the young man. "Then answer this," she said. "Why were you, an Israeli Jew, chosen to save me and so many other Witnesses?"

Lapin shrugged, then smiled, "I guess Jehovah knows a good doctor when he sees one."

"So do his Witnesses."

He started to speak, but a large lump found its way into his throat. Instead he just smiled, waved, and started to back out the door slowly.

"Doctor," she said, stopping him. Her tearful eyes glistened; her voice, though still strong, began to waver. There was a radiance--a glow--about the woman which came from a peaceful understanding of things to come. "Doctor, I know how important this night is . . . for you . . . and for all of us."

Lapin still couldn't speak.

Mrs. Simmons continued, "I just wanted to thank you . . . for the sacrifices you've made and for everything you've already done."

He tried to speak again. There was still no sound.

"Know this, dear doctor, we are all praying for you . . . you are not alone . . . you are in Jehovah's hands."

He went to an empty nurses' station and wept openly. The responsibility he'd taken on was awesome. *I'm only one man*, he thought. There was deep comfort in the fact that he was not really alone. The Witnesses shared his human emotion, and he was truly in Jehovah's hands. He looked to the heavens and whispered, "I will not fail." Tears flowed freely down both cheeks and disappeared into his beard. *I will not let these people down. I won't.*

"Doctor Lapin," the P.A. announced, "call the operator, please . . . Doctor Lapin."

He picked up a nearby phone. "This is Doctor

Lapin."

It was Mrs. Gonzales. Lapin had instructed her to call just as soon as the plane took off. But something was seriously wrong. The woman was nearly in hysterics. Her sentences intermixed Spanish with English, so it was difficult to understand anything she was saying.

"Whoa, whoa . . . wait a minute. I can't understand what you're saying. Slow down."

He could hear her gasping for air. She composed herself somewhat and spoke. "They won't let my husband ride on the airplane."

"What!" Lapin couldn't believe what he was hearing.

"He looks bad, doctor. He's real white. I had him on board, but the stewardess said he was too sick to travel and wouldn't let him stay." She drifted back into Spanish.

"Wait, wait, wait," Lapin said. "They wouldn't let him on the airplane?"

"He was too white. . . ."

"Give me a minute," he said. "Let me think." He put his hand over the receiver and pressed his eyes tightly together.

A hundred thoughts raced through his mind as he drew from his past survival techniques. "Mrs. Gonzales," he said, "I want you to do what they do out here in Hollywood."

She didn't understand.

"Put make-up on him . . . give him back some color."

"What?" she replied.

"If it's good enough for Burt Reynolds, it's good enough for your husband, too. Trust me. Put some rouge on him--it'll work. Just do it and put him on the next plane. Then call me with the new flight information."

He was right--it worked. Mrs. Gonzales pulled it off. She applied the make-up as instructed and snuck her husband aboard the next Delta flight out of Miami. Before leaving the airport, she managed to call Lapin with the new arrival time. She returned home and prayed with a few friends for her husband's life. She also put in a good word for the surgeon.

Lapin and his people were busy. The arrival time had been delayed to nearly ten o'clock. The ambulance would be waiting when the plane touched down. The Fluosol was in place and waiting. The team was ready and waiting. The surge of energy was electrifying.

146

Everything came off without a hitch. The plane was on time, and the patient was transported to the hospital on schedule. The transfusion of the Fluosol also went well. Considering that it had never before been used for a pre-operative situation in the United States, it was remarkable that each aspect went precisely as outlined.

When the first unit was transfused into Gonzales, history was made, pictures were taken, and anxiety peaked. But any celebration would have to wait until the patient was stable enough to undergo a successful surgery.

It was nearly midnight on December 7, 1979, when they opened the drip valve on the IV bottle.

They waited through the night . . . Lapin, Herk, Donnelly, Jan, Mikie, Dixie, Marilyn, Smitty, Rana, and many interested observers. Even though they monitored the patient in shifts and had adequate time between watches, not one of them slept. They didn't want to miss a single moment of the medical miracle taking place.

Together, they watched through the night as the patient's color improved and his chest pains disappeared. It was nearly eight o'clock the following morning when Lapin made the decision. "Prep him . . . we're going in."

During the forty-five minute operation, Lapin removed half of the man's stomach, cut the vagus nerve to reduce the excessive acid production, and completely controlled the bleeding.

They watched closely for any reactions or complications. There were none whatsoever! Mr. Gonzales' chest pains had developed because of his heart's starvation for oxygen. Since the Fluosol particles were much smaller than blood cells and could carry the oxygen through the arteries easily, the pain subsided.

"Those Japanese are a clever bunch," Lapin remarked to the team. Gonzales' abdominal wall was closed, and he was promptly taken to recovery.

Lapin dictated his post-op report with a profound sense of pride. It was magnificent. He'd been the first one on the mountain. He'd charted new ground and opened doors that had never been approached by fellow surgeons. His deepest sense of joy and happiness, however, was for Gonzales himself. This Cuban refugee escaped Castro's regime, had the courage to crawl on an airplane, disguised, and then flew three thousand miles--all to defy prejudice and stand firm on his convictions.

Observing integrity like that brings genuine happiness and celebration . . . and certainly revitalizes someone working for human rights.

The recovery process went well. Gonzales was moved to ICU, and the monitoring continued. All eyes were on Lapin and his now-famous patient. Gonzales came through the entire process with flying colors, and no make-up. The Fluosol and the operation had both been incredibly successful.

The long-awaited celebration had to be postponed. There was another emergency patient--another ideal candidate for Fluosol--being rushed by helicopter to the emergency room.

Amid the flurry of publicity about Fluosol and its long-range effects on our society, Gonzales left the hospital only ten days after the ambulance first brought him. Glenn Atrat, one of the brothers, drove him to the airport for his return flight home to Miami. His blood count had returned to a near-normal level. As he thanked Lapin and the team just prior to leaving, he told them he felt better than he could ever remember. Mrs. Gonzales, who had made the trip later, was sobbing quietly. It was a truly joyous moment.

Members of the news media were calling the hospital at an ever increasing rate. They all wanted to talk to Lapin, the bloodless surgeon. Lapin chose to remain low-keyed regarding the success of Fluosol until more concrete data had been accumulated.

With the increase of unwanted publicity filling the news wires, the hot line phone was now ringing off the wall. Lapin realized for the first time that he'd created a center where Jehovah's Witnesses could be safe, at least for the time being.

Without any premeditated planning, he had established a social-medical front that was crusading for civil rights within the confines of a run-down, forty-four bed hospital.

Things were going almost too well and Lapin couldn't relax. His sixth sense alerted him to keep his gaurd up and to prepare for the next shot directed at him . . . a shot that would no doubt be fired through the barrels of mediocrity and jealousy.

148

It was a crusade outside the hospital; a battle within. The place was full, busy. Lapin had fulfilled his promise, but they hadn't. The facility was still in desperate need of repairs. Repeated arguments, logical and emotional, fell on deaf ears.

The publicity had brought news media reporters to the hospital like never before. These people were in a position to expose existing safety hazards, so understandably the administration began to get nervous.

It wasn't the actual publicity that bothered the administrators or the owners; it was the State of California that caused their sleepless nights. If the State picked up on the publicity and decided to investigate, the odds favored them closing the hospital until necessary improvements were made. The State wields ominous power in medical matters.

Lapin was informed in no uncertain terms that all his bloodless surgical procedures would be reviewed by an outside surgeon and that he would have no further say in the matter. He would be microscopically scrutinized by strangers unfamiliar with his techniques.

The administration stopped admitting patients who had financial difficulties. The Cormans were the first ones to be turned down. They lived locally, in Santa Ana, and visited Lapin at the hospital.

"But, Doctor Lapin," Corman said, "why can't we arrange to make payments every month? We don't want to go to the County Hospital where they won't respect our beliefs."

"I'm sorry," Lapin sympathized. "These decisions aren't up to me. They're made by the administration."

Mrs. Corman raised her hand, silencing her husband's next question.

Lapin continued, "I can't operate on you because of

the hospital administrators' policies. I don't agree with them, but they're afraid something might go wrong. I know it's difficult, but please try to understand their position."

Mrs. Corman was the picture of serenity. "Oh, I do, Doctor Lapin. Believe me, I understand completely."

"You people amaze me." Lapin's frustration was evident.

"What I don't understand is why you're angry." And she was right--he was. The anger didn't go away.

Donnelly and the rest of the team clearly sensed his frustration later that afternoon during surgery. There was no idle conversation. There was no conversation at all. There was just the surgeon expertly removing a malignant breast. Blood loss: less than one fifth of a pint. Operating time: forty minutes.

Lapin removed his gloves and threw them into a receptacle. The team, his family, waited patiently. They could tell he had something to say. He didn't direct himself to any one individual, but used them collectively as a sounding board.

"They can't do this," he said. He stared at the patient as his people transferred her to a gurney. "It's wrong."

The room was still. No one spoke. They gave him all the space he needed.

"It's happening again," he said, nodding his head. "They're doing it to us--you know that they are. It was only a matter of time. First, they wouldn't fix this place, and now they've taken control of patient admissions."

His words were followed by momentary silence. Then Donnelly spoke. "I talked with the administrator over at Esperanza, not specifically about us, more about what we were doing."

"To move there?"

"We've had to move before."

"Esperanza's more of a convalescent home than a hospital," Lapin said.

"They've got the facilities," Donnelly replied. "They just don't use them very much."

Lapin thought about it, then added, "One crisis at a time. We'll talk about it later. I'm late for another ludicrous review meeting."

He was late by about twenty minutes--that always irritated the other members of the staff. But the patient came first to Dr. Lapin . . . always.

Blackledge, the administrator, cleared his throat and shifted uncomfortably as Lapin entered the room. Some of the other department heads and surgeons around the table parroted his actions.

"Go well?" Blackledge asked.

Lapin nodded as he took his seat at the far side of the room. The mood characterizing the group was so strained it almost seemed hostile. *They're probably just paranoid,* he thought to himself. *No big deal, let's just get on with it.*

The conference table became an obscure background as it supported large stacks of files in front of everyone attending. Blackledge shuffled through some papers in one of his folders. "I think we're in agreement that the procedure used was appropriate." He glanced around the table as everyone nodded. Then he picked up another file. That brings us to Dr. Lapin."

Several men cleared their throats. The administrator leafed through the thick stack of paperwork. "A busy month."

"Not really," Lapin answered.

"Are all of these patients Witnesses?"

Lapin nodded his head and sighed. He knew what was coming. "Most of them."

Blackledge sighed in turn. The stage was set to do battle. "Dr. Lapin, with the increased attention the hospital is getting, we feel it's necessary to. . . ."

"What is it you're trying to say?" Lapin interrupted.

"Just that this hospital can't exist in a vacuum."

"A vacuum," Lapin repeated.

"Dr. Lapin, it's not just a question of how you or I feel about it; there's the entire community to consider."

"Leo," Lapin answered wearily, "this is a hospital, not a church. I don't conduct religious services, I just operate."

Blackledge remained calm and in control. "There's a standard of medical care that we're supposed to maintain."

"Leo, these people--these Witnesses--don't know anything about the AMA or State regulatory agencies, and what's more, they don't care. There are nearly a million Witnesses in the United States. They're not bad people. They're not criminals. They don't hurt anyone." Lapin's voice was beginning to rise. "But if they get hurt, they can't go to a doctor or to a hospital and get help. There has to be a different standard of care for these people--different from the community standard of care."

"We don't make the rules."

"The hell we don't," he shot back. "If we don't help these people, who will?" He looked around; most eyes were fixed on the table top in front of them. "I'll tell you who--the quacks, the charlatans, and the butchers." He lowered his voice and continued, "I saw a woman today. . . ."

"A Witness?" Blackledge asked.

"Of course," he replied. "If she hadn't been a Witness, I wouldn't have seen her. She had a pain, small at first, so she went to see some guy in Wisconsin. He put her on a raw vegetable diet and had her drink soup made from wheat grass." At least Lapin had now regained their attention. "Strangely enough," he continued, "that didn't seem to make the cancer in her gut disappear. So next, she and her husband went to a clinic in Mexico. They gave her enemas--coffee enemas."

"We know all about such things, Ron."

"We can afford to hate the place and the things they do--we don't have to go there . . . but, we force the Witnesses to go."

"It's their choice," Blackledge answered.

"No!" he nearly shouted. With regained control, he explained, "We're their only choice. You know, sometimes they hear that there's this *meshugenuh* doctor out in Orange County who believes they're entitled to both their religion and first-class medical attention. So what do they do? They show up here. The woman I saw today--the one who used to have a little tumor--now has a tumor the size of a watermelon in her belly. Why don't some of you go talk to her about the standard of medical care in this community?"

Blackledge patronized, "We can't allow the patients to dictate procedure."

"We're not talking about procedure; we're talking about their deepest convictions. How dare we place our precious procedures above their beliefs? Are we so high and mighty all of a sudden that we can't bend to God?" Now he'd done it. Now he'd really offended them. Physicians were accustomed to hearing the analogy between themselves and God, but that analogy

152

was always made by lay people. This accusation was coming from one of their peers. To top it off, he had the audacity to allude to them as having elevated themselves above the Almighty. They seethed in silence.

Finally Blackledge spoke. "Doctor Lapin, we've granted permission for nearly all of your operations because of the specific nature and background of the cases. Since we've started, the ground swell from these Witnesses has created problems for this hospital that are far greater than your sense of justice and fair play."

"What are you trying to say?" Lapin repeated.

"That the State requirements must come first."

"In other words?"

"Operating exclusively on Witnesses has got to stop. They're not our problem. This meeting is adjourned."

***

Lapin and Donnelly stopped for a drink on their way home that night. It had been a long afternoon and they were both tired. Being mentally and physically exhausted seemed to come with the territory they were trying to establish.

Donnelly, by now, had heard all about the meeting. "You know our days are numbered here," he said, "at least if we continue with the Witnesses."

Lapin slowly sipped his drink. "Where's Jehovah when I need him?"

Donnelly smiled. "You know, it's not you that makes them nervous; it's the Witnesses."

"Yes, but I won't play their game."

"So you make waves. I know you're a better surgeon than most of them, maybe all of them. I've been around. You know perfectly well why most of them fight you on the transfusion issue. They're not good enough or fast enough to use your techniques. With blood, they have more time to be mediocre in the OR. Without blood, it's like working without a net . . . and they're not about to do that."

"So I should be held back because of them?"

"Aha! Now you've come face to face with the real issue. You're willing to put it all on the line for the Witnesses and risk hurting yourself. They're not. Every time you operate on a Witness, every time you go in there and keep your promise not to use blood, you're putting your neck on the block. That takes guts. Every time you tell them that the patient comes first and not the AMA standards, you're rubbing their faces in it. You're reminding them of how mediocre they really are. And you know what, my friend?"

"No, what?"

"They don't want to hear that, so don't waste your time. You're bothering a lot of people . . . and some big people at that. Just be careful, that's all."

Lapin stared into the distance, through the hanging blue smoke in the dimly lit bar.

"So tell me about the guy," Lapin finally said.

"What guy?"

"The guy at Esperanza . . . I want to talk to him."

Donnelly smiled, nearly chuckling out loud. He touched his glass to Lapin's, and the clink caused several heads to turn. "Here we go again."

And there they went again. From Bristol to Esperanza. The move was reasonably uncomplicated. Only a few of the actual inpatients had to be transported. It went well, all except for the administration at Bristol.

The same people who tried to stifle the young surgeon only three weeks earlier were now threatening to charge him with stealing their personnel. The truth of the matter was that their allegations were false.

The only team member who worked directly for Lapin was his secretary, Jodie, who maintained steadfast loyalty through ordeal after ordeal. The others, Jan, Dixie, Mikie, and the rest, were hospital employees. They all saw the other side of the mountain while working with Lapin. Their days--and sometimes nights-- in the OR were always filled with learning and, more importantly, with accomplishment. They assisted in resolving the kind of challenges that had become commonplace in Dr. Lapin's case load, even though equivalent problems had never been discussed or even touched upon while they were still in school.

To return to a "normal" surgical situation and work with a "regular" doctor would have been an immense backsliding that professionally none could afford. They asked Lapin if they could go with him and resigned en masse.

Rana and Donnelly, being staff members, could practice anywhere they chose. It was clearly apparent to the administrators that when the two of them left Bristol to work with Lapin, they were unlikely to ever return. The die had been cast. Decisions had been made on a personal and individual level. Lapin hadn't stolen anybody. They had all attached themselves to a man whose talent, ability, and courage they respected. It was just that simple. *Why*, Lapin questioned so many times, *couldn't other things be that simple? Why?*

Esperanza was about five years old, and Lapin's earlier appraisal had been accurate. The operating room was only being used about three times a week. This struck Lapin as strange in that the facility itself was quite modern. It had good equipment that could easily be upgraded into a first-class facility.

It was twice the size of Bristol, one hundred and six beds. Everything seemed right--everything, that is, except the occupancy rate. For unknown reasons, it hovered between a mere five to ten percent of its capacity.

From discussions with Jay Piersal, the owner of the hospital, William Fancher, the hospital administrator, and Donnelly, Lapin fit together the primary puzzle pieces. At least enough pieces were in place to make his decision to move there.

The hospital's interest in Lapin was purely self-serving. They were right on the verge of bankruptcy. Piersal had called Lapin nearly six times a day during the three week interim. He knew Lapin could fill the beds quickly and wanted to make sure that Esperanza was getting his profitable practice. During one conversation, he distastefully remarked to Lapin, "I won't care if you fill the beds with Borneo headhunters." He laughed and added, "You can even bring in people who, God forbid, ring doorbells on Saturday morning."

Piersal wasn't necessarily being critical or insensitive; it was just his offbeat sense of humor poking through. Lapin wasn't amused in the least. Piersal tried to reassure Lapin by explaining that, less than a year ago, the beds had been filled and everything was great. Then in a very short period of time, the surgeries had come to a screeching halt. Admissions hit bottom because the three staff surgeons, Williams, Tyler, and Mitchell, sent all their patients to other local hospitals and heavily influenced various staff members to do the same. Their influence seemed to hold sway. The hospital was dying.

"The only thing I can figure out," he told Lapin,

"is that they're trying to run the hospital into the ground so they can buy it at a substantially deflated price, build it back up, and retain ownership themselves. Either that, or force a sale of the place to a hospital chain."

A scenario giving an opposing view of the situation was uncovered during conversations with Williams, Tyler, Mitchell, and some other staff members. Lapin learned that the hospital's biggest problems were a direct result of Piersal's basic dishonesty and lack of integrity. Each, in turn, told him the same story. Piersal owned a hospital in Northern California that was doing quite well, but then had also formed a limited partnership with several doctors here to create Esperanza. Even though Esperanza grew and made money, Piersal, as the general partner, cleverly managed to lose the profits on paper.

They revealed that Piersal had reneged on several other business deals with the same group of doctors. Understandably, they became disenchanted with the entire money-losing proposition and, after several unsatisfactory attempts to reconcile, decided to take the matter into their own hands. They, along with other investors, built another hospital in the same area and were admitting all their patients there. The thread of logic behind this expensive ploy was that Esperanza would be forced to lose a lot of money. This, they deduced, would eventually force Piersal to sell out to one of several institutions who'd been unsuccessful in their previous attempts to buy the hospital. Only in that way would the original investors have their money returned, and probably with a large profit.

But Piersal refused to buckle under. He advertised for physicians in medical journals throughout the Southwest, offering a first-class facility. He used funds from the hospital up north to keep Esperanza afloat. It was a struggle and a financial drain.

Finally Piersal received a reply from a doctor in Arizona--a busy general practicioner. Together they formed a partnership and built a medical center near the hospital which did very well. Piersal didn't want to lose the hospital and now had his sights set directly on Lapin to turn it around. Persistently, he called the young surgeon at least six times a day.

Fancher, the administrator, was an employee of the owner, and as such, obviously leaned in the company's

156

direction. He also had a great personal interest in the matter. During one of the meetings with Lapin, Fancher mentioned a rumor he'd heard about Rana. As the admitting internist, the story went, Rana wasn't doing his share of the work. He was cutting corners instead of providing the proper work-ups.

Lapin, heavily weighed down with more important concerns, passively defended Rana and said he'd take care of any problems that might exist among his people.

Fancher shrugged and let it go. He'd gone as far as he could, without creating problems. His job was to help solicit Lapin and fill those beds for Piersal.

Williams, Tyler, and Mitchell, the three surgeons who wanted to force the sale of the hospital, were already at work undermining Lapin's team. They riled key staff members and told nurses and other personnel that their jobs would be in jeopardy as soon as Lapin became entrenched. The news of Lapin's pending appointment brought more behind-the-scenes excitement to the hospital than it had had in years.

Lapin unwittingly set off another round of subterfuge. His primary concern was needing a safe place to operate, and needing it soon. If his joining the staff at Esperanza would spoil the plans of its three most powerful staff members--the chief of staff, Tyler, the chief of anesthesiology, Mitchell, and the chief of surgery, Williams--he would have to deal with that as the next thing down the road.

Piersal had at least been honest enough to warn Lapin of the friction between the hospital and the three physicians. Lapin, not being one to cower in the face of any controversy, decided to face it head-on. He arranged a meeting between himself and his adversaries at what he laughingly referred to as "neutral ground." Hutchins went with him, acting as considerably more than just an interested observer.

The restaurant was full that Saturday night as the waitress led the three men to Lapin's table. They stood and went through the formality of introductions although they already knew one another. Then they sat down in silence, waiting to see how it was all going to start.

Lapin cleared his throat and began, "You're probably wondering why I've invited you here."

"I'm curious," Mitchell said, never taking his eyes off the man.

"As you know, we're bringing all the Witness patients over to Esperanza. I want to turn things around there, and I want you gentlemen to help me." He paused for a second, giving them an opportunity to respond. When no one did, he continued, "The place is a first-rate facility, and there's no reason why it shouldn't stay in business for a good long time."

Williams, Tyler, and Mitchell looked intently at each other. Did they really just hear what they thought they heard?

"You want us to stay on?" Tyler finally asked.

"That's the idea."

Mitchell glanced at Tyler as if checking for approval. "I assume you know we're trying to force the sale of the hospital."

"And that you're sending all of your patients to other hospitals in the area," Lapin added.

Tyler was noticeably irritated. "That's about the size of it, Lapin. So what?"

"Relax," Lapin said. "I'm not making any judgments about what you do. Hell, I don't care who owns the place. All I know is I've got lots of patients who need beds and doctors. What do you say?"

This Lapin guy is shrewd, Tyler thought. "As long as you don't move your practice into Esperanza . . . just yet."

"Oh?" Lapin injected, raising an eyebrow. "When would you suggest?"

"Give it about three months," Tyler answered.

"Why three months?"

"Because we believe we can force the sale of the hospital by then."

The three men smiled and nodded.

"I appreciate your advice, gentlemen," Lapin responded, "but I'm moving in tomorrow."

"That might prove to be a mistake," Tyler hissed.

"Wouldn't be my first."

"No doubt," Mitchell replied. Then his voice went cold--ice cold. "But it could prove to be your last. We'll get rid of you in our own way. Good night, Doctor Lapin."

Hutchins watched the three walk quickly through the crowd and wryly commented, "Did they just threaten to do something very unpleasant to us?"

Lapin smiled. "Why, I believe they did."

***

The first day was hectic. Actually, the entire first month was hectic--transferring patients, re-arranging schedules, and trying to create a team spirit among the people who would now be working together. There was a tremendous increase in patient admittance, so new nurses and support personnel had to be hired. Williams, Tyler, and Mitchell did everything they could to throw obstacles in the path of progress, openly criticizing or condemning nearly all of Lapin's moves.

Witnesss came from across the country to see Dr. Ron Lapin, even after hearing of his relocation. From their experiences while under his care, many assigned him affectionate nicknames, but he never did feel worthy of those designations.

Things were going smoothly. The hospital was filling up, critical cases were being undertaken successfully, and, most importantly, lives that would probably have been unnecessarily lost were being saved.

Fluosol was used three times in quick succession with total success. The first patient was Gina Carlton, a Witness from Hemet, California. She was a delightful young woman: bright, vibrant, full of life --at least until she developed a large tumor in her uterus. Massive vaginal bleeding had caused her hemoglobin to drop to four grams. Like many Witnesses preceding her, she'd gone from doctor to doctor only to be rejected, accused, and criticized for religious beliefs that they labeled suicidal.

The last doctor to see her was in an emergency room setting. Like his colleagues, he refused to touch her without transfusing. The physician made a cold, cruel, heartless attack on her beliefs and finally told her husband to take her home and let her die. Gina went home--prepared to die. She was at peace with herself, unafraid, and determined to maintain her integrity.

Her husband, also a Witness, had nearly accepted their fate. He prayed with his wife and knew that she was in the safest of hands. But he had one more call to make--a call to a Jewish surgeon in Orange County, California.

And as usual, Lapin said, "Bring her over right away."

All necessary calls, including those to Washington and Green Cross, brought full approval to use Fluosol. It was delivered and used to stabilize the brave young woman and prepared her for a successful hysterectomy.

159

Gina's bleeding stopped, and seven days later she returned to Hemet a happy young woman--as bright, vibrant, and full of life as ever.

The entire ordeal, the Fluosol and the bloodless surgery, was later reinacted for *That's Incredible,* the ABC television show.

Two local TV stations came to Esperanza to interview Lapin. Film footage was shot both in and outside the operating room. People and patients were interviewed. Days were spent following Lapin around to capture the innermost workings of the man and his hospital. Lapin was frank, open, honest, and realistic. The interview was fair and good, owing to the fact that it was a candid portrayal of Lapin and his real life existence in a life-and-death world.

One night after the second TV crew had packed their equipment and gone home, Lapin stood in the hallway just to observe the surroundings. There were nurses and gurneys. There were meals being delivered to patients who finally had a place to be treated. There was a flurry of activity, an aliveness.

It occurred to him that the last time he stood in that very same spot just six weeks earlier, the scene in the hallway had been just the opposite . . . deserted, empty, and lifeless.

It's been a good day, Lapin thought to himself as he walked to the front parking lot. He'd parked his car there early that morning. He felt good, relaxed for a change. *Finally*, he thought. *Finally. And isn't it about time?*

Then he saw it . . . on the other side of the street, across from where his car was parked. It was a no parking zone, clearly marked with signs and large block lettering on the curb that said "No Parking" every ten feet. Someone had decided to express their feelings by adding some lettering of their own. Lapin read the new printing. His day was shattered; he was stunned. Now every ten feet, the curb read: "No Parking - Ron Lapin . . . No Parking - Ron Lapin . . . No Parking - Ron Lapin."

***

It was a silent vigil at home alone that night. Hutchins called to see if he was all right . . . and of course he was. No big deal. Just some crank. By now somebody from the hospital had painted over the additional writing to return the curb's message to its original form.

Herk told Ron to forget it--sort of like a judge telling a jury to disregard the previous statement. It can't be done . . . not after they heard it . . . not after Lapin saw it. It was blatantly clear that the turmoil was starting all over again.

The phone rang. He hoped it was someone on the hot line he could help--something he could throw himself into.

"This is Doctor Lapin."

There was complete silence . . . no voice, no dial tone.

"Hello . . . this is Doctor Lapin."

Then a low, muffled voice responded, "Listen, Jew boy, and listen good."

"Who is this?"

"We don't want you or your kind in Yorba Linda."

"Who is this?"

"You take your weirdo Jehovah Witness patients and go the hell back to where you all belong . . . 'cause if you don't, Jew boy, we got ways of dealin' with you."

Lapin hung up and stared at the phone.

***

He was in surgery the next morning at six-thirty. It was business as usual. There was another long day ahead of him. Lapin had eight procedures scheduled for the day and a meeting with a group of Witnesses that night.

The P.A. announced "Code Blue" and everyone's ears perked up. The operation continued without interruption, but all talking ceased. Code Blue indicated that a hospital patient had gone into cardiac arrest. Teams were summoned to the appropriate room to take whatever measures were necessary.

Dixie, without being asked, left the OR and walked to the nearest wall phone. When she returned moments later, she just stood inside the door. Her surgical mask managed to hide most of the emotion written on her face.

Lapin looked up from his patient. "So?" he asked.

"It's Mrs. Carmen. . . ." That's all Dixie seemed able to get out.

Lapin continued working; he didn't look up. "What

about Mrs. Carmen?"

"Somebody . . . made a mistake last night." Then
she stopped again.

"Dixie, what mistake?" Lapin asked, beginning to get
irritated. "What happened?" Lapin's irritation was
justified, considering he had operated on Mrs. Carmen
two days earlier. It was a routine gall bladder
surgery, and she had been recovering nicely.

"Well," Dixie began slowly, "last night someone
turned her IV on full."

"Opened it all the way?" Lapin's voice rose, but he
never took his eyes off the patient.

"All the way! She went into heart failure after
taking in two liters of fluid so rapidly. They're
working on her now and trying to reverse it."

Lapin was quiet for a minute while he concentrated
on a delicate cut and then cauterized several small
vessels. "Someone tried to kill her," he finally
said. No one answered. They all knew his words rang
of truth. "Who did it?" he asked.

"Nobody knows," Dixie answered.

"What do you mean, nobody knows?"

"Her chart's in order. It hasn't been touched. None
of the night shift nurses know anything; as far as any
of them know--or will say--the IV wasn't touched."

"Where's Jan?"

"She's with the Code Team."

Lapin looked up at his able assistant. "Herk?"

"I'll close," he said without hesitation. "You go
on."

Lapin tore off his mask as he left and ran down the
hallway to the patient's room. She was just beginning
to come around. The thought of this criminal act
haunted Lapin for a long time to come.

***

That night he spoke to a group of twelve Witnesses
in the hospital cafeteria. After recovering from her
surgery, one of the sisters had asked Dr. Lapin to
talk with some friends from her Kingdom Hall, and he
readily agreed.

The sister who arranged the meeting had had cancer
of the thyroid. She'd been refused treatment, been
ridiculed for her beliefs, been desperate enough to go
to Mexico, and been told she was going to die. Like
so many others, she'd been through the whole ordeal

162

before finding Lapin.

This was the first meeting of its kind. The purpose was to explain some of his methods and techniques to the people who someday might need them--the people who someday might not have anywhere else to go. In his heart, Lapin hoped that would never be the case and that other surgeons would someday soon see the advantages of not using blood.

He quoted from an article in a United States government publication which said, ". . . donating blood can be compared to sending a loaded gun to an unsuspecting person; like the loaded gun, there is a safety lever governing blood transfusions. Yet, how many persons have died from gunshot wounds because they believed the safety lever was on?"

Lapin imparted information from *Jehovah's Witnesses and the Question of Blood,* a brochure published by the Watchtower Bible and Tract Society of Pennsylvania.

He quoted Winfield Miller from *Medical Economics:* "No biological product has greater potential for fatal mistakes in medical practice than blood. More than one doctor has learned, to his sorrow, that every bottle of blood in the blood banks is a potential bottle of nitroglycerin."

Dr. J. Garrott Allen, a leading expert on the blood problem, estimated that blood transfusions kill at least three thousand five hundred Americans each year and injure another fifty thousand. *The Southern Medical Journal* suggests that the estimated three to thirty thousand deaths per year attributed to transfusions is probably conservative.

Dr. Robert J. Baker reported in yet another publication that the danger of adverse effects from blood is far greater than previously believed, with one out of twenty patients developing a reaction.

Lapin wanted his audience to be keenly aware of the fact that their aversion to taking blood, based on their religious beliefs, was acceptable to him. He pointed out that their opposition to transfusions was also valid from a medical standpoint. He read a list from a hematology textbook which cited twenty-two different types of reactions to blood transfusions. Most were highly technical, but the ones most often discussed among laymen were hepatitis, malaria, syphilis, and bacterial contamination.

However, one of the most critical problems exists within hospitals themselves. Blood mismatching, often

163

described as a clerical error, results when one blood type is requested but another is delivered from the blood bank and then transfused. It's a human error that occurs at an alarming rate.

In the United States alone, thirty thousand cases of post-transfusion hepatitis result in fifteen hundred to three thousand deaths annually. That statistic is serious enough, but the U.S. Center for Disease Control additionally points to a conservative figure of two hundred thousand cases of hepatitis B occurring each year in this country from blood transfusions.

Professor H. Busch, a director of transfusion medicine, concluded his report at a German surgeons' convention by saying, "Blood should be considered a dangerous medicine and should be used with the caution of, for example, morphine."

The Witnesses' stand against blood, Lapin reiterated, was valid. He ended the discussion by showing them an article that had appeared in the *Las Vegas Sun*. It told about a patient, a Witness, who had been promised by her surgeon that he absolutely wouldn't use blood. But during surgery her doctor got into trouble. He obtained a court order to transfuse, and did so immediately.

The small audience was shocked and saddened when Lapin told them that the patient died a day later--a result of being transfused with mismatched blood.

***

Somehow the surgical unit seemed to be slowing down. Lapin couldn't put his finger on the exact reason, but he knew it wasn't the team. They were working together as a finely tuned unit. Skin-to-skin time had been reduced, and that was critical with the type of patients Lapin served. It was more a problem of getting support. For one thing, supplies were being delivered to the floor late. Worse yet, those supplies sometimes hadn't even been ordered. If that were the case at hand, Dr. Lapin was forced to improvise and that should have never been necessary.

The most detrimental part of all this was having floor care for post-operative patients that was slower than it should be. Lapin reprimanded the nurses about the problem more than once; he expected their best efforts as professionals. The last thing he wanted, however, was another confrontation with anyone. He'd had his fill of that. He just wanted proper care for his patients, that's all.

Problems, though, are an integral part of a surgeon's life. These doctors actually live in a world dominated by problems and try to do everything in their power to find acceptable solutions.

This was the case when one patient called and explained with great certainty that he'd been charged for an examination he'd never had. The problem and its solution really belonged to Rana since he was responsible for the examination in question. But Lapin, being closer to the patient than Rana, volunteered to look into it. When he ran into Rana later that morning and confronted him with the problem, it was explained away as some sort of clerical error. Partially satisfied, Lapin instructed him to be more careful with his billing procedures. Of course Rana agreed, and that was that. Problem solved. Back to the operating room.

Mitchell, Williams, and Tyler had controlling positions on the executive committee of the hospital and tried everything in their power to block Lapin's permanent staff appointment. They tampered with his application folder, removed important documents, and leaked sensitive information to hospital employees about his resignation from Hope Hospital eight years before. They also spoke with a newsman from the *Register*, an Orange County newspaper. The reporter immediately smelled a hot story and began an investigation of his own.

In an impromptu emergency meeting, the executive committee tried desperately to summarily remove him from the staff and cancel his next day's surgical schedule. Thanks to the valiant efforts of Doctor Hill, an older, stately orthopedic surgeon who exposed their real motivations, they didn't succeed.

Smarting from their failure to remove Lapin and realizing they couldn't sink the hospital, all three resigned from Esperanza. They gave full warning that they'd be heard from in the future. Everyone seemed to ignore their threat and passed it off as "sour grapes." Everyone, that is, except Lapin. He knew they had little to lose and that their behavior, at best, would be irrational or even desperate.

How he wished that his instincts about those three doctors were wrong. But time proved him right; their retaliatory actions demonstrated how unscrupulous and vicious they were.

***

Inquiries on the hot line steadily increased, and admittances continued to rise. The expanse of their work load required that they take on a new team member, Dr. Stanley Kaller.

Kaller had come to Esperanza with Piersal's new partner, the GP from Arizona, but after repeated disagreements, was no longer working with him. As an associate with no private practice of his own, he was literally packing his bags and getting ready to leave. Lapin intervened by proposing that he work with the team. His case load was building and there was room for another good physician. Rana wouldn't mind; he was busy and already beginning to cut corners with his patient work-ups. Kaller readily accepted the offer and unpacked.

Lapin had a meeting with another group of local Witnesses that night. He told them about the case he'd had a couple of years earlier involving Rusty Barnes, the youngster who'd accidentally shot himself in the leg. Lapin pointed out that giving Witnesses immediate medical treatment was critical. This was the first time he used the Rusty Barnes situation to make a clear-cut analogy, but he would use it a thousand times over because it was one that people could relate to and understand easily.

"Bleeding internally," he began, "is a slow and sometimes painful process. Its especially critical for you people because you can't find anyone to stop it. It's much like watching a bullet . . . in slow motion . . . coming straight at your head . . . and there's nothing you can do about it. To move or duck would mean violating your own religious conscience. I, for one, won't ask you to do that. I never have, and I never will. It's imperative for you to be armed with information so that you can avoid such potential disasters."

Applause filled the room. This time the crowd numbered sixty-five. That meant sixty-five more people now knew they had a place to go where their beliefs would be respected, should they ever have to face that terminal bullet hurtling toward their head. Still in Jehovah's hands? Absolutely. But now, they had an alternative to the certainty of death; they had

166

someone they felt Jehovah was using to care for His people.

For nearly an hour, Lapin answered questions, every single one of them. He chuckled when inevitably asked, "Are you a Witness?" His stock answer had become, "No, I just sound like one."

He was pleased that so many Witnesses told him in all seriousness that he actually was a Witness, but just didn't know it.

***

The night was clear, calm, and peaceful. It had been a fine day. He'd done good things for good people. Even the inner workings of the hospital had gone smoothly. He held his good feelings in check. It was a habit he'd been acquiring, and this night it proved to be of value.

The contentment of the evening was immediately disrupted when Lapin reached his new car. There he found that the left front door had been badly gouged. *Whoever did it probably used a screwdriver or an icepick*, he thought to himself as he ran his finger over the torn metallic paint. *Or maybe a scalpel*, he added as an afterthought.

It was ruined. *Probably have to repaint the entire car to get it to match.* The grooves were cut deep, really deep. He took three steps backward and just looked at the door. He tried desperately not to hate the people responsible for what he saw.

But he'd seen that insignia so many times as he grew up in Israel; seen it, hated what it stood for, and hated the people behind it. Now here he was, a million light-years away, a surgeon in Orange County, California, just trying to help some courageous people live a little longer. Here he was, a Jewish surgeon with a large, ugly swastika scratched deeply into the side of his car. He was angry, confused, and very hurt. He could only ask, "Why?" "Why?" "Why?" More problems were yet to follow, some subtle, some blatant.

***

Patients came from all over the country by plane, train, bus, motorhome, and automobile; they came to Orange County to a one hundred bed hospital. They came to see Lapin and his young staff of doctors who respected their beliefs.

Their persistence and dedication disproved the suicide theory that was so often thrown at the Witness population. Their will to live was superseded only by their refusal to violate God's Holy Word. Their trust and confidence in Lapin was something he in turn considered sacred. His commitment to their beliefs and principles had become as deep-rooted and unbending as their own. He had formed a strong and lasting bond with them, a bond dedicated to life.

***

The phone call at five a.m. wasn't the hot line, but oh, how he wished it had been. Hutchins wouldn't say exactly what was wrong at the hospital, just that he'd better get down there as soon as possible. Whatever it was, it had to be serious.

Can't be a patient, Lapin thought. *Herk would have told me if it was a patient.* He dressed quickly. He was a master at that. *And what the hell's Herk doing at the hospital this time of the morning anyway?* The ride to the hospital brought still more questions, each more disastrous and less answerable than the last.

The hospital was quiet. That much was expected for five-thirty a.m. There was very little activity. *How different*, Lapin thought as he rushed through the deserted halls toward the operating room. *Wouldn't it be nice . . . wouldn't it be nice if it were always like this--quiet, peaceful, empty?*

He turned the corner and walked into the OR. Herk was there, so was Donnelly, and so was Dixie. They stopped what they were doing and watched as he entered. The first thing Lapin saw was their faces-- stark, drawn, angry. Dixie's mascara still stained her cheeks from crying. Their faces asked questions that they couldn't answer . . . or could they?

Lapin turned his head to the left and visually swept the room in slow motion. In an instant, his face matched those of his friends. He was struck by a combination of shock, frustration, and despair. The room was a shambles. Surgical equipment was strewn across the floor. The anesthesiologist's monitoring devices were knocked over and smashed into irreparable pieces. Towels stuffed into the sinks had caused them

to overflow and flood the entire room; the water line
on the far wall was nearly a foot above floor level.
Hutchins and Donnelly were attempting to mop up the
mess. The supply cabinets had been turned over, and
the walls were splattered with chemicals. The oxygen
hoses had all been cut.

Lapin was speechless, totally speechless. He inched
his way around the room, touching things as if they
weren't real . . . as if he were in a nightmare . . .
as if he'd lost faith in his eyesight and was forced
to rely on his sense of touch to confirm the tragedy.

He looked at his three friends, one by one, then
spoke. "Who would do such a thing?" The tone was
filled with pain. He was incapable of understanding
how anyone could commit such an act.

Hutchins shared the feeling. He, too, spoke slowly.
"Who could do such a thing?"

"I don't know," Lapin replied. "Tyler, Mitchell,
Williams . . . take your pick."

Lapin grabbed a damp towel and began wiping the
chemicals off one wall. The motion was more mechanical than anything else. His mind and his heart were
elsewhere. His friends watched him, just watched, as
he wiped the wall. Faster . . . then faster . . .
then faster! He became frenzied in his attempt to
eradicate the travesty.

Sweat poured from his forehead. The others watched,
sharing his pain, perhaps not equally, but sharing it
nonetheless. The only sound was the swish, swish,
swish of the towel as it flew across the stained tile
walls.

Finally he stopped. There was a long, deep inhale
. . . and a slow, drawn-out exhale. He whispered,
"It's like desecrating a church. How could people--
especially doctors--do such a thing?"

The room was quiet. No one offered an answer. Then
Hutchins picked up a towel and started mopping. The
others followed suit.

***

The operating room was filled with nurses and
orderlies that afternoon. Lapin's anger was outwardly
controlled, but still raged within. He called a
meeting. This was going to be the showdown he had
hoped to avoid, the final confrontation.

With perfect diction, he was explicitly clear in

stating that someone right there at the meeting was either responsible for what had happened, or had at least been aware of it.

He paused to let his statement sink in, but there were no voluntary confessions.

He went on to remind them of the sanctity of medicine and the healing process, and of the responsibility with which they'd all been entrusted.

Still no volunteers came forward.

He talked about the strides they'd made together, the medical history that had been accomplished, the lives they'd saved, and the other good things they had done. He told them he couldn't comprehend how anyone could have done this horrible thing.

The room was as quiet as it had been at five-thirty that morning.

He waited until the silence itself created an intolerable atmosphere.

Three senior nurses and a nursing supervisor finally stood up and left the room. Each of them had been clearly supportive of Tyler, Mitchell, and Williams and their plan to sink the hospital. Later that afternoon, the four of them resigned from the staff.

Lapin was relieved. He thought he was through with them . . . that he'd heard the last of them. He was so wrong.

7

It wasn't unusual for Lapin to ride in the ambulance to meet a patient arriving at the airport. This particular case, though starting the same as many others, seemed to warrant more immediate attention than most.

The frail, pretty young lady had just turned twenty-four when she developed mandibular osteo sarcoma, cancer of the lower jaw. It surfaced over two and a half years ago with some throbbing and minor irritation in her gums and jaw.

X-rays failed to pinpoint the cause of the pain; nevertheless it intensified with each passing day. It was a shooting, stabbing pain that never went away. Finally a biopsy was done when the discomfort became severe; a thin slice of tissue from the lower jaw was removed and examined under a microscope. That's when her cancer was first discovered.

Lapin shook his head with frustration and complete dismay the first time he heard the story. *It's so ridiculous,* he thought to himself, as they weaved their way through the heavy late afternoon traffic. *If someone--anyone--would have dealt with the tumor when it was first diagnosed, none of this would be happening. We wouldn't be dashing madly to the airport, and this young woman wouldn't be dying from starvation and suffocation.*

But, alas, that wasn't the case. The young woman was one of Jehovah's Witnesses. She was unable to find a doctor who would even consider removing the tumor without transfusing massive amounts of blood.

And so her personal trek began, doctor to doctor, treatment to worthless treatment, and trips to Mexico for expensive laetrile injections. Nothing worked. Nothing helped. The tumor continued to grow inside her mouth, disfiguring her attractive young face. The drugs helped to ease the pain in her mouth, but not the one in her heart. That was the real pain, the frustration of being helpless and alone and having nowhere to turn. Yes, that was the real anguish, two and a half years' worth. Only her complete faith in Jehovah kept her going, and that faith was aided strongly about a year and a half earlier when she met and fell in love with Gary Chapman.

Her inner beauty shone through the grotesque mass growing steadily inside her mouth. Together, they decided they could face any obstacle and overcome it. The love they shared was stronger than anything life could throw in their path.

They were married. No longer would she have to face her pain and frustration alone. They prayed together, searched for help together, and grew more deeply in love. And, oh, what a love it was. It was the kind of love that most people can only dream about. Their dedication and commitment to each other was totally without reservation.

It was Gary who heard about Lapin from one of the friends at the Kingdom Hall. Never during their entire relationship had he questioned that they'd eventually find someone who would save his wife's life.

It was Gary who had called Lapin earlier in the week. The young man sitting on the airplane beside his dying wife recalled the conversation verbatim. He remembered telling Lapin that the tumor had grown so huge that it forced her mouth open. It was actually the size of a large orange. His wife was unable to speak and had only been able to ingest small amounts of liquids over the past several weeks. She was having great difficulty swallowing and now even breathing had become arduous. She had dropped from a hundred and ten down to eighty pounds. It was a horrendous, living nightmare. Yet after all this searching for someone to help her, she still kept her faith even as she now struggled to breathe.

"Tell you what," Lapin had interrupted, "you make arrangements to get over here as soon as you can, and we'll fix it."

There was much celebrating at the Chapman household in Nevada that evening. Gary and the frail-bodied Katie held onto each other like never before. Finally they had found someone who would give them the time together they so desperately desired.

And now they moved even closer to that moment. The plane was taxiing to the terminal and the ambulance was waiting on the field apron. When the 727 stopped short of the telescopic passenger tunnel, steps were rolled out toward it. The flight attendant opened the door so Gary and Katie could depart from the aircraft to meet their special ride.

Handshakes and introductions were warm and friendly; they were also hurried. There was an important passenger to get to the hospital.

Lapin took an immediate liking to the young couple. He learned during the ride that she was a Paiute Indian and had been a follower of Jehovah since she was sixteen. Gary was studying the Truth, but had not yet been baptized.

Lapin was intrigued with them as a couple. Here was a frail, thin, eighty-pound, five-foot woman and Gary, a six-foot-two, stocky ex-Green Beret. Gary had served fourteen months in combat in 'Nam. His toughness from the ordeal showed, but then, so did the tenderness, compassion, and love that he felt for his wife. Nightmares and flashbacks from the jungle still bothered him, but he was getting better as time went on, or so he thought.

The ambulance was nearly half way to its destination when Katie began to choke. At first it was a suppressed coughing with guttural sounds emanating from deep within her throat. Gary tried to grab her, but Lapin pushed him out of the way. He had her sit with her back straight, leaning slightly backward, and extending her neck. He was trying to create the easiest angle for air to enter the windpipe. It wasn't working at all. The gasping worsened.

Gary tried to muscle his way toward his wife. Lapin pushed him back again.

Lapin had Katie lie on the gurney and talked a mile a minute to the frightened young lady. He was reassuring and comforting as he tried to put her at ease. He reached inside one of the carefully labeled built-in drawers and produced a scalpel.

Isn't this strange, Lapin thought; *these people come all this way to be taken care of by a bloodless surgeon, and I greet them with a regular scalpel in my hand.* It was ironic.

But there was little time for thought. It was time for action, the kind of mechanical action that requires no thought. Years of experience made it second nature. Lapin had no time to waste; Katie was beginning to turn blue.

Gary panicked. "What are you gonna' do?" he shouted. The veins in his temples began to protrude.

Lapin remained calm and continued to prepare. "She can't breathe," he said. "She's choking to death."

The gasping intensified with each wretching hack. She was wheezing. Then her face became dark and ashen.

"She's turning blue," Gary screamed, trying again to get to his wife. Then louder, he demanded, "What are you gonna' do?" The gasping stopped. So did Katie's breathing. "Oh, my God . . . oh, my God. . . ."

Lapin quickly said, "Katie, I know you can hear me." He reached into another drawer and fumbled until he found the clear plastic tubing. "We'll have everything fixed in just a minute."

He removed the sterile wrap from the scalpel and held it in his right hand. Then he moved it toward Katie's throat. Now Gary didn't move. He became absolutely quiet.

"I'm going to do a tracheotomy . . . in just a minute you'll be able to breathe again. Just hang on. Everything's going to be fine."

Lapin quickly pushed the knife through the membrane in her windpipe and made an opening. By this time the siren was screaming and the ambulance was traveling as fast as possible through the city streets. The war-scarred veteran sitting at Lapin's side was beginning to lose his color.

The surgeon wiped away the precious blood that trickled down both sides of her neck. Then he quickly inserted the plastic tubing. There was a second of hesitancy, then another. Her chest began to move slowly. With a few deep breaths, everything was back to normal. She was turning a beautiful shade of pink again.

Gary was crying. Katie's eyes were sparkling, and a slight smile of gratitude could be distinguished beyond the horrendous tumor distorting her pretty face. The ambulance screamed into the night.

***

"Good morning," Lapin said. His voice was warm and filled with compassion. Katie's eyes opened slowly and focused on her visitor and her new surroundings.

When she recognized Lapin, her eyes seemed to almost dance. Months without speech had intensified her need to develop other methods of communication.

"This is Brother Hutchins," Lapin said. Katie turned her head to view the man. Lapin went on, "In addition to being a Witness, he's also one fine surgeon. Wouldn't do anything without him."

Herk touched Katie's hand. "Good morning, Katie. It certainly is a pleasure to meet you." She clasped her hand around his and squeezed it. Together they shared an understanding based on their religious beliefs. "This is a good place for you to be. You're in good hands . . . the very best."

Katie reached for the pad and pencil by her bed. The doctors watched as she hurriedly printed a message for them. When she handed it to Herk, it read, "I know this is a good place . . . and that I'm in good hands . . . thank you both. And, it is a very good morning."

The doctors were touched. It was quiet for a moment. Then Herk asked, "Is there anything we can get for you?"

She shook her head "no." She'd had some morphine earlier that morning and was holding up nicely. But then she lifted her right hand and used her index finger to point toward her mouth. Then she turned her hand around and pointed away. The message couldn't have been more clear: "just take this thing out of my mouth." Both Lapin and Herk were again touched, realizing that her unspoken request was delivered with a very sincere "please" attached. They smiled back warmly.

"We're going to do just that," Lapin said. "I just wanted to drop by this morning to see how you were doing, and also to introduce you to Doctor Hutchins."

Katie nodded appreciatively.

"We'll be back later this afternoon to visit and let you know what we plan to do."

They both touched her tiny hand and walked out of the room into the busy hallway. Neither spoke for several steps.

Herk finally muttered, "Uhh . . . I've never seen anything like that."

"Neither have I," Lapin agreed. "And she's really something, isn't she?"

"I should say."

"You ever feel such strength . . . especially from a

patient that little?"

"You do know where she gets her strength, don't you?" Herk asked needlessly. The two men smiled at each other; Lapin knew. "Now what are we going to do?" Herk continued.

"We're going to take it out."

"Ron, we've never attacked a tumor like that. That's the worst tumor I've ever seen. How are we going to do it?"

Lapin was unshaken. "I don't know yet, but I do know that we have to take it out."

"But," Herk started.

"There's no way we're going to let that little girl lay there and die . . . no way."

"You are something," Herk said, "really something."

"Yeah," Lapin smiled, "I guess that's why everybody likes me so much."

***

Katie Chapman was a perfect patient. Her sparkling eyes and unrelenting faith literally lit up the hospital and each life she touched. She was constantly passing notes of encouragement to other patients and lending an interested, concerned ear. The entire staff fell in love with her; it wasn't a hard thing to do. Her own pain was constant, but she never complained--not once. Her life was in the hands of Jehovah, and she was totally comfortable and at ease with that knowledge.

After much testing, Lapin concluded that radiation and chemotherapy treatments were the best route to take initially.

"Are you sure that'll be okay?" Gary asked, grimacing slightly.

"Well, this is what the consultants recommended," Lapin said. After studying Gary's expression, he asked, "Am I missing something here? What do you mean, 'Am I sure that'll be okay'"?

"Radiation . . . the baby. . . ."

"She's pregnant?" Lapin asked with a heavy sigh. "Why didn't you tell me?"

"I'm sorry, doc," Gary responded. "I thought I did. I really thought I did. . . ." The voice was sincere. He meant what he was saying. The emotional stress over the last few days had been far greater than he'd anticipated. Gary was spending his nights alone and two of them had ended with recurring Vietnam nightmares. He was put on tranquilizers.

"How far along is she?" Lapin questioned.

"Two months," Gary answered in a low voice.

"Well," Lapin said slowly, "I'm going to have to talk with Katie about it."

Grave concern filled his face as he discussed it with her.

"Will the chemotherapy and radiation hurt my baby?" she wrote.

Lapin, usually the epitome of confidence and optimism, nodded his head. He would never compromise his honesty. "It probably will," he choked.

She nodded understandingly, and began to write again. Lapin watched with consuming interest. She handed him the slip of paper that read, "Then this plan of yours is out of the question."

Lapin pursed his lips, considering the young woman's constant agony. "Katie, we. . . ."

She held up her hand and stopped him in midsentence. That was a feat not often accomplished. She started to write again and seconds later gave him her message. "Doctor Lapin, I'm going to have this baby."

He shook his head. "Katie," he whispered, "without the treatment, we can't even be sure you'll live long enough to deliver. I think you should consider taking the risk."

He saw the smile in her eyes that couldn't be expressed with her deformed mouth. He felt such empathy for her, such anguish. He wished somehow he could transfer the pain from her small weak shoulders to his own. *What's a little more pain?* he thought.

Katie was busy writing again. She gave him her final words on the matter. "I'm not going to do anything that would jeopardize the birth of my baby. I know you'll keep me alive long enough to deliver."

Again, he was moved. He wanted to speak, but was choked with emotion and feared it would give him away. He nodded with a slight shrug of exasperation and quietly left the young woman.

Where does she possibly get all that strength and courage, he asked himself. He explained to Herk and the team that they were going to operate on Katie the next morning. Their happiness was clouded by their concern for what they would find and how he'd go about the procedure. There were so many unanswered questions.

Lapin didn't have the answers. One of the basic ground rules surgeons learn is that they don't have all the answers and can't be one hundred percent sure of what they'll find when they operate. They learn that much of surgery is discovery--discovery that only comes from the human eye or the human touch. The science of medicine, even with all its marvelous testing processes and "science fiction" equipment, is not absolute. The surgeon, with his trained eye and unwavering hand, is still the most integral part of the complex process.

He spent most of that night reviewing the latest surgical literature regarding such tumors. He also restudied for the hundredth time the anatomy of the head and neck.

The room was filled with anxiety as Donnelly began the anesthesia. Tension was much higher than usual. Most patients enter the hospital shortly before their surgery, are seen by the team only during the actual surgery itself, and are discharged soon after. Katie's situation was different. Time had allowed most of the team to come in contact with her on several occasions. Their respect and admiration for this brave young lady ran deep. She had won their hearts, every single one of them.

Now, as she slept on the table, it was all up to Lapin, Hutch, and, most certainly, Jehovah.

Lapin's cutting was sure and swift. He first approached the major blood supplies to the tumor and tied them off. In the next two hours he removed the tumor, part of her jaw, and the floor of her mouth. Corrective and reconstructive surgery was then performed. Katie would speak when she came out of the anesthetic. It was considered a major success by any standard.

"Lapin has done it again," Herk murmured. He had gone where textbooks hadn't preceded him, treaded waters where no one was certain of the depth, and finished what few others would have even considered starting.

When Katie regained consciousness, her ability to verbally thank those who had both cared for her and done so much for her was an emotionally moving experience for every person involved. Her very first words were spoken with an incredible smile as she asked, "Where's my good Doctor Lapin?"

She rested for another week and continued to share her warmth and compassion with everyone in the hospital before she and her husband returned to Nevada. One small measure of their gratitude was demonstrated when they vowed to return and have Dr. Lapin deliver their child. Lapin hadn't delivered a baby in ten years, but promised them he'd brush up on his techniques.

Their future, however, was filled with uncertainty. There was a strong possibility that the tumor would return to plague her again, but no one could accurately pinpoint the time. Nevertheless, this probability did little to dampen the emotional outpouring that occurred as Katie and Gary drove away from the hospital.

***

Another patient complained to Lapin about being charged for a physical exam that was never performed. Lapin again spoke to Rana, who just mumbled and promised to be more conscientious.

"This is the second time," Lapin said, "and it better be the last. No more clerical errors, no more excuses, no more anything . . . period. Your records show that you admitted this woman to the hospital twice this year and that she had a normal uterus. The only problem is . . . she had a complete hysterectomy twenty years ago! You show a full history and physical on her chart, but the truth is you never examined her. Admit it! Now don't let this happen again."

Rana was overly apologetic, but this time Lapin wasn't satisfied. *Could I have been fooled? Was it carelessness, incompetency, or just outright dishonesty?* Whatever the case, Doctor Lapin knew he had to find out what was wrong.

Lapin was more troubled than usual. Consciously, he tried to concern himself only with his next operation. That was his style. Subconsciously, he underwent a fierce twenty-four hour struggle as he did some intense soul-searching. It was a grueling search deep within that tied his mind and psyche in knots. *What should I do about Rana?* he kept asking over and over. *What should I do?*

It was on the previous day that an attorney from New Jersey called and asked Lapin to testify for the prosecution--for one of Jehovah's Witnesses--against another doctor. It turned into a long day as Lapin found himself questioning the unwritten medical code of ethics and the widely accepted physicians' conspiracy of silence.

It was a big trial, a malpractice suit, and it was only four days away. Lapin had to make the right decision in a hurry. The prosecuting attorney's main problem was not being able to find a medical expert anywhere in the country who'd testify against a fellow doctor and say under oath that something had been done incorrectly.

This story, like so many others concerning the Witnesses, really moved Lapin. He felt distressed, bothered, pained. The attorney explained that a young Spanish-speaking woman in Newark, New Jersey, had fallen on ice during the worst snowstorm of the year. She had been rushed to a hospital where a locally respected orthopedic surgeon wanted to put plates in her forearm to correct the broken bones. Interestingly enough, the surgeon was a graduate of Maimonides, the same hospital where Lapin had done his residency.

The doctor explained to the woman, through an interpreter, that it was a very bloody operation and that it would definitely require a transfusion. Hearing the words in Spanish, the woman's facial expression turned from pain to shock. Her answer was an absolute refusal and was clear enough in her native tongue that the bilingual third party became unnecessary.

The doctor then suggested they put a cast on her arm and that, by doing so, she would heal just as well. Lapin knew this was incorrect even before the attorney pointed it out. It clearly indicated poor judgment on the part of the East Coast surgeon. Lapin was also aware of the fact that a plate insertion in an appendage wasn't at all a bloody procedure if the surgeon applied tourniquets and a reasonable degree of caution. Her surgeon never once suggested that she seek another opinion, nor did he refer her to someone who would perform the operation without blood.

The attorney explained that when the cast was removed, the patient's arm was predictably and grotesquely twisted. It was severely damaged, he said, and for all practical purposes, a non-functional extremity.

180

The patient was then patronized, being assured that the situation would eventually correct itself. After two long years of agony, the condition had only worsened.

She explained to her attorney that the worst part of the ordeal, well beyond the pain, involved her two young daughters. Both of them had hair that was very long and beautiful. Each of the girls had cultivated a loving bond with their mother as she sat and talked with them for hours while combing their hair. But because of the senseless, unnecessary disfiguration, she hadn't been able to do that for over two years. Her tears came from that pain, from wanting that experience back. And that, the attorney told Lapin, was what motivated her to sue the orthopedic surgeon. The lady had been badly harmed mentally and physically.

The attorney emphasized that without testimony from a medical expert, the young woman's chances of winning were hopeless.

Lapin's first consideration was always for the patient's welfare; after all, they were his priority. The Witnesses and his personal ethics were both immensely valuable to him. Lapin was not a man to violate his own principles. This case could be no exception.

After rearranging a demanding surgical schedule, Lapin was set to arrive in New Jersey two days before the trial date. His consuming thought during the entire coast-to-coast flight was, *If I don't defend their rights today . . . who will defend mine tomorrow?*

Upon his arrival, he was briefed on the intricate details of the case. He was distressed and disheartened as he watched both attorneys eliminate over one hundred prospective jurors in their search for eight people who weren't openly prejudiced against Jehovah's Witnesses. He was appalled as he watched the legal process in action.

Before the trial began, Lapin contacted over a dozen orthopedic surgeons who were, by reputation, favorable to the Witnesses. None of them, however, would openly demonstrate that support by coming forward to help him or the Witnesses. All-in-all, Lapin felt the situation painfully paralleled events of early Christianity.

The trial began, the opening statements were made by

both sides, and the young Spanish woman was called as
the first witness. The eyes of the courtroom,
particularly those of the jurors, watched closely as
she tried to put her badly mangled right hand on the
Bible. She couldn't do it. And she couldn't control
the tears flowing from her eyes.

She won her case, making it another landmark
decision for Witnesses everywhere. Later she came to
Orange County, California, where Lapin repaired her
hand without the psychological crutch of transfusing
blood.

***

Esperanza was indeed busy. The hospital was usually
full, even though surgery was considered only as a
last resort after other medical treatment failed. It
became common for cases of elective surgery to be
postponed until there were available beds.

Most of the staff surgeons had never seen a hospital
this active. The dissension among their ranks was
becoming commonplace by now and, in reality, even
expected.

Amidst this absolute flurry of activity, Lapin
somehow found time to develop and perfect a new
device. It was an invention that would give peace
of mind and confidence to women faced with the
horrible possibility of a complete mastectomy.

Because of deadly cancer, Lapin had been forced to
perform many breast removals--more than he cared to
remember. With each procedure, he became more
remorseful over the lasting deformity each woman had
to bear. He understood the pain they felt in losing
an important part of their personal identity and being
left branded by unsightly scar tissue. His empathy
ran deep.

Each time he did a mastectomy, he wondered why
someone hadn't found a better way to reconstruct these
breasts. He poignantly knew that psychological
devastation raged inside these women, sometimes for
years, sometimes forever, while they lived with the
feeling of being only half a woman.

But what can I do? he'd ask himself. *I'm only one
man.* Each radical mastectomy he was forced to perform
drew him like a magnet closer to the solution.

"I'll do it myself," he finally announced in the
operating room late one afternoon. "I'll just do it

182

myself."

When a decision like that was verbalized, it signaled Lapin's total commitment. Even though repeated attempts had been unsuccessful, no one on Lapin's team doubted that he would eventually carry out his proclamation. He said it, and they knew he'd do it.

Amid his extraordinary surgery schedule, he made time for the necessary research. It often required working nights, weekends, and holidays. It was a new driving force in his life. It meant having the will and determination to eliminate some of the unnecessary pain and suffering in this life. It meant having the desire to make a contribution to healing the whole person, mind as well as body.

Day after day, test after test, trial after error, he unrelentingly pressed on, accepting each failure as moving him one step closer to success. He refused to bend, let alone break.

Finally he did it. He accomplished what he had promised. He developed a skin stretcher, an expandable implant which could be placed under the skin after a mastectomy. Its primary purpose was to stretch and shape the remaining skin so that it would match the other breast.

Dow Corning investigated, ran their own series of highly complicated, technical tests, and now considered marketing Lapin's product internationally.

At lectures arranged for the purpose of explaining bloodless surgery and Fluosol to Witnesses, Lapin would show slides of breasts that were reconstructed and challenge his audience to determine which one was restructured. They were seldom right. That's how good the procedure was. Lapin was pleased, but well knew--as he'd read in Roman literature--that all glory is fleeting.

***

The hospital was swimming in a sea of activity that by now was considered normal. It was filled with patients--patients who were being helped. But this particular morning as Lapin walked through the busy hallways, he was alerted by his uncanny, usually-correct sixth sense. Something was different; something was wrong. It wasn't another typical crisis. It wasn't an emergency case where a patient

183

was critical and expected to die simply because few
surgeons have the confidence or talent to step beyond
vaguely-defined medical standards. It wasn't the
professional jealousy from colleagues that seemed to
riddle Lapin's entire career, if not his very
existence. It was something more, and the young
surgeon could sense it.

A cloud of uncertainty hung suspended in the
hallways. Its effect registered on the faces of staff
members going about their appointed rounds. The
rounds themselves appeared strangely different to
Lapin. There was an obvious change of pace as people
moved more slowly than usual through their daily
tasks. Each footstep taken on the cold linoleum floor
sent forth an echo of caution. The faces Lapin
encountered were pleading for answers as if silently
questioning him, *Why? Why?*

The spirit-dampening cloud infiltrated the operating
room. Jan and the rest of the team were just standing
there waiting. "So," Lapin asked, trying to brighten
their spirits, "nobody sick today? We have nobody to
operate on?" His attempt at humor failed miserably.
The room remained solemn and silent. Glances were exchanged in an attempt to select a spokesman. Who was
going to tell him? Who would be the one?

Jan, taking a deep breath, began in a pain-filled
voice. "Ron," she said, "the Department of Health
Services is here at the hospital."

"Yeah," he responded apprehensively.

"Three people are here from the State." After
another deep breath, she continued, "And they're going
to investigate allegations filed against the hospital."

"By whom?"

"They wouldn't disclose the charges. It's supposed
to be a secret or something."

Now Lapin took a deep breath, but it failed to have
a calming effect. "What's the bottom line?" he asked.

"The man in charge of the investigation said that
their findings . . . could result. . . ." She stopped,
unable to force out the words.

"It's okay," Lapin reassured her, "go ahead."

"Their findings could result . . . in revoking the
hospital's license," she concluded.

Lapin stared straight ahead for a second, then
nodded with some degree of understanding. He raised
his eyes to the ceiling, but was really looking far

past the structural limitation that confined him and his friends. He reached into the depth of his soul for strength. "Well," he finally said, "there must be somebody around here we can operate on. Smitty, why don't you go get us a patient?" Then he walked to the sink in the hallway and began to scrub.

***

Throughout the day, Lapin made several unsuccessful attempts to talk directly with the State investigators. He wasn't after a confrontation; he was only interested in their reasoning . . . and the truth. As is so often the case, the truth was like an elusive butterfly.

No one from the State would speak directly with Lapin or his team throughout the entire investigative process. Lapin was perplexed by their highly unusual method of operation. *Why don't they want to hear the truth?* The investigative procedure was unsettling. It wore down people's nerves like the grinding of a dentist's drill in unskilled hands. It strained relationships. It eroded the very framework of communication and understanding that supported the staff's ability to better serve patients.

Why? Lapin asked himself so many times. *Why are they doing this without an explanation? Why don't they just leave the Witnesses alone?* The State still refused to reveal their formal charges. The closest accounting they offered for their persistence was an illusive response, "The place isn't safe." But it didn't wash. It just didn't wash.

An unrelenting barrage of State agents reviewed patients' charts and meticulously examined every record in microscopic detail. Through it all, the constant, nagging question of why they were conducting such an investigation was never answered.

Could it be, Lapin posed in silence, *a professional backlash, a negative reaction to my testimony against the doctor in New Jersey?* "Altogether possible", he answered in a whisper. *But who knows, who really knows. It's just as likely*, he also thought, *that the trial had nothing to do with this. And why all this secrecy? Why don't they just tell us what's going on?* He knew he had offended a string of people with his demands for perfection. He'd irritated some colleagues. He'd left others with sharply defined

wounds that penetrated too deeply for that magic
elixir, time, to ever erase. But wounded egos didn't
matter to Ron Lapin; patients did.

The State agents continued to wield their mighty
power as they pressed on with their "examination."
Files, charts, and records were copied. Private
records that were the personal property of the
patients were removed from the hospital without
authorization or approval. The code governing both
medical ethics and privileged information between
doctor and patient was violated repeatedly.

One of the greatest injustices in the State's
relentless attack on Lapin and his affiliation with
the hospital was the illegal public disclosure of
patients' personal files. Potentially damaging
private information--given to one's physician but not
necessarily to a husband or a loved one--could now be
given to someone other than their doctor. Although
these records were perhaps not earth-shattering in
general, they could be potentially devastating to the
individuals involved. A doctor-patient relationship
is a sacred trust that should never be violated, yet
these State investigators virtually opened private,
personal files and made them available to nearly
anyone wanting access to their contents.

For months, teams of staunch, impersonal State
investigators rode roughshod over the hospital.
Without exhibiting any real concern for others, they
managed to disrupt the morale of the entire staff.
There they were, stern-faced, emitting a general
distrust for everyone. After awhile, the personnel
felt like they were each nothing more than a
microorganism on a glass slide.

Even the head of the State task force descended on
the hospital one afternoon. His visit was disguised
under the auspices of checking on the Medicare and
Medi-Cal records--supposedly the State's right when a
hospital is being subsidized by government programs.

In actuality, it was merely another ploy to gain
illegal entry into the records. It gave the State yet
another opportunity to review patients' charts under
false and misleading pretenses.

Operating a hospital under optimum circumstances is
difficult enough, but trying to function with team
after team of State investigators swarming in the
hallway made the task virtually impossible. Personnel
became unnerved under the constant glare of these

clipboard-carrying strangers.

***

The *Awake!* magazine, one of the primary publications
of Jehovah's Witnesses, carried an article about
Hutchins, Lapin, and the team. Without an actual
endorsement, they praised the work being done at
Esperanza and discussed several extreme cases in which
patients were refused care by the medical community at
large before being successfully treated by Lapin.

Because readership of the *Awake!* soars into the
millions, the hot line buzzed with calls from people
who had been seeking quality medical care. Lapin
thereby discovered that it wasn't only clinics in
Mexico that offered a "haven" for the Witnesses.
There were others in South Africa, throughout Europe,
and around the world. They charged more than their
counterparts in Mexico, but provided only the same
mysterious treatments with the same dubious results.

Through the *Awake!* article, people became aware of
the Southern California group of physicians who
treated only Witnesses and the bloodless surgeon
who guaranteed to respect their religious beliefs.
They read about the man who refused to bow to the
dogmatic attitudes and witchhunt tactics of his
anonymous accusers in order to give them impeccable
medical care.

In spite of positive responses from the Jehovah's
Witnesses toward Dr. Lapin, the State continued its
constant harassment without directly confronting Lapin
or anyone on his team.

One morning the operative theater was staged. Lapin
was dressed and scrubbed and the surgical staff had
all the necessary instrumentation prepared. The
patient lay sleeping under the dark blue paper
covering which exposed only the portion of the abdomen
to be opened. Monitoring devices were affixed to
critical areas of the body.

Then something very unusual happened. A stranger
dressed in surgical greens entered the operating room
unannounced and stood by Lapin's side. He was an
elderly man, about five-five with thick grey hair and
clearly defined Jewish features. The way he stood
staring down at the patient clearly indicated his
unwillingness to speak and could have actually been
interpreted as a challenge.

Lapin, scalpel in hand, visually polled Herk, Smitty, and the others to see if they knew what was going on. Their eyes and subtle shoulder shrugs indicated they, too, were in the dark. There was an uncomfortable moment of silence, then Lapin spoke. "Something I can do for you?"

The rest of the team smiled behind their masks. The stranger in their midst didn't. Nor did he reply.

Lapin tried again. "Excuse me, but this is a private operating room in a private hospital. . . ."

The man turned and looked Lapin straight in the eye. His voice was as filled with Jewish heritage as Lapin's own. His mood and tone were both dead serious. "I'm going to observe the operation," he said, returning his eyes to the patient.

"I see," Lapin responded slowly, "and I presume you have the patient's consent to do that."

"I'm board certified," the man said, avoiding Lapin's question.

"I don't give a damn about the board certification. Do you have the patient's consent to observe this procedure?"

The man was unshaken. He took a deep breath. "My name's Cowen," he said, "and I don't need the patient's consent, or yours, or anybody's."

"Uh huh," Lapin replied. "You must be pretty important." Lapin's annoyance gained momentum. He had a patient asleep and had to get on with surgery.

Cowen's voice and demeanor were unwavering. "I am the State." His announcement carried the strangest hint of a threat. The mood was clear. The stage was set. "I can observe any operation, anywhere, as I see fit. And I see fit to watch you, Doctor Lapin, the famous bloodless surgeon."

Lapin just looked across the table at Herk and shook his head. He laid the scalpel down, turned, and stared directly at Cowen. "I'm not the State." He nearly spit the words out. "And I need the patient's consent for you to be in this room."

Cowen started to speak but Lapin stopped him cold by placing a surgical-gloved finger in his face. "That's the end of it." He turned to Hutchins and announced, "Cancel the case . . . wake her up," and started toward the door.

Cowen was seething with rage. He was absolutely furious. Blood vessels on both sides of his neck began to protrude. "Wait a minute, doctor," he screamed. "I have the power to close down any hospital at will."

"For what reason?" Lapin shot back.

"I don't need a reason."

"That makes a lot of sense," Lapin added sarcastically.

"I don't need a reason because seventy-five percent of all surgery done in the United States is unnecessary."

"Seventy-five percent, huh?" Lapin said.

"That's right."

Even through his anger, Lapin had to suppress a smile at the stupidity of Cowen's statement. "Dixie," he said. "How many cases do we have scheduled today?"

"Ten, doctor," she replied.

With a delivery that was Oscar-worthy, he announced to the room in general, "Fine . . . cancel seven and a half of them. Have a nice day, Doctor Cowen."

***

Later in the hallway, when voices returned to a normal speaking level, Cowen actually told Lapin and Hutchins they should be performing two-thirds fewer operations on the Witnesses. "Then," he added, "you and the hospital will have no further confrontations."

Lapin was astonished by the statement. "Where are you from?" he asked, collecting his thoughts.

"New York."

"What was your specialty?"

"General surgery," Cowen answered, wondering where Lapin's line of questioning was leading.

"And how long has it been since you've practiced . . . since you've actually operated on a patient?"

Cowen cleared his throat and ran five stubby fingers through his grey hair.

"Seven years," he finally said.

"I see," Lapin nodded. "Well, let me tell you something about your 'two-thirds less' theory. The people who come through this admitting room are sick. Some have been denied proper medical care most of their lives."

"That's not your problem."

"I'm making it my problem. And I'll tell you something else. I don't know how to decide which third of the people who make it through those doors downstairs are sicker than the other two-thirds. We just do our best to take care of them all."

Cowen didn't budge. Lapin continued, "How's this? You sit in the admitting room and pass judgment on the people who show up from all over the world. You play God and decide on life and death and guarantee me you'll be absolutely right--one hundred percent of the time. You do that for me . . . then I'll do what you say."

Cowen, in his blindness, mistook Lapin's commitment and dedication for arrogance. "I'm warning you, doctor. . . ."

"Get in line . . . it's a big club . . . and you better bring your lunch."

8

Lapin was thrilled when he heard that Katie Chapman and her husband, Gary, were returning to Esperanza to have him deliver their child, but the news was bittersweet. He learned that the grotesque tumor he'd previously removed had grown back to an even larger state inside her fragile mouth. It was a shocking blow not only to Lapin, but to the entire hospital staff.

It was a heart-rending repeat performance of their first visit as the frail young lady was checked into the hospital. Once again the blockage had sealed off all possible air entering through her mouth and she would require a new tracheotomy within the next twenty-four hours.

She was three weeks from her delivery date. Various tests indicated that the baby inside her was fine. Even through the intensity of her pain, Katie beamed with that special glow reserved exclusively for expectant mothers.

Lapin's first emotion was anger as he viewed the killer tissue protruding from her mouth. She was lying very still. There was that same calmness about her . . . only the inner peace had deepened and intensified since they'd last seen each other.

"Are you back to bother me again?" Lapin teased. Her eyes lit up as she heard the voice of the young surgeon who meant so much to her. She raised her hand as if to grasp his, but instead produced a note gripped tightly in her fist. Lapin gritted his teeth behind his smile. He had to be strong. The note, so painstakingly written while she had waited for him, read, "Dr. Lapin . . . I told you . . . I'm going to live to see this baby."

Lapin's smile hid neither his heavy sigh nor the

anguish he felt for her. Words came hard; he tried to choose them carefully so as not to require any written responses from her. "Just listen," he whispered. "I know how important this baby is . . . I really do." He paused for a second. "We have to re-do the trach in the morning. It's going to be difficult because of the scar tissue."

Katie nodded acceptingly. No further response was necessary.

Lapin was going to say more, but she held up her hand and stopped him. She wrote something and handed it to him. "I trust you," it read, "I know you'll keep me alive, at least long enough."

Emotion gripped him, but he knew he had to continue. "When the operation is over, I really feel you should start radiation treatments or chemotherapy."

A nurse entered the room and gave Katie the shot of morphine Lapin had ordered. As she did, Katie wrote, "No treatments until my baby is born. . . ."

Tears welled up in Lapin's eyes as he was consumed with a feeling of helplessness. He softly pleaded, "Katie . . . I don't know if I can keep you alive that long." But Katie's own eyes reassured him of the profound trust she had in her heart. This remarkable young woman, whose strength and commitment had touched the lives of nearly everyone in the hospital, was able to express without words a wealth of understanding he'd never known before. Her eyes explained that no matter what happened, everything was going to be okay because she had hope in the resurrection. Lapin knew, he just knew, that she was telling him that she and her soon-to-be-born child would, in time, live together in the earthly paradise.

Lapin cared deeply for Katie. He was touched by the parental concern and self-sacrificing love she felt for her unborn child. He was especially touched since his own childhood had been completely void of such family devotion.

There were twelve people in the operating room that next morning, all with emotional ties to the brave young woman lying on the table. Prayers for Katie came from nearly every room in the hospital. Her breathing had become more seriously impaired during the night, and she was literally struggling for her life and for the life within her.

The room was silent, dead silent. No operating room chatter this morning. After the local anesthetic was injected, Lapin opened a small hole in her throat and inserted the clear plastic tubing which would allow her to breathe. Her lungs instantly filled with air, that precious commodity most of us so take for granted. As Katie's color returned to normal, she and her twelve friends in the operating room shared their emotions and cried openly with happiness.

Through all of this, the State investigators continued their insensitive probing of charts and files. But it now spilled over into the actual interrogation of several patients. One was literally threatened. Being hospitalized is an emotionally stressful experience that could best be served without any additional, undue, or unnecessary outside pressures. But continue they did.

***

Lapin and Herk both stayed at the hospital for the next four days. Alternately sleeping in the Intensive Care Unit, one was always awake to watch and monitor Katie. Their greatest fear, premature labor, came to pass. The child she so desperately wanted to bear was on its way.

Katie's battle for life was a losing one. There was no stopping the cancer; it had already won. It was just a matter of time and even that had nearly run out. The labor pains came as a blessing to Katie since she wanted this baby more than life itself. She'd certainly proven that over and over.

The pain of the impending childbirth was no match for the intense agony she endured as cancer ate away and destroyed her already tiny body. With the labor pains, there was time in between for rest. But, even with the morphine and other pain killers, her cancer pain was always present. The halls of Esperanza were filled with empathy for this kind, dear person who had given so much of herself to others.

Once again faced with a life-or-death situation, Dr. Lapin had to act fast. He decided that a normal delivery would be too risky. He also decided it would be better to transfer Katie immediately to the University of California's hospital in Irvine. Unlike Esperanza, they had an excellent facility for premature babies.

Arrangements with the university surgeon included his guarantee that he would perform the caesarean section without transfusing blood. The ambulance was ordered, and Katie was on her way.

She drifted in and out of consciousness as the gurney was lifted into the ambulance. She was too weak to know what was going on. She only knew that soon she'd give birth to her precious child.

As the ambulance sped into the warm summer night, several members of the hospital staff watched the taillights fade in the distance. Their jubilation for the birth that was about to take place was overshadowed by the disquieting realization that they would never see this special young woman alive again.

Once Katie arrived, the university hospital surgeon momentarily balked at the guarantee he'd made not to use blood. After the required release forms were signed, however, he reluctantly agreed again to keep his word. Katie was prepped, rushed to the operating room, and anesthetized. She gave birth to a four-pound baby boy and was then taken to the recovery room where they hoped beyond hope she'd awaken.

An emergency had kept Lapin at Esperanza. Missing the actual moment of birth was one of the great disappointments of his life, but at least he was comforted by the fact that she was in good hands.

When Katie regained consciousness, her first written words were, "My baby . . . I want to hold my baby."

To fulfill Katie's fondest desire, a nurse was sent to the premie ward for the baby. As they waited, the joyous parents decided to name their son George Henry.

Their most special moment was nearly upon them. The nurse entered the room carrying a small bundle. It was unheard of for such a tiny newborn to be removed from the ward, but this was a highly unusual situation. Katie was experiencing massive hemorrhaging and she knew her time was running out. No one had to tell her. But right now, right this instant, that didn't matter. The only thing that mattered was her infant son and being able to hold him.

The actual moment for which she'd sacrificed came when the nurse handed the child to Katie. Sweet tears of joy rolled down her cheeks. She felt with a certainty that her sacrifice had been rewarded far beyond her hopes and dreams. She cradled the baby in her love and affection, hoping to protect him in a blanket of motherly care and concern that would endure throughout his lifetime. In those few short moments, she tried to instill in her son a lifetime of

understanding and compassion for his fellow man. She
most of all hoped to imbue in him her infinite love
for Jehovah and her eternal faith in Him as the true
source of strength and endurance.

It was time for George Henry to return to the ward.
Five hours later . . . Katie Chapman died.

***

A special memorial service was held three days later
and was attended by most of the staff and personnel
from the hospital. A young secretary at Esperanza had
seen Katie almost daily during her treatments.
Through tear stained eyes and a voice weighted with
emotion, she offered the poem she'd written about her
friend. "Unselfish Faith," she began. "Unselfishness
filled every bone of her body--and carried her through
until the end--when her most accomplished deed
unselfishly took place and she delivered her gift to
the human race. Never has a child been created more
out of love--for there was nothing else to rely on for
sustenance. You see, his mother's body was broken
before he began and it most definitely took a great
hand to bring him into this life. She fought the
fight of a most fatal disease. But the look in her
eyes was the adept expertise of a loving mother so she
quietly walked through those painful months as proud
as she could be--for she carried her most prized
possession--her infant son she would set free. I have
written of many people, circumstances, places and
things, but I have never seen such love in action or
faith take flight as she cared so lovingly for this
unborn life. And so, special lady--if I could have a
talk with you now--I would make you understand that
your faith and strength will help to guide my hand.
For I shall not forget the lesson you've taught us.
Although small and depleted your body appeared to be,
you've added a new dimension to all eternity--for none
of us who walked in your presence will ever be quite
the same. You see, you've taught us of a different
love and you have brought honor to your name."

The last few sentences were the most difficult to
deliver, but Katie's strength seemed to prevail at the
service and her friend managed to complete her
tribute.

A Witness seated in the back row had a heart attack
during the reading of the poem, and Lapin went to his

195

aid. Once the man had been cared for, Lapin rose to
speak. He told the audience that Katie had given him
much more than he could have ever given her. He spoke
of her having the strength, balance, and courage of a
true Witness of Jehovah. He closed his comments by
saying that Katie's integrity to Jehovah and the
rights of her unborn child were the things for which
she'd given her life.

Later that day, Katie's body was transported back to
Nevada. Little George Henry remained in the hospital
until he weighed enough to be released.

Less than a year later, tragedy struck the Chapman
family once more. While Gary was holding the baby
during his feeding, he had another Vietnam flashback
and dropped George Henry. The baby's head was crushed
and he died instantly . . . just months after his
mother had given her own life for his.

***

The State investigators and the Board of Health task
force kept a constant surveillance. Their presence
was disturbingly conspicuous as they bothered and
disrupted the hospital routine with their persistence.
They were the proverbial "thorn in the side" as they
scrutinized nearly every piece of paper on the
premises. Patients who preferred not to be interviewed
were interrogated and badgered. Through all of this,
the investigators still never gave a realistic or
acceptable explanation for their inquisition.

Under a veil of secrecy, one investigator deviously
pushed to the limit in an attempt to force a patient
to testify against Lapin. He threatened to brand this
young St. Louis Witness as an unfaithful wife by
insidiously claiming she'd had an affair with the
doctor. This agent was frustrated by her firm refusal
to lie or to defame the only doctor who had helped
her. This agent's infamy did, however, contribute to
the breakup of her marriage.

This same State agent publicly boasted on several
occasions that after "getting" Esperanza, he would
concentrate all of his time and energy on eliminating
Lapin. Lapin didn't buckle, nor did he bend. He just
kept doing what he did best.

As Lapin's experience widened out, so did the range
of his skills. One such experience occurred as an
aftermath of a critical operation when the suction

device wasn't working as efficiently as he felt it should. Logic fueled by emotion was the forerunner of yet another technical advancement. Lapin perfected the electric knife by adding suction to its tip and by creating its own self-contained light source. It was named, quite appropriately, the "Lapin True-Cut II."

The refined knife was used on a man who finally found Lapin after four long years of agonizing rejection from the medical world. Based solely on the man's religious objection to accepting blood, he was refused treatment by doctor after doctor. Skin cancer had distorted the man's face to the point where it was emotionally devastating for him to appear in public. The psychological scars were so deeply imbedded in this poor man's psyche that his ego had eroded almost as badly as his twisted, grotesque face.

The man had found Lapin through the hot line and came to California for help. Lapin took before-and-after photographs of this patient and showed them regularly at his lectures to the Witnesses. By now, these lectures were occurring on a regular basis. Each time he showed slides of the astonishing distortion in the man's appearance, the audience was stunned. Then when he showed the second slide, the audience erupted into applause. It was visible proof of what could be accomplished by a surgeon who operated with his heart as well as his hands. Lapin was pleased with the sensitive responses from the audience.

He showed slides of a taxi driver from Canada who had a forty-three pound tumor on his right shoulder. Forty-three pounds! The growth was three times larger than the man's own head and still growing. For three years, he'd searched in vain for help. Meanwhile the growth had pushed his head into a position that made it impossible for him to raise it off his left shoulder. He finally heard about Dr. Lapin at a local Kingdom Hall.

When Lapin showed the "after" slide, the audience was once again moved to applaud. Through these lectures, audience after audience became aware of a place they could go right in this country if ever they became seriously ill and needed help.

One early morning in February of 1981, Lapin received a hot line call from a small two-hundred-year-old hospital in the town of Ripratransone on the East Coast of Italy. A translator informed him that two very critical Witnesses were in need of help.

The hospital chief surgeon, a devout Catholic, was treating Witnesses from all over Italy and Europe. The surgeon, Cezar Buresta, told Lapin that the patients needed immediate surgery. He said that they'd need a hospital with better facilities and more advanced surgical skills than he could offer. Without hesitation Lapin replied, "I'll be there on the next flight. Just pick me up at the airport in Rome."

Buresta informed Lapin that they couldn't afford to pay him. Lapin's only response was, "I pay my own way."

Smitty and Mikie helped Lapin pack every piece of equipment they thought might be needed. Six hours later, he was on his way to Italy.

A large contingency of Witnesses waving the *Awake!* magazine greeted Lapin in Rome. They drove for three and a half hours over hilly, winding roads to the sixty-bed hospital in the country. Doctor Buresta, a man in his late forties, met Lapin with a broad smile and a warm handshake. In the week Lapin spent as Dr. Buresta's house guest, the two men became the closest of friends, even overcoming the language barrier.

Three hours after his arrival, Lapin and his Italian colleague successfully operated on both of the patients. Lapin had employed every trick he knew. He even taught as he went along, imparting valuable knowledge every step of the way. Although Lapin only expected two patients, he ended up operating on eighteen more.

While on daily visitation rounds with Buresta, Lapin couldn't help but notice how easily identifiable Witnesses were, even in a foreign country. They all seemed to have a warm smile, a friendly attitude, simple dress, and the ever-present Bible.

During a three hour dinner one evening, Lapin became aware that Buresta was experiencing the same problems with his medical colleagues and State regulatory agencies regarding the treatment of Witnesses as Lapin was having in the United States. It seemed ironic that in two places separated by over ten thousand miles, the same bigotry and prejudice loomed larger than ever. It was also ironic that a devout Catholic and a Jew would stand hand-in-hand to stem that evil tide.

He left Ripratransone with a heavy heart but promised to return if he was needed again. He left

behind all the equipment he had brought with him . . .
but more than that, he left behind a large part of
himself. As his car pulled away from the old hospital
some thirty Witnesses cheered him on his way.

A week later, he was back at Esperanza and his
routine schedule of an eighteen hour workday. He
would, however, continue his scientific and
humanitarian missions on behalf of the Witnesses in
Israel, Holland, Germany, and Japan.

As Lapin continued to perform both classically
routine and astonishing surgical procedures, he
received more opposition from Timothy Basket. As the
assistant attorney general for the State of
California, Basket accused Lapin of being "the Jim
Jones of Orange County." Basket further claimed that
the Jehovah's Witnesses were a 'cult' and that he
personally was going to rid the state of them.

He theorized that if they got rid of Lapin, the
Witnesses would stop coming to California for surgery
and things would then be better for everyone
concerned.

The flow of opposition continued. Chuck Michaels,
another investigator, was heard bragging at a cocktail
party that he was going to get Lapin. It didn't
matter to him what it cost to do it; it was just going
to be done.

Scott Brian told friends and associates he'd
received a promotion from the State as a direct result
of his tireless, persistent, dogged attack on Lapin
and Esperanza.

It had also been discovered that Dr. Cowen, head of
the State task force, had been disciplined in New York
for the unwarranted removal of a patient's gall
bladder. This was the case that caused Cowen to
become so antagonized when Lapin asked him how long it
had been since he'd seen a patient or performed
surgery.

Dr. Craig Boyd was the State investigator assigned
to oversee and analyze the charts that the task force
had illegally removed from the hospital. But Boyd was
a pediatrician and had no background or practical
knowledge in surgical procedures, anatomy, or
documentation.

Meanwhile, Lapin saw a new patient who had been
experiencing increasingly severe abdominal pains. She
had also continued to gain weight despite an
assortment of dieting regimens. Nonetheless, a string

of doctors insisted that nothing was wrong. The woman had grown obese and was almost a candidate for a mental institution.   Through a friend, she finally learned about the hot line and called Dr. Lapin.

Precisely two weeks later, Lapin removed a huge, benign ovarian cyst from her abdominal cavity.   The tumor weighed thirty-nine pounds.

It was around this time that a lawyer for a Witness in Canada called Lapin.   He needed a surgeon's testimony to defend a child's parents.

"Go on," Lapin said, removing his surgical mask.

"We have a case of a twelve-year-old girl who was suffering from acute auto-immune hemolytic disease."

"You mean her blood cells were breaking down rapidly," Lapin clarified.

"That's right.   She suddenly developed the disease while in a small town up in northern Canada.   They took her to the local hospital, but the doctors there couldn't treat the case and called the nearest major city, Thunder Bay, Ontario."

"Right. . . ."

In painstaking detail, the attorney explained how the doctor on call, a pediatrician, hadn't initiated the standard medical treatment.   He should have prescribed high doses of cortisone to retard the breakdown of the blood cells.   The doctor had also received permission to fly the child down to Thunder Bay, but refused that option.   Instead, he had the child transported nearly four hundred miles--by land-- with little medical support.   By the time the little girl arrived, she was moribund, literally at the point of death.   Despite her critical condition, she was not placed in the ICU.

Then, of course, the pediatrician in charge of the case insisted on blood transfusions.   Those fruitless discussions caused an additional waste of valuable time.

The hospital had access to a hyperberic chamber in which oxygen under high pressure is forced into the patient's tissue.   It's much like the device used to reduce the bends, the painful condition deep-sea divers sometime suffer when returning to the earth's surface.   The chamber wasn't even discussed with the parents, let alone used.   And, of course, the doctors seemed to know nothing about Fluosol.

The attitude of the doctors seemed to be that the child would die regardless of what treatment might be administered.

Sadly accepting the clearly inferred opinion of these doctors, the parents decided to at least provide a comfortable environment for their daughter in her few remaining hours of life. With the help of several local elders from the nearest Kingdom Hall, they quietly snuck the child out of the hospital.

Four hours later, the little girl died.

"Now", the attorney concluded, "the government is trying to convict the parents on charges of negligent manslaughter." The Crown was going to make this trial a showcase and would spare no expense to obtain a conviction against the parents. "And," he added sadly, "after weeks of trying, I haven't been able to find an expert--or anyone for that matter--who could testify about surgery on Witnesses or the use of Fluosol."

Lapin hung up and immediately called a hematologist, Dr. Mac Becker. After listening to his friend recount the atrocity, Becker agreed to accompany him to Canada.

Upon their arrival, they discovered that the prosecution had in fact gone all out to get the parents who, according to newspaper reports, "kidnapped their own daughter and let her die . . . a result of some pagan religious belief."

The trial originally was to be held in the local court house, but the resounding throngs of people attending each day forced its move--an unprecedented occurrence--to the ballroom of the Prince Albert Hotel across town.

Five hundred Witnesses came each day. "It was like being in church," Lapin later related. There was a prayer every day before the trial began, another at lunch, and another when court was adjourned for the day.

Lapin and his friend wore jeans and other casual attire as they attended every session. Listening with astonishment at the injustice and prejudice that crossed the bench, Lapin felt like he was right back at Esperanza.

The Crown's attorney, the prosecutor, had noticed Lapin from the first day's opening statements and one day asked him who he was.

"Just an old friend of the defense attorney," he calmly answered.

It was late on a Thursday afternoon when the Crown

concluded its overwhelmingly biased case. Friday, Lapin went to court in a three-piece blue pinstriped suit and was called to the stand. It was time for the defense.

On the stand, Lapin answered that he is an assistant professor of surgery who has specialized in bloodless operations and has performed them on over four thousand Jehovah's Witnesses during the last eight years. The Crown's attorney gasped and immediately asked for a recess.

In one and a half hours of testimony, Lapin quietly responded to the questions of the defense counsel. The attorney demolished the case that had been built against the parents over the last seven days.

Counsel was good, Lapin thought to himself, *but the truth is there really was no case.* Lapin believed in truth.

While Lapin was in Canada defending the civil and religious rights of Witnesses he'd never met, Rana was back in California trying to undermine Lapin and his practice.

Rana had been courting an executive of the insurance company which specialized in Witness coverage. He used statements like, "Lapin's no good for the JWs" and "I'm the only viable alternative."

Lapin heard the news from the other side of the continent. He called Rana for a firsthand explanation, but received no straight answers. Even though Rana was attempting "to play politics" with the Witnesses, Lapin knew that their integrity and religious convictions would protect them from falling for such devious maneuvers.

Of course Lapin stopped trusting Rana at that point, but allowed him to remain as a cursory consultant due to the intense pressure still being applied by the State. His thought was that closely scrutinized unity was better than division, even with a "Judas" among their ranks. He was wrong. The war raged on . . . and on . . . and on.

Two months later, the judge in Thunder Bay vindicated the parents. They were indeed innocent. Lapin's presence had once again been felt.

9

He hated to be involved in redoing total hip re-
placements and the case he and Chuck Bonnett were
tackling that particular morning was certainly no
exception. For two hours, both men struggled to free
broken and loose proximal components in a fifty-two-
year-old JW from Canada. She had been crippled with
excruciating pain for the past two years--ever since
she fell in a British Columbia snowstorm and broke
her prosthesis. She had endured this agony because
none of the Canadian orthopedic surgeons she consulted
would consider operating on her without transfusing
blood.

"I'm going to make a small window in the bone and
see if I can pound this damn thing upward while you
pull on it."

"Sounds good," Lapin replied.

Skillfully using a power saw, Bonnett made a small
opening below the estimated end of the prosthesis and
began pounding on the tip of the stubborn device in an
attempt to dislodge it.

"Let's not fracture this old bone," Lapin offered.

"Don't worry; I remember the last case," Bonnett
said, reading his mind.

"Of all the cases we work on together, I dislike
these the most. They're just too messy."

"I don't particularly enjoy them myself, but
somebody has to do them," Bonnett said, continuing to
pound away until he dislodged the fragment.

"That was excellent, sir, excellent," Lapin
commented. "Now let's put in a new prosthesis and get
out of here. This patient's wound is already half
healed," he remarked jokingly. Bonnett laughed and
continued to work.

"What's the blood loss?" Lapin asked the circulating nurse.

"About 350 c.c.s," she answered.

"Hey, Chuck, do you know what the definition of Jewish foreplay is?"

"No, tell me."

"An hour and a half of begging."

The room erupted in laughter. They had needed something to break the tension of the difficult case. "You seem to be in a good mood today, Ron," Bonnett said.

"Yeah, I guess I am. I had a nice evening last night, and I feel just great today."

"Anyone I know?" he replied nosily.

"No, Chuck, no one you know."

The operating room door opened and the secretary walked in. "Dr. Lapin, there's an emergency call for you."

"Not now. Please take a message and I'll call back when we finish here."

"Dr. Lapin, it's Jan Jordan from Esperanza and she says that this can't wait."

Lapin shook his head in dismay. He should have known his happy mood was too good to last. "Chuck, can you manage without me for a couple of minutes? I'll be right back."

"Sure, go ahead."

Lapin removed his gown and gloves. He walked into the office and picked up the extension with the flashing light. "Okay, Jan, what's up?" he asked, annoyed.

"I'm really sorry I had to call you out of surgery, but I think you should get over here right away."

"Why? What's going on now?"

"The State just left here. They're closing Esperanza Hospital to your patients--effective immediately. We have until two o'clock to make arrangements to move out all twenty-two patients, including the five or so that are critical."

He could feel the blood leave his face. His heart pounded in his chest as he pounded the desk with his tightly clenched fist. The outburst was over quickly. Calm and reason returned. "What reason did they give for closing it down?"

"I don't know exactly. The State apparently told the administrator that the hospital either wasn't clean enough or safe enough for patients."

"That's garbage. . . ."

There was a moment's hesitation. Jan could sense the frustration and anger Lapin was experiencing. "Yes, I know," she said sympathetically.

"Jan, I can't leave here until this case is finished. It'll probably take an hour. In the meantime, get in touch with Samaritan Hospital-- they're the closest facility I have privileges at--and see if they can accommodate the patients today. Find Attorney Garner wherever he is. Tell him it's imperative that I meet with him this afternoon. And tell everybody on the team to stay calm. Oh yes, we'd better play it safe on this one and put Donnelly on valium! Inform the patients and their families that I'll be in the hospital shortly to explain what's going on . . . if I can figure it out myself."

"By the way, Ron, this should interest you; I found out that St. Jude Hospital bought the place and will take over this afternoon." After waiting momentarily for a reaction, she continued, "They don't want either you or the Witness patients here anymore."

"That's interesting. . . . Is St. Jude a Catholic-supported hospital?" he finally asked.

"I think so."

"I see. Do they also discriminate?" The question was redundant.

"I don't know, Ron . . . I just don't know anything anymore . . . I'm too upset."

"You hang in there, lady . . . just hang in there. I'm going to need a copy of the accusations they served on the hospital. Please try to get that for me right away."

In a purely protective voice she added, "Listen . . . when you get here, come in through the back entrance because the front entrance and the lobby are swarming with reporters and television cameramen."

He hung up the phone, went back to the sink, and re-scrubbed. His mind was racing. The survival instinct in him was rapidly taking over. Once again, the wandering Jew would have to search for a new home for his patients.

As Lapin walked back into the operating room, Chuck looked at him and knew something was wrong. "Anything I can do, Ron?"

"No . . . it's okay. I'll handle it."

Bonnett knew Lapin well enough to know when not to pursue matters.

"I see you're ready to cement the new prosthesis," Lapin said, trying to control his composure.

"Yes, she'll be as good as new. She'll even be able to continue her missionary work in Micronesia. I didn't even know they had Witnesses there, did you?"

"No, can't say that I did."

"Well, they do. How 'bout that?"

Lapin generally enjoyed assisting other specialists and was good at it. Now, however, he was all thumbs and clumsy. Chuck saw it and finally offered, "Look, Ron, the hip is reduced into place. Why don't J.D. and I close, and you just go take care of whatever you need to? I'll call you later. How's that?"

"Thanks, Chuck, I appreciate that. Will you remember to speak to her husband in the lobby?"

"Sure I will. You just take care of yourself."

Lapin walked out of the OR and into the doctors' lounge where he changed clothes before leaving for Esperanza.

Later, entering the uncommonly quiet hospital, he found Jan in the nurses' lounge. Together they visited each patient to explain the transfer to Samaritan, which had fortunately agreed to accept the patients. The Witnesses, as usual, were remarkably calm and understanding; they weren't strangers to doors being slammed in their faces.

When they finished making rounds, Lapin asked, "Have you seen Rana today?"

"No, but when I reached him at home earlier, he sounded distant, almost secretive."

"Do me a favor, Jan; get some ambulances over here to transfer the patients after the reporters leave. Okay?"

"No problem; I'll take care of everything. Don't worry!"

"You're a doll. What would I do without you?"

"Probably nothing! You just get out of here."

As they walked toward the back door, a number of strangers carrying clipboards passed them. "Who are all those people?" Lapin whispered.

"They're the new owners from St. Jude Hospital."

"The vultures can't even wait for the body to get cold."

Through the back door window they saw several television cameras surrounding his car. "I guess they figured out from the 'NO BLOOD' plates that that's mine. Look at them just waiting. Can we trade cars?"

"I'm parked out front," she said, handing him her keys.

"We can trade back later this afternoon at the office. Thanks."

"Be careful, Ron, please," she said as she handed him a copy of the State accusations.

"I will." He headed out the side door through the loading dock and drove over to Samaritan Hospital where he made the necessary arrangements for beds and additional nurses to take care of his patients. He was careful to have his calls screened by the operator in order to avoid the press. At two p.m., he drove to the American Airlines terminal at L.A. International to pick up his New York attorney, Gerald Garner.

Garner could offer no explanation as to what was behind the closure, but agreed that they needed to find a hospital immediately to replace Esperanza.

"I know a place we might look at," Garner said.

"Where?"

"Bellflower City Hospital."

"Bellflower? Where's that?"

"In L.A. County."

"That's a little far for us, isn't it?"

"We don't have too many options, Ron."

"I guess you're right. When can we see it, Gerry?"

"It's on the way . . . how about now?"

"Perfect . . . just give me directions."

Fifteen minutes later, they pulled into the nearly deserted parking lot.

"Is this place open?" Lapin asked.

"I think they have a few patients here from time to time."

"How many beds do they have?" he asked, walking toward the main entrance.

"About a hundred and fifty, I think."

"Why are they so slow here?" Lapin asked.

"Probably for a number of reasons. First, they were severely underfinanced when they opened the hospital. Second, they had some serious problems attracting new doctors to move into this older area of the county. I mean, the town needs emergency revitalization. It's not exactly the area a young doctor would choose as a great place to practice."

They walked into the administrator's office, and Garner introduced Lapin to a Mr. Needman. After brief amenities, Needman offered to show them the facilities, and of course Lapin jumped at the opportunity.

Now he could evaluate the hospital on a firsthand basis.

After crossing the empty lobby, they took the elevator to the second floor. The first wing held seven patients, four medical and three surgical. The alcohol rehabilitation unit housed another ten patients. The other two wings were closed. A pungent smell of idle decay permeated the deserted hallways and was hard to ignore. The older section of the hospital had been converted into clinics and doctors' offices. As they inspected this section, Mr. Needman pointed out a large, unused area on the first floor and suggested they convert it into a J.W. clinic.

Lapin was thrilled with the concept. He could visualize a place where "Nobody's People" could walk in off the street and be treated, without compromising their religious beliefs.

Back in his office, Needman made the customary promises. He said he'd do everything possible to help them make a smooth transition to Bellflower. He aspired to revive the hospital and was absolutely thrilled at the prospects of having Lapin's team and daily surgical load.

As he walked them to their car, Needman even pledged the cooperation of the staff and promised Lapin he'd have no problems at all at Bellflower. "All I want is good medicine and good patient care," Lapin said.

On the way back to his office, Garner talked about the hospital. In a monalogue of facts and figures, he mentioned capital expenditures, square footage, equipment leasing, and current fiscal strategies. Lapin was not listening. He was engrossed in the thought of moving to a third hospital in only five years. He knew the payoff for revitalizing a financially troubled institution like Bellflower: staff confrontations and bitterness that would eventually force him to move elsewhere. He recalled that the feeling was clearly one of *deja vu* when Mr. Needman told him how good Bellflower would be for his patients.

"Do you think we'll have a problem with their team about moving over there?" he asked Garner.

"I don't know; you can never tell."

"I anticipate problems with Rana, and maybe even Donnelly," Lapin said sadly.

"Why do you say that?"

"Well, Rana couldn't be reached today, and I've

known for some time now that he's been politicking with officers of the insurance company and some of the Witnesses. Then you have Donnelly, an opportunist who'll stab anybody in the back if it moves him forward. If push comes to shove and he thinks Rana can get the Witnesses to follow him to Samaritan Hospital or even back to Bristol, I think he'll go with Rana."

"You think Rana can do it?" Garner asked, surprised.

"Yes. For three years he's tried to emulate everything I've done. He might have the background to pull if off."

"The only thing he's missing is a surgeon," Garner added.

"That might slow him down, but it won't stop him. Whatever he and Donnelly can't accomplish in fair competition, they'll deal with underhandedly. I've seen both of them in action before."

"But do you really think Donnelly will go with him? I know he respects you."

"He'll go. It's only a matter of time," Lapin answered.

"Should I set up a meeting between the three of you? According to the newspaper, the Board of Health Services handed Esperanza's records over to the Board of Medical Quality Assurance for possible disciplinary action against eight doctors. BMQA would love nothing more than to see the team split up and attack one another."

"Well, Gerry," Lapin responded slowly, "if the Gestapo is really after me, I can assure you that both Rana and Donnelly will give them their total cooperation--even against me--if they think it will save their own hides."

"What possible derogatory information could they give the State to use against you?"

"I can't think of a thing. Everything we ever did together was completely aboveboard."

"I know that. You operated on my daughter Robyn at Esperanza, remember? I'm still going to try to get that meeting going."

"Hey, that's okay with me."

He stopped to drop off Garner at his office. There was, without question, much work to be done.

***

As Lapin walked through the crowded waiting room of his office, Jodie motioned to him to stay out of his private office. She whispered, "Four reporters are still waiting in there for your statement about the hospital closure."

"Tell them to call the hospital lawyer. I can't help them."

Jodie's pretty face showed distress. "There were two TV crews outside. They left fifteen minutes ago to take care of another assignment and said they'd be back in a little while."

"Interesting, huh? I'm getting to be a real celebrity, aren't I? I don't have anything to say on or off camera, so just get rid of them next time. You know the press seldom plays fair. All they really want to do is make headlines by playing up the sensationalized angles."

He walked back into the waiting room, apologized to his patients for being late, and saw each of them in turn. He was exhausted by the time he finished at seven-thirty that night and nearly collapsed into a waiting room chair. Jodie brought a much needed cup of coffee and announced, "Jan just called and said she'll be here in fifteen minutes."

"Thanks, Jodie. What would I do without you!" he stated appreciatively. "Are there any hot line calls I need to answer?"

"No, I took care of most of them and referred the others to Herk and Stan to handle."

"Do we have any cases scheduled for tomorrow?" he asked.

"Well, we had seven, but I canceled them until we know where to admit them."

Lapin closed his eyes and grimaced slightly from the day's pressures. "We can take everyone who's critical to Samaritan and the elective cases to Bellflower."

"Bellflower?" she questioned. "Where's that?"

"I'll tell you later." His voice faded and he dozed off.

Jodie answered the ringing phone and woke him up just as Jan Jordan walked into the waiting room. She shook her head in empathy and sat down beside him.

"There's a Remmy O'Neal on the phone," Jodie said.

"What's a Remmy O'Neal?" Lapin asked, rubbing his tired eyes.

"Ordinarily, I'd say it's some kind of a rare cognac, but I think it's your ex-wife with a new name.

I recognize her voice."

Lapin shook his head. "What does she want now?"

"I don't know. But I know it's not money because I mailed her alimony check ten days ago."

"Then I can't see why she's calling me. Tell her I'm not available."

As Jodie returned to the phone, Lapin turned to Jan. "How'd it go today?"

"It went okay. There were some minor problems, but nothing to worry about. We have an entire wing at Samaritan."

"Have you seen Donnelly or Rana at all today?"

"I saw Rana walking around Samaritan with some insurance company directors. When I walked up to them, Rana pretended not to see me. I don't trust him, Dr. Lapin; I just don't trust him at all."

"Join the club, Jan; I haven't trusted him or Donnelly for a long time."

"Do you think they'll try to interfere with your patients?" Jodie asked, joining the conversation.

"I won't be surprised if they pull some pretty underhanded stunts. I even look for them to start their own hot line."

A worried look filled Jan's face as she asked, "What can we do about it?"

"Nothing. All we can do is to keep right on doing what we do best. We're going to take care of patients, and we're going to do it at Bellflower. And then we're going to hope and pray that our operation can be rebuilt to the point we're at today."

Jan smiled. How she admired the man's courage! "Why don't you take us out to dinner tonight, Dr. Lapin?" she prompted.

"You got it. Let's go to the Hungry Tiger. But first . . . Jodie, will you go out to the parking lot and make sure there aren't any reporters hanging around my car?"

***

Over dinner the three discussed plans to move the entire operation to Bellflower and to replace Rana as soon as possible. They all agreed that Doctor Kaller was not only an excellent physician, but also the best choice to replace him. Lapin, expressing a degree of concern, hoped Kaller could withstand the pressures ahead of them.

"Don't worry," Jan said, "we all helped train Rana, so we'll certainly help someone as nice as Dr. Kaller."

"Well then, let's start first thing in the morning."

"Okay, fearless leader. But can it wait until nine-thirty? I have to take my daughter to the doctor," Jan said smiling.

"It can wait," Lapin said as he paid for dinner.

Arriving home that evening, he read the State's accusation and became livid at the incompetence and sheer ignorance shown by the State investigators in drafting their report. As an example, the hospital was cited for permitting a Pap smear before Lapin performed a D&C, because, they claimed, a D&C was more accurate. Their error wouldn't have even been made by a mere medical student. Ignorance of anatomical knowledge was evident as they described another of his cases. This patient had a diastasis recti reported as being a rectal prolapse instead of a bulging stomach. Further criticism that it was inappropriate for Lapin to "dictate" a discharge summary on a post-operative patient was read with exasperation.

***

For the next three months, Lapin and the team worked long and hard to rebuild their operation and upgrade Bellflower to their demanding standards. Even though Mr. Needman and his administrative staff stood by their promise to provide all the technical assistance they needed, the Bellflower project was predictably ensnarled in roadblocks. The reticent attitude of the nursing administrator and medical staff toward both the team and the Witnesses became increasingly pronounced. Unfortunately, Lapin's past experience with similar obstacles at Bristol and Esperanza proved to be of little benefit in reaching the predominantly Oriental staff at Bellflower. Their attitudes and reactions were primarily motivated by the complacent way that they formerly practiced medicine.

With the sudden influx of patients and the increased hospital activity challenging the staff, some felt threatened. Their resentful attitude was further intensified by the endless confrontations that erupted during surgical committee meetings. Even though many such occasions resulted in outright warfare between the existing staff and the new group of physicians,

Lapin hoped they'd still become friends.

Previously, the director of nursing pretty much had the run of things at this low-keyed, slow moving operation. Now, she was faced with acutely ill people who needed intensive care. Due to the increased nursing shortage in hospitals throughout the country, she found herself working with marginal, transient part-timers from the flourishing nurses' registry, an organization providing little more than semi-interested "bodies." During their eight-hour shift, they performed their specified duties, but they seldom did so with real interest or out of purest concern for the patients. Occasionally appearing on the scene were competent nurses who enthusiastically offered constructive solutions to acute medical problems. Because she found them threatening to her own position, the nursing director discouraged these talented nurses from staying on full staff for any period of time . . . or just eliminated them outright. Repeated requests by Lapin to change the nursing hierarchy fell on deaf ears, so he notified the administrator that he himself would be sleeping at the hospital until the nursing shortage was corrected. It was Lapin's way of assuring his patients that they would no longer be at the mercy of inadequate staffing. Soon after, the necessary changes were made.

The dream of a JW clinic became a reality. It began slowly, but due to medical competence, its fame spread quickly throughout the Witness community. Doctors volunteered their services and covered the clinic in rotation. A nominal fee, charged only when patients could afford it, was plowed back into the operation to help pay its staff of Witness employees.

Simultaneous with the opening of the Witness clinic, Lapin's dream of one day establishing an Institute of Bloodless Medicine and Surgery became a reality. A nucleus of over seventy specialists, committed to patient care without the use of blood, became the foundation of medical care for Witnesses on a regular, controlled basis.

Realizing he could not care for the spiritual needs of the hospital patients nor the social and interpersonal problems of the outpatients, Lapin began to search for a Witness family who could care for such needs within the clinic on a regular basis. He was indeed fortunate to find a family with the ability to offer his international group of patients the support system they so badly needed while in an unfamiliar environment.   Lapin's   requests   were   as follows: (1) administrate the entire clinic, (2) find accommodations for out-of-town patients and their families, (3) arrange transportation for patients from the airport to the hospital, (4) visit the patients daily, (5) arrange for Bible studies during the week, and (6) start a monthly news bulletin. Ron and Heidi Austin have accepted the challenge and have met it admirably.

First a group of medical specialists had been acquired to cover all medical problems, and now the Witness family would provide for the ancillary needs of the patients.   Lapin and Hutchins diligently pursued the educational aspect of their health care program, emphasizing the fact that vital information must be presented to Witnesses so they in turn might avoid major confrontations with the medical profession. This intensive educational program took both men across the United States and abroad.

Dr. Hutchins was unable to keep up with the pace and showed signs of increased heart failure. He had been cared for medically by Rana for the past three years, but Rana never did seem to get his heart problem under control. At Lapin's insistence, a well-respected cardiologist performed another angiogram. He disagreed with Rana's diagnosis and recommended that Herk have an aortic valve replaced surgically. Herk, however, decided to wait a little longer. Considering Herk's condition, Lapin minimized his responsibilities in the operating room and on the lecture circuit so that he'd be as rested as possible when he chose to undergo surgery.

***

During the process of rebuilding their operation at Bellflower, Rana capitalized on the desires of some of the Witnesses to go to Samaritan. First of all, he promised to admit them there if they were personally referred to him.   Then he promised that, through a bond issue, the Witnesses would own the hospital without paying for it. And just as Lapin predicted, he soon started another hot line and increased the rift between them.

Rumors reached Bellflower that Rana, out of concern for his own hide and career, had informed the State in writing of his disassociation with Lapin and his team. It was later rumored that the State planned to prosecute Lapin on the basis of misinformation supplied by Rana. Lapin was obviously upset, but dismissed all concern about the rumors. He knew in his heart that everything he'd done for his patients had been ethically sound.

Meanwhile, even more patients complained about being charged for tests that were never given and being billed for examinations that Rana never performed while they were in the hospital. Lapin discussed the situation with Donnelly, but he remained uncommitted and acted indifferently. Donnelly did, however, provide quite a sideshow, constantly bickering with staff anesthesiologists while continuing to work with Lapin at Bellflower.

***

On Labor Day, 1981, the State of California filed accusations against Lapin, charging him with being incompetent and negligent. Donnelly, acting like a stranger, grew even more unapproachable. One morning before surgery, Donnelly demanded that Lapin and the hospital guarantee him a certain minimum income. Lapin was flabbergasted and turned him down flatly. Since each man's services were paid for directly by the patient, Lapin couldn't guarantee a set fee to anyone.

In early October, Lapin, Garner, and Frank Barbaro-- the California attorney retained in the defense--began working long hours to put together a defense against the vicious and groundless accusations filed by the State.

Donnelly called Lapin's office and told Jodie that unless he got a contractual guarantee, he was "firing" Lapin as a surgeon. Later that afternoon, Lapin met with Fred Garcia, a stable, competent anesthesiologist he'd known for some time. Lapin was delighted when Garcia agreed to step in and take over Donnelly's job.

Later in October, rumors hit Bellflower that Donnelly and Rana were extensively involved in meetings with the BMQA to discuss Lapin's patients and activities. Copies of their conversations with State officials were later made available to Lapin and his legal defense team through the discovery process. Exerting considerable pressure, Lapin's two attorneys persuaded him not to file legal action against both physicians. "There will be plenty of time to nail them after the hearings. Let's not worry about that now."

An electronic survey of Lapin's office revealed that his phone line circuits had been changed. He could only presume by whom and for what purpose, but couldn't prove it.

After a remarkable transformation, the clinic and hospital flourished. And though it was true that the medical staff hadn't quite adopted the attitude of "brotherly love," their animosity had become more muffled and less of a problem.

It was at this time that Jodie's health began deteriorating. She suffered from a chronic inflammatory disease of the small intestine that had worsened considerably in the last eight months. After requiring five hospitalizations for treatment, it became apparent that she needed surgery and that she wouldn't allow anyone but Lapin to do it.

The possibility of operating on both Jodie and Hutchins in the same year generated a great deal of anxiety in Lapin. He, quite naturally, tried to postpone their cases as long as he reasonably could.

The time arrived, however, and he had to cut short a trip to Maine University that December. Jodie had developed an acute internal obstruction. Lapin needed all the moral support he could get and decided to perform the operation with Hutchin's assistance. Everything went well. Jodie was back working in the office eight days after part of her small intestine was retracted and hasn't been besieged by recurrent symptoms since.

***

Lapin was never to forget New Year's Eve that year, nor would his entire crew. Early that morning he received a call from Vince Timson from Cleveland. Timson was distressed and very angry.

"Calm down, Vince," Lapin said. "We'll help you. Just tell me what's been going on."

For the next five minutes, Vince related a typical JW horror story. Even though he'd heard similar stories over the years, Lapin's blood still boiled as if he were hearing these accounts for the very first time. He had remained keenly sensitive to the

216

discrimination and mistreatment the Witnesses endured over and over again.

"I took my wife, Joan, to the hospital six days ago," Vince began with a shaky voice. "She was scheduled to have our second child by C-section, and the gynecologist promised to respect the blood issue. Surgery went okay, according to the doctor, but she began to experience heavy vaginal bleeding in the recovery room. The gynecologist then told me he'd have to take Joan back into surgery to stop the bleeding. After talking it over with my wife, I gave my consent. It was terrible! She was lying in a large pool of blood. Ten minutes later the doctor came back into the recovery room and told us the name of the anesthesiologist, but then he stopped abruptly. I said, 'What's wrong?' He told us that the anesthesiologist wouldn't put Joan to sleep unless they could use blood. So I said, 'What can we do, doctor? We can't just watch her lie here and die while the nurses keep changing the bloody sheets. It's inhuman to have to watch such a slow, agonizing death without being able to do anything about it!' I asked him if there wasn't another anesthesiologist he knew who had a heart. You know what he did? He shook his head. So I said, 'Not one? Not even one?' My wife kept saying to me, 'It'll be okay, honey. Don't worry.' But I was worried, doc, real worried. She was getting pale, real pale, and was dripping with sweat. Her breathing was very shallow and faint."

Lapin clenched his teeth. He grimaced. His empathy and mental anguish transcended the miles. Vince went on, "The doctor promised us he'd look around Cleveland for an anesthesiologist who'd go along with the blood issue. He said he'd try real hard, doc." There was silence on the line for a moment, but Lapin knew Vince would continue. "Doc, Joan and I have a two-year-old child at home, and my wife's only twenty-six years old." Lapin could sense that the emotional outpouring came from this man's heart. "I'd like--if it isn't too much to ask--for this child to have her mother. The doctor can't even face me now. He said he tried everything he could . . . but he wasn't able to find anyone in Cleveland who would help us. He's been looking for the last five days. . . ."

Lapin composed himself. "What's your wife's situation now, Vince?"

"She's in ICU and her hemoglobin is down to five

grams."

"That's very low, Vince," Lapin said softly.

"Yes, I know, Dr. Lapin; I know that. But what can we do?"

"Well, we can stop the bleeding, that's for sure. But we might have to take out her uterus to accomplish that."

"That's okay, just don't let her die. I love her so much! I don't know how I could go through life without her."

"Vince, listen carefully. Call the airport and find out how quickly you can get a private jet to airlift her to the Long Beach airport."

"One problem, doc," Vince interrupted. "The hospital's chief of staff has already given us a lot of problems. Now he says he won't accept any responsibility for her transfer because she's too sick to travel."

"Damn it, Vince, listen to me! He hasn't accepted any responsibility for her up to now. You just tell him you'll release him and the hospital from any responsibility and that you'd rather have her die up in the air than watch her die of neglect right there on the ground in their hospital."

"Okay, doc. You got it! I'll do just that."

"Vince, keep your cool . . . you have to. Call me back with your anticipated time of arrival at Long Beach."

"Okay, Dr. Lapin, I will. And thanks . . . thanks a lot. You're a life saver!"

"Cut it out, Vince; you're wasting valuable time."

He hung up the phone, then slammed his fist on the bed stand in anger. The sound was sharp enough to wake Ethan from his sleep at the foot of the bed. Lapin dialed the nursing supervisor at Bellflower and told her to keep the operating crew in full force until he released them.

"Do you know what day it is?" she asked with obvious irritation. "I hope you can explain it to your crew."

"Well, first I have to explain it to a very nice lady that I was supposed to take out tonight."

"You know, Dr. Lapin, you can get to be a pain sometimes. But I have to hand it to you, you never ask anyone else to do something you wouldn't do yourself."

"Thanks . . . thanks for understanding. Just keep the crew in the operating room."

218

"Okay, doctor, I will."

After hanging up, Lapin called Doctor Gough, a brilliant, talented gynecologist who'd recently joined the team, and asked him to stand by for the emergency case coming in from Cleveland. Gough wasn't thrilled, but he understood and promised to be there. He also knew how much Lapin put himself out for others.

At noon, Vince called back and told Lapin he'd found a Lear jet that could bring them to Long Beach with an ETA of eleven p.m.

"Nothing sooner?" Lapin quickly asked.

"No . . . I couldn't get anything sooner. Is that a problem?"

"No, not really. It's just that it's New Year's Eve, and the crew and I all had plans."

"I can understand that," Vince said.

"It's okay, Vince; just get her out here as soon as you can. I'll be waiting for you on the runway."

"How will I recognize you, Dr. Lapin?"

"You can't miss me, Vince. I'll be the only one on the runway with an ambulance, a black beard, and a car with license plates that say 'NO BLOOD' . . . and there won't be a sleigh or any reindeer."

"I'm looking forward to meeting you tonight, Doctor Lapin. I truly am."

"So am I."

The sleek Lear jet landed on schedule at eleven o'clock that evening. Lapin was parked directly in front of the ambulance by the terminal. Vince jumped out first, followed by the gynecologist who had operated on Joan. Lapin thought it was great to find a doctor who cared enough about his patient to actually make the trip.

As Joan was placed in the ambulance, Lapin directed Vince to his car. They followed behind, with ambulance lights flashing and sirens wailing. The adrenalin in their bloodstreams pumped at maximum speed. As they sped through red lights on their way, Vince remarked, "I thought you'd be much older, Brother Lapin."

"Fooled you again, Vince . . . twice. I'm not a Witness."

"You're not?" Vince asked with a startled look. "Then why are you doing all this for us?"

"Well you know, Vince, we Jews have nowhere to go on New Year's Eve anyway. We celebrate our New Year about three months earlier."

They shared a warm smile as the ambulance pulled up at Bellflower's emergency entrance.

Joan was taken to surgery immediately and had to undergo a complete hysterectomy to control the bleeding. The crew and the exhausted physicians celebrated the coming New Year with Cold Duck poured into plastic cups. Vince sat holding his wife's cold hand in the Intensive Care Unit. Ten days later, Joan and Vince were back in Cleveland taking care of their two beautiful children. It wasn't until months later that Lapin found out the family had mortgaged their house and everything they owned in order to pay for the fifteen thousand dollar one-way airplane trip to Los Angeles.

***

Ari was doing well at Occidental College, though torn between his love for music and his unexplained secret desire to go into medicine. His father, hearing him play both the piano and clarinet with perfection, realized that his music should be encouraged. Ari argued with some degree of conviction that he couldn't earn a living as a musician. He was just being practical. But his father wisely responded that he could enjoy life infinitely more in the field of music and that the issue of money was secondary at best. Having seen firsthand the torment and agony his father lived with from the time Ari started at Occidental, he decided on a career in music and has been at peace with himself ever since.

Weekends held a special joy for Ari because they allowed him time to get to know and love his father. With each reunion, the bond between them grew deeper and stronger. Watching them interact, one could not imagine that they'd lived apart and seen each other so infrequently over the past eighteen years.

10

It didn't look like any ordinary letter. The envelope bore Hebrew print and a red Star of David in the upper left hand corner. The colorful stamp was postmarked March 14, 1982. Lapin's hands were shaking as he tore the envelope open. The words looked so familiar and yet so strangely different. He read it over and over in his mother tongue, a language he had seldom used in the past twenty-four years--a whole generation, a lifetime. The letter was from the director of the Israeli Red Star of David, which is the equivalent of the American Red Cross although not recognized by it. Director Kafir, a retired Israeli general, was inviting Lapin to come to Israel and deliver a series of lectures on Fluosol and bloodless surgery to his staff and the army medical corps.

Lapin sat in his office staring at the bookshelf. Thoughts were racing through his mind in a bizarre, uncontrolled stream of consciousness.

Why me? Is Syria planning to attack Israel? Or maybe it's Libya this time. How will I be able to leave Israel after the lectures? Will Customs detain me because I'm Israeli born? Who do I still remember there after all these years? Are they expecting an attack from Jordan and anticipating a need for Fluosol to take care of the potential blood shortage? Will any of my old high school classmates recognize or remember me? Will they want to? Will they ask why I left them with the task of defending the Jewish dream of a homeland in Israel, while I lived in comfort in the land of Mickey Mouse, Corvettes, and disco lights? Or will they just stare in agonizing silence? Does the house in which I spent my childhood still stand? How many Israeli pounds does one get for a U.S. dollar? And what about Dina? Is Dina still alive?

Where is she?

The office door flung open and Jodie, his secretary, marched in. "There are twenty-six patients in the waiting room. Can we get started, please!"

"Not just yet."

"What excuse do you want me to give them this time?"

"Hmmm . . . tell them . . . tell them that I'm in a conference; they'll understand that. Tell them anything. I'll be out soon."

"Oh, sure," she replied, unconvinced.

"By the way, do I have a valid Israeli passport?"

"Do you have a what?"

"An Israeli passport?"

"Why on earth do you need an Israeli passport when you have an American one?"

"You don't understand. If you're born there and leave, you need an Israeli passport to get back in."

Jodie stood stunned with a look of disbelief written all over her pretty face. "You aren't planning on going to Israel, are you?"

"Yes, I am," he replied, avoiding eye contact.

Jodie, who had watched with great anxiety as Lapin's international travel schedule got out of hand in the last two years, knew he could pack his bags and travel anywhere at a moment's notice to lecture or trouble shoot any medical problem involving Witnesses or bloodless surgery. She walked in front of him, put her cigarette down, and placed her hand on his shoulder. "They will never let you out," she warned.

"I'll take my chances," he replied.

As if stunned by a poisonous snake, Jodie pulled back and said, "You never get tired of looking over the charging bull's horns, do you?"

"I guess not," he answered. But Jodie didn't hear him as she quickly left the room.

He saw thirty-seven patients that afternoon but remembered little about his work load that day. His mind was drifting east. For him, Jerusalem was becoming a tangible reality for the first time in a generation.

Three weeks later, armed with both a sixty day entry-exit visa and an Israeli passport, he was driven to the Los Angeles airport by his son. Ari's lively mood was in tune with the fast-paced trip to the TWA terminal. By contrast, Lapin was in a somber mood and was deeply absorbed in his own thoughts.

"I'll park the car while you check in, okay, dad?

Dad?"

"Yeah, that's fine, son. I'll meet you at Gate 28."

"Okay, dad . . . and hey, cheer up, will you?"

Most of the passengers had boarded the plane, but Ari was nowhere to be seen. Lapin started to become irritated and was walking over to page him when he saw Ari running up the stairs.

"What took you so long, Ari?" he asked, visibly annoyed.

"Well, dad, when I parked the car, three people came over and asked me to explain your personalized 'NO BLOOD' license plates. So, not wanting to be rude, I explained what you do. One of the men asked what my last name was. When I answered, they smiled, shook my hand, and told me that they had read about you in the *Awake!* magazine. When I told them you were going to Israel, they asked me to convey their support and appreciation for all the good work that you were doing in their behalf."

"I wish I was going to Israel with you, dad," Ari added softly. He suppressed his tears as the two embraced tightly.

"Next year, Ari . . . next year, Jerusalem."

***

At New York Kennedy Airport, Lapin transferred to EL-AL Airlines and boarded the plane after undergoing an extensive security check, complete with a body search. The tight security reminded him of the problems still prevalent in the Middle East: danger, terrorism, and fear of the unknown. Lapin was relieved that he'd drawn up a will before he left.

The blue and white 747 displaying a large Star of David on its tail was crowded and uncomfortably warm inside. Two anemic-looking young Orthodox men, dressed in traditional black attire and round fur hats, occupied the seats next to Lapin. They carried on a lively conversation in Yiddish, the first language Lapin was taught by his paternal grandmother. It was this grandmother who raised him after he'd been abandoned by his mother as a one-year-old child.

Lapin's beautiful seventeen-year-old mother left Palestine to live a more glamorous life in Paris after an ugly divorce from his father, twenty-three years her senior. The words, the feelings, the pain, and the past were all slowly coming back. Entrenched

deeply in thought, he gazed through the plastic
covered windows into the dark, clear night.

The two men beside him began to study the Talmud in
a muffled cacophony of monotonous tones.

How different I am from them, he thought. *Jewish--
but oh, so different!*

In the seat in front of him, a young father was
helping his son assemble a puzzle. He was encouraging, coaxing, teasing, teaching, loving. Lapin,
observing the scene between the cracks in the seat,
watched with obvious envy as the two took delight in
that lengthy interchange. Such strong bonding between
parent and child always gained Lapin's admiration,
even though this closeness had been sorely lacking in
his own childhood.

His own father was a cold, dictatorial, and physically brutal man who managed to teach his only son how
to hate him. While his father enjoyed all the
comforts of life, Ron learned firsthand about hunger
and doing without necessities much too early in his
young life.

"What will you have to drink with your meal, sir?"
the flight attendant asked in a mechanical voice.

"Red wine if you have it; kosher, of course."

The two men sitting next to him had brought their
own kosher food on board and proceeded to remove it
from two large brown paper bags. Lapin, plastic knife
in hand, began attacking his microwaved piece of
dried out meat with minimal success. His pious
neighbors became engrossed in an elaborate prayer
before eating. Feeling guilty, Lapin stopped trying
to master the mysterious meat until they finished.
While eating, the two men kept making sly remarks in
Yiddish about the "*goy*" next to them; they were to
make a number of such remarks during the trip, secure
in the knowledge that he would not understand them.

Lapin didn't respond. He enjoyed catching people
off guard in the unpretentious act of being themselves. The meal was terrible; the wine, good enough
to finish the bottle. Settling back in his seat to
gaze out the window, Lapin basked in a strange
sensation of warmth as the plane carried him closer to
a long-lost dream.

The night passed quickly. As the brilliant sun
began to wash the blue skies with light, the plane
started its descent toward the Israeli shore. The
Israeli national anthem played over the P.A. system

as the plane crossed into Israeli territory. Lapin's heart pounded in his chest and tears streamed from his eyes at the sound of the music. He felt like an emotional volcano erupting with ferocity after many years of dormancy.

He left his seat as soon as the plane pulled up to to the terminal building. His body was aching from the long flight, but his spirit soared. In perfect homespun Yiddish, he wished the two men seated next to him a pleasant and productive stay in the Holy Land and a speedy return to Brooklyn. His eyes lit up as he watched their anemic faces become even whiter. He deplaned and walked to the terminal building, but not before kneeling down and kissing the ground. He was home!

Outside the terminal building, his eyes caught sight of a large hand-held sign in Hebrew saying, "Welcome to Israel, Doctor Lapin." As he gazed at the sign in amazement, a group of ten people approached him. *A welcoming committee from the Red Star of David*, he thought to himself.

"Welcome to Israel, Doctor Lapin. We are so glad you came. We recognize you from your picture in the *Awake!* magazine," said Dan, their spokesman, as he shook his hand.

"Witnesses?" Lapin asked in disbelief. "JWs in Israel? You must be joking!"

"No, I am not joking. We have five Hebrew-speaking congregations and six Arabic-speaking congregations here."

"Well, I'm very glad to know that," Lapin replied.

"We're having a lot of problems getting medical care in Israel, Dr. Lapin. It's because of our stand against blood transfusions. So we're grateful that you came."

"Wait just a minute, Dan. I'm here at the request of the army and the Red Star of David to lecture about my techniques and artificial blood replacement," Lapin said.

"Yes, we are aware of that," another Witness answered.

"You know? How do you know? How do you know anything? How did you find out I was coming to Israel in the first place?"

"We have a very effective grapevine system of communication," Dan answered with a sly smile.

"I guess you must."

"Would you teach some of our doctors how to operate without blood so the friends won't have to die seeking medical help?" asked one of the young Witness women.

"I'll try; but please, just give me a chance. I've just returned to Israel for the first time in twenty-four years and I don't want to make waves just yet. I have a meeting in Jerusalem this evening and I'm very tired, so maybe we can continue this conversation tomorrow."

They understood. "We will be honored to drive you to your hotel in Jerusalem," one of the Witnesses offered. Lapin warmly accepted.

As the small caravan of five cars made its way to Jerusalem, it passed through Bab-el-wad, the gate to the valley which had been conquered with a great number of casualties and much bloodshed. Lapin was getting an earful about the difficulties the Witnesses were having in Israel with both the government and the medical profession. As Dan spoke, Lapin refused to accept all that he was hearing. *Not in Israel, too . . . not here . . . it's just not possible . . . not in the land of democracy.*

Dan helped him check into the Jerusalem Hilton. "I would like to assemble all of our congregations some night next week to hear your lecture," he said.

"You don't quit, do you?"

"I am an Israeli, like you," Dan said with conviction.

"Okay, Dan, okay. We'll do it next Monday night. It's my last night in Israel, but it's the only free night I have."

"By the way," Dan said, "you've become very famous in Israel. You made the front page of the evening newspaper as well as the news program on the radio." Dan handed him the newspaper. Lapin opened it and read the headline in the middle of the front page. It read, "Israeli Born Pioneer in Bloodless Surgery and Artificial Blood is Here for a Lecture Series." His eyes were fixed on the newspaper headline as he thought to himself, *I am a celebrity in the world but a dog in Orange County.* "I suppose that I have you to thank for leaking all this information to the press."

Dan merely smiled, nodded his head and said, "*Shalom.*" Then he turned to walk away.

"*Shalom*, friend, *shalom*," Lapin bid him farewell.

Many messages awaited Lapin as he checked into his room, mostly from the press. But one made him freeze in amazement. It said simply, "Dina called from Ginosar," and gave the telephone number. Dina was his former teacher, housemother, and friend from the agricultural high school of Nahalal. He spent those three and a half years of his formative life supported by a social agency, while his greedy, wealthy father was jet setting throughout the world. The school was the first real home he ever knew; Dina and the forty boys and girls who made up his class became his family. Dina had been the center of his life--the key to his survival. She kept him in touch with what was left of his tender, battered, human emotions. She held him up, defended him, clothed him, and pushed him to excel in his studies. She became his new-found basis for a healthier reality. For a woman who was divorced, self-supporting, and raising a young daughter, her energy to keep up with forty young people's problems--twenty-four hours a day--was nothing short of amazing.

Lapin vividly remembered the gray, rainy morning when she brought him to the bus stop, six months before he was to finish his last year in high school. He had chosen to leave Nahalal and return to Tel Aviv and care for his grandmother who had suffered a disabling stroke. Since his father, as usual, was nowhere to be found to care for his ailing mother, Ron felt compelled to step in and carry the load just as he had done many times before.

Dina's parting words that day were: "Only I know what a great sacrifice you are making today for your grandmother. I am sure now more than ever, in spite of this temporary setback to your education, that the academic world will one day hear again from Ronny Lapin."

When he boarded the bus for the trip to Tel Aviv, leaving a sobbing Dina behind, he had no idea that twenty-four years would pass before he would see her or the school again.

He picked up the phone and dialed Ginosar. The few rings seemed like an eternity to him. Finally she answered. The voice, the warmth, the sense of humor-- all had remained the same, though somewhat older and wiser. They spent over an hour talking about old times. He learned that she was now a grandmother, had two grown children, and was remarried. She had kept in touch with all the living members of the class from Nahalal. She seemed to know a lot about Lapin from

227

American newspaper clippings supplied to her by Kafir, who had not only arranged Lapin's trip but had also located her. This initial conversation had been an emotional experience for both of them, and they ended it by agreeing to meet in Nahalal in three days.

He sat motionless by the phone for a long time before hanging up. *Is this really happening? Am I really in Israel after such a long hiatus, or is it just a cruel joke, a bad dream?* A strong, warm gust of wind from the Judean desert blew the window open, startling him back to the present--a deeper reality now, born out of fabulous imagery from the realm of dreams.

The next day was spent sightseeing in the old city of Jerusalem. As if a giant sponge, he busily absorbed the sights, sounds, and smells of the eternal city. He followed the crowds to the Wailing Wall, Judaism's most revered shrine, and remembered being brought there by his grandmother at the age of four. He recalled her stuffing small pieces of paper containing her handwritten messages between the cracks of ancient stones and praying quietly while she rested her snow white head on the wall. He soon joined the group of Orthodox Jews in prayer by the wall and was amazed to find that prayers which he had not uttered in an eternity flowed freely from his lips in perfect Hebrew.

He searched in his pockets for a piece of paper on which to write his wish, but could only find an old blue prescription blank. He wrote, "Dear God, help me to continue doing your work for the benefit of all mankind." He stuffed the prescription blank among thousands of other pieces of paper in the cracks of the wall which, half as old as time, continued to stand tall supported by nothing more than prayers and tears.

As he prepared to leave, his eyes caught sight of the opening services for a Bar Mitzvah at the far end of the wall. He strolled over to watch the boy, who was about to become a full-fledged Jewish man at the ripe old age of thirteen, recite a passage from the ancient Torah. The small boy strained under the weight of the heavy scrolls as he placed them on the crisp, white linen covering the small wooden table.

Lapin thought of Ari, who had had his ceremony at the wall. When his mother brought him to Israel, she knew all too well that his father couldn't be present for this especially important occasion. As he watched the boy perform admirably, he pretended he was watching his son become a man. Just being part of the entire scene, Ron Lapin relived the richest of warm feelings, proud to be a Jew, thrilled to be surrounded by its tradition and history.

Rediscovering a sense of pride in his own heritage, he was still aglow as he began walking over to the Arab section. He had never seen it before, and he was looking forward to the exploration. He had been cautioned at the hotel to be careful in that area of the city and, preferably, to avoid it altogether. Due to considerable unrest among the Arabs on the West Bank, massive demonstrations and a general strike now paralyzed the commercial and industrial sectors. Lapin predictably ignored the warning and walked into the Arab sector.

A burst of automatic rifle fire came whirring from the direction of the Golden Dome Mosque, causing him instinctively to dive for cover. Within moments the square in front of the mosque was filled with Israeli paratroopers firing Uzi submachine guns in the direction of the magnificent Arab shrine.

Sirens wailed as the air became heavily saturated with the smell of gunpowder. In great haste, an army jeep evacuated him from the danger area and out of the city. "What the hell is going on in there?" Lapin asked the young soldier driving the jeep.

"An American who emigrated to Israel took over the Mosque of the Rock and is firing an M-16 rifle. He's already killed two people . . . but we'll get him."

"Why did he do it?"

"Who knows why. Maybe he's just crazy."

"This whole area is crazy. People are crazy. The world is crazy. Nothing makes sense anymore. Nothing. . . ."

The driver didn't reply as he continued to drive Lapin to safety.

Visibly shaken from the day's experience, he sat in the dimly lit hotel bar and ordered a desperately needed double martini. He downed it in a hurry and started to order another when a tall, distinguished, gray-haired man approached his table. "Good afternoon, Dr. Lapin. I am Mr. Kafir. Welcome home."

"Thank you very much, general," Lapin replied, shaking his hand.

"I heard about your close call today in the old

city. I'm sorry."

"It's not your fault. I guess it's just one of those things that happen here regularly. But, you must forgive me . . . it was an emotionally devastating experience."

"How so?" Kafir asked.

"As you know, I left here in 1958. A generation later--a whole lifetime later--things haven't changed. Oh sure, there are lots of new roads, tons of expensive new cars, crazy drivers, and new restaurants and disco clubs. But the fighting, the hatred, and the killing still go on . . . unchanged . . . on both sides."

Somewhat embarrassed by Lapin's assessment, Kafir replied, "Things have changed, not as fast as we would have liked to see, but changed nonetheless. You must recognize, doctor, that in an area of the world where living by the sword has been a way of life since the beginning of time, it takes cooperation and understanding on both sides to turn the tide of bloodshed. It's going to take patience and time, lots of time. But we will have peace here one day. There is no other way. We must have peace."

"When am I scheduled to lecture?" he asked, changing the subject.

"Tomorrow, at one-thirty, to the Surgical Society; Wednesday, at noon, in the Red Star of David Headquarters to my entire staff; and Friday, at one o'clock, to the army."

"That sounds fine. I guess this schedule will allow me to visit a few old friends."

"I'll have my driver and my car at your disposal for the duration of your stay in Israel."

"You're very kind indeed."

"Is there anything else I can do for you before I leave?"

"Yes, in fact, there is."

"Anything! What is it?"

"As you know, I do all of my work and research with Jehovah's Witnesses."

"Yes, I know."

"Well, I met a few of them yesterday and they complained that it's impossible to get medical care here because of their stand on the blood issue. Is that so?"

Kafir nodded. "As a director of the blood bank industry in Israel, I can only tell you that we have

230

had a lot of problems with these people."

"But this is Israel," Lapin said. "This just can't happen here."

"And why not? What does being a democratic country have to do with treating people who refuse to comply with the standards of our medical society?"

Not again, Lapin thought. *Not the same old speech again.* He had heard it in a hundred different ways before, but never in Hebrew. It somehow sounded sacrilegious and out of place.

"Well, Mr. Kafir, can you suggest anything I might be able to do here in such a short time that could change the situation without causing too many bruised egos?"

"I guess you can try to convince one of the surgery professors to try your methods, and get all of the Witnesses to go to him if he agrees. . . ."

Lapin was not overwhelmed with the sincerity of his reply. "Can you introduce me to anyone?"

"I know most of them; I just don't know who will be sympathetic to your needs. Wait, wait just a minute . . . this is incredible . . . I know one doctor you can meet right now who might be able to help you." With that, Kafir got up, walked to the end of the bar, and began talking with a man sitting alone by the window. Soon the two men walked back toward Lapin.

"Dr. Moshe Feuchtwanger, I would like you to meet the bloodless surgeon," Kafir said jokingly. The two men shook hands and then sat down. "I'll leave you two eggheads alone and run back to Tel Aviv to finish my work," Kafir said. "I'm looking forward to seeing you at the headquarters on Wednesday, doctor. *Shalom.*"

"Safe trip," Lapin responded, and then turned to the man sitting beside him. "Well, Moshe, what do you do for a living?"

"I'm the professor and chairman of the Department of Surgery at Ben-Gurion University," he replied in perfect English.

Lapin was impressed and went right on in his crusade to find an ally to the Witness cause in Israel. "How busy are you there?" Lapin questioned his guest.

"Very busy. But it's mostly routine procedures or busy work, so it's frequently boring."

"My practice was that way until I started working with the JWs, and it's been anything but that ever since."

"I'm very interested in your work, Dr. Lapin.
That's why I'm here in Jerusalem, to hear your lecture
tomorrow."
Lapin was delighted that the man was interested.
"What are you doing for dinner, Moshe?" he asked.
"I have no plans as yet."
"Great, let's have dinner at the Intercontinental
Hotel, where I'm told you get the best view of the
city, and then I can tell you all about my work."
"That sounds good."
"Eight o'clock in the lobby okay?"
The two men stood, smiled, and warmly shook hands.
A bond of camaraderie had been established.

***

Lapin was happy as he walked back to his room to
shower and change for dinner. Through the bathroom
door he could hear the phone ring and ran, dripping
wet, to answer it. Dina was calling to confirm the
Thursday meeting in Nahalal. He reassured her that it
was still on and told her of his meeting with Moshe.
She knew all about him. Her daughter, a surgical
nurse, had worked with him for two years and had great
respect for both him and his work. Lapin beamed as he
hung up the phone; he was making headway.
The view from the Intercontinental Hotel was
breathtaking. The food was satisfying and the wine
was acceptable, but the conversation was outstanding.
For three hours they enjoyed a panoramic view of the
old city--its array of lighted monuments glittering
like jewels--as they covered such diverse topics as
politics, cooking, artificial blood, Israeli art, and
a smathering of other things as well. Lapin told
Moshe all about his techniques, citing a number of
difficult case histories to illustrate his success
with bloodless surgery. It was quite evident that the
professor was impressed. They closed the restaurant
that evening and still managed to find a taxi to take
them back to the Hilton. Each sat quietly absorbed in
his own thoughts as the cab sped through the now
deserted streets of the city.

***

Lapin loved to lecture, especially about bloodless
surgery and Fluosol. In the last two years he must

232

have addressed well over a hundred different audiences across the United States and throughout the world. He skillfully aimed at shocking those in attendance with his graphic slide presentation. Long-neglected, grotesque tumors flashed on the screen first and made an awesome impression. Then came untouched photos-- visual success stories as it were--of the post-operative results. Horror stories of surgical patients with stringent, death-defying hemoglobin counts were dramatically captured in living color. All-in-all, the slide presentation validated the mastery of bloodless surgery at the hands of Lapin's skilled team. He toyed with the skeptics. He enjoyed disarming them with a harmonious blend of Jewish humor, scientific fact, Talmudic logic, and a pinch of sarcasm. He seldom lost an argument with his audience and always moved them to do some reflective thinking about his talk long after it had taken place.

The lectures in Israel were no exception. Moshe drove him to Tel Aviv following the meeting. After emphasizing how much he enjoyed Lapin's talk, he asked him to become a visiting professor in his department. He also expressed his willingness to care for any JW referred to him, as long as Lapin helped with the case in the beginning. He then suggested a meeting with heads of the Witness congregations in order to establish an Israeli branch of the hot line.

"How do you assess the audience reaction to the talk today?" Lapin inquired.

"From the comments I heard, you run the complete gamut of genius to nut-job."

"So what else is new?" Lapin responded bitterly.

"I've been a surgeon for twenty-two years, and I still can't understand why surgeons seem to resent everything that's new and challenging."

"Easy," Lapin replied quickly. "A glass blower has never created anything as fragile as a surgeon's ego."

"*Touché*," Moshe responded with a smile.

***

The Blood Bank staff received the information about Fluosol with great interest. Their receptiveness resulted in a feasibility study to consider Fluosol for emergency cases.

Early Thursday morning the driver picked Lapin up for the two-hour trip north to Nahalal. He sat motionless; only his eyes traced the landscape as the car raced the coastal city winds. He searched out landmarks that were etched in his memory, but found that most had yielded to their overpowering adversaries, time and change.

Dina was waiting in front of the Administration Building as the car pulled up. She looked tired, heavier, and much older, but her warm facial expression and her compelling deep-brown eyes remained unchanged. They embraced dearly, trying in vain to hold back the tears. Playful school children passing by on their way to class were insensitive to the touching emotional tenderness being expressed.

"The beard suits you well," she said as they began their walk through each building on the school grounds. They were trying unrealistically to recapture the past. When they entered dormitory room number seven, the small, airy quarters where he'd spent his first school year, he noticed that all three beds were in exactly the same location with exactly the same blue bedspreads. The young dark-haired boy sitting on the bed Lapin had once occupied was absorbed in studying a biology textbook. Lapin introduced himself and said, "Be careful son, this bed is contagious. Everyone who sleeps in it is destined to become a doctor."

Dina beamed with pride as he spoke. The boy managed a faint smile and in Talmudic fashion responded, "From your mouth to God's ears." Before leaving the roomful of memories behind, he turned and asked Dina, "Do you remember how Itschak, Vaspi, and I used to turn this place upside down?"

Dina remained silent as he went on recalling some things that the three roommates had done. After they left the room and headed toward the staircase, she softly said, "They are both dead."

Her words had a devastating effect on him, ripping open old wounds, bringing forth a massive wave of long-suppressed guilt and sorrow. *Where was I when they were out there dying? Where?*

Itschak had been a brilliant artist who could work equally well in any medium. Vaspi was a scholar. What a waste. What a loss. And all for what?

"How did they die?" he asked, almost whispering.

"Vaspi was a tank battalion commander who died in the major tank battle on the Golan Heights in 1973. Itschak was a major in the paratroopers and died that

234

same year trying to rescue a wounded soldier in the
Sinai Desert."

"Do they have families?"

"Yes. They were both married and each had three
children."

"Did anyone else in the class die?" Lapin asked
hesitantly.

"Yes . . . a good number. . . ."

"Please don't tell me any more names . . . just let
me pretend that we're all here together like we were
in the past . . . one close family."

As they passed the bus stop on their way to the car,
she asked if he remembered her parting words when he
left so many years ago.

"I remember," he replied.

"I was right, wasn't I?"

"Yes, you were right. But you were always a lucky
guesser!"

"That wasn't luck, Ronny. I saw in you the ability,
the intelligence, and the burning desire to reach for
the stars. I'm extremely proud of you." He had not
been called Ronny in years. They left Nahalal by car
and headed north to Kibbutz Ginosar. The morning
proved to be physically and emotionally exhausting for
both of them.

"Have you heard anything from your mother?" she
inquired as the car passed the town of Nazareth."

"No, I haven't heard from her in over eleven years.
I'm not even sure if she's aware of my father's death
four years ago."

"She lives with her American husband in Belgium now,
and she's very ill. In fact, she had heart surgery
last year--a double coronary bypass operation. I
received a letter from her husband a few months ago.
I got to know him well when he visited us in the
Kibbutz years ago."

"That's nice." Lapin replied, hoping she would
change the subject.

But Dina persisted. "Why don't you call her? I'm
sure she'd love to hear from you, especially when she
reads all about you in the newspaper."

"Dina, when I first saw my mother, I was eighteen,
lost, and alone. But I was delighted to have a chance
to know my real mother and put to rest my imaginary
substitutes. She promised to send me to medical
school in the United States and I was the happiest man
alive. Then a month after leaving Israel--which for

235

me was the most difficult decision that I've ever had to make in my life--my mother informed me that she wasn't going to send me to medical school after all."

"Did she give you any explanation, any reason?"

"She simply said my younger half brother came first and that they were going to save the money for his schooling. That was it."

"Why did you leave their home?"

"My stepfather--her husband--gave me a choice of either joining the American Army or leaving. So I left . . . and worked my way through Monmouth College and Indiana University Medical School."

"And did you enjoy it?"

"I loved the studies, once I got a handle on the English language. That was the tough part. I didn't, however, enjoy starving or living on less than minimum wage for eight years to accomplish it. But with God's help, I managed."

"I can see that. Are you sure you don't want me to give you your mother's address?"

"You could probably be a good matchmaker, Dina, if you decide one day to leave the Kibbutz; but in this case, the answer is still no. I've lived through too many disappointments . . . far too many . . . from both parents. The birthdays without celebrations or presents. No one around for parents' day in school. No one there at graduation. Then my very own mother teamed up with Ari's mother to prevent him from coming to stay with me. The way that I see it, my father is dead and my mother is just a mirage, and a bad one at that."

"I hate to see you so bitter, Ronny. I wish you could see life in a more optimistic light."

"I'm old enough to know better--and yet--still young enough to dream. But, Dina, long ago I substituted my rose-colored glasses with two very black eyes."

They walked a few steps in silence. Then Dina spoke, "How's Ari?"

"He's great. He's finishing his first year in college and taking up classical music, playing both the piano and the clarinet."

"The apple doesn't fall far from the tree."

"He's very happy in school, and I'm delighted that he decided not to pursue medicine."

"But why?" she asked in amazement.

"Because I want him to enjoy his life."

236

"Was it really all so difficult for you, Ronny?"

"It wasn't easy," he concluded in what was to be the greatest understatement of the day.

After meeting Dina's family in their modest apartment situated on the shores of beautiful Lake Tiberias, they all went up to the communal dining room for lunch. Dina was radiant as she introduced him to her friends, many of whom knew all about him from recent newspaper articles and radio broadcasts.

Later that afternoon they drove up to the military cemetery. It was built in an olive grove on the side of a gentle hill overlooking the valley and lake below. They had come to visit the final resting place of his two fallen roommates. A warm breeze seesawed to and fro as they stood by the graves with bowed heads. The essence of the moment was captured. As he laid a single white carnation on each headstone, he could only bring himself to mumble, "What a waste . . . what a waste. . . ." Dina finally led him away.

They drove off to visit Vaspi's widow and her three boys. Sarah had also been a classmate of his. Lapin anticipated seeing bitterness or accusation in her eyes, but found only warmth and friendliness. Over coffee and fresh fruit, they spent the afternoon reminiscing about old times. She told him that since her husband's death nine years ago, her youngest son sits by the window overlooking the Golan Heights, awaiting his father's return.

A number of other classmates living in the surrounding settlements began drifting in to join the impromptu homecoming celebration for the long-lost member of the class.

He was exhausted when he returned to the Tel Aviv Hilton late that evening. Before leaving Dina, he promised to meet her in his hotel on Monday evening so she could attend the lecture he'd be giving to all ten Witness congregations.

The lecture to the army medical corps turned out to be an interesting scientific duel between Lapin and a major who endorsed a different system of blood substitution. That system, relying on blood as its primary source, was based on obtaining the free hemoglobin directly from the blood. Neither man was able to budge the other from his stand, but the audience was able to observe the fine art of playing mental chess. Impressed with Lapin's thinking, the major suggested that he train some new battalion surgeons in his techniques. Lapin gratefully accepted.

Following the lecture, he asked the driver to take him to the home where his grandmother had raised him. It was one of the first houses built in the city of Ramat-Gan about fifty years ago.

When they arrived, he found that it had been abandoned and condemned. The property had been sold, and an apartment building was scheduled to be built on the grounds once the house was leveled and the old orange grove in the back yard was uprooted. As he walked through what remained standing of the old house, he remembered many things he'd long since buried in the depths of his subconscious mind. Still standing in the back yard was the old oak tree on which he had built his first tree house and swung from branches pretending to be Tarzan.

He could still remember every crack in the trunk and the exact location of each branch. To the young driver's amazement, Lapin took off his shoes and began climbing the trunk of his old, silent, leafy friend. Halfway up, he came upon a carving he had made some twenty-six years ago. It was a heart surrounding the names Miri and Ronny.

He ran his finger over the letters he'd carved for his first love and wondered what had become of her. He remembered her beautiful golden hair and deep blue eyes. He remembered how much he'd wanted to marry her and how she had longed to have his children. He also remembered not being able to tell her that he was leaving Israel in search of a medical career and chose instead to tell her in the letter he mailed after he'd left the country.

I wonder where she is now, he thought, running his fingers across the letters as he traced the outline of the carved heart. He felt the pain of stark loneliness. He had had many casual relationships, but still continued to search for intimacy of the heart, for bonding, for stability, for a commitment . . . but could find none.

There was a definite void in his life, a vacuum which needed to be filled. But as the years passed, he found that satisfying his needs became an elusive fantasy. Oh, how he wished he could go back those twenty-six years for even the briefest of moments . . . to walk down the street holding hands with

Miri. . . . But he was never again to capture the intensity of those feelings.

The driver gave him a thumbs-up signal as he swung from branch to branch, completed a perfect flip and landed on the ground in an upright position. He photographed the house from every angle so that he could show it to Ari when he returned to America. He tried so very hard to capture mementos of his broken dreams with 35mm living-color slides.

On Sunday, Lapin drove down to the ancient fortress of Masada where a handful of Jewish Zealots had held off the mighty Roman legion for many months. Finally, when it became apparent that they would be conquered, they had all chosen to commit suicide rather than be taken as prisoners and forced to violate their religious convictions.

As he walked among the ancient ruins, he recaptured the spirit of defiance all over again. He vowed to continue fighting for human and religious rights as his ancient forefathers had done, regardless of the price--any price--that he might personally have to pay.

After a two-hour press conference on Monday, he and Dina had dinner before going to his scheduled lecture. As they entered the large auditorium, over 800 people stood up and gave them a standing ovation. Lapin was choked with emotion while Dina had no difficulty showing her pride. He spoke in Hebrew for two hours explaining all of the problems that Witnesses should be aware of before entering a hospital: how to avoid court orders, how to select a physician, and how to practice preventive medicine. He informed them with joy that Ben-Gurion University would now accept them as patients and respect their stand on blood transfusions.

His last statement brought down the house! It took a number of attendants well over five minutes to quiet everyone so that he could continue. After the lecture, he stayed more than an hour to shake each person's hand and answer all their questions.

He and Dina were finally ready to leave when an old Arab gentleman walking with a cane approached them and said, "My name is Yusef and I am a Palestinian from Jerusalem. I was born in Jaffa and was a pharmacist all of my life. I got my first job as an assistant from your grandfather, Aaron Lapin, who owned the only pharmacy in Tel Aviv in those days. I'm sure Aaron would be proud of the sacrifices his grandson is making to defend people who are not even Jews and proud that you are following in his footsteps."

"My dear friend," Lapin said with a trembling voice, "I hope that my grandfather in heaven will use all of his influence with God to protect me and my team as we continue to fight for the rights of Jehovah's Witnesses so that maybe one day they can be treated as equals regardless of their stand on blood."

"*Inshallah* (God willing)," the man replied.

"*Inshallah*," Lapin responded.

* * *

"I don't know when I'll be back," he told Dina prior to boarding the flight to L.A.

"I hope it won't take you another twenty-four years. I don't think I'll live that long."

"I'll keep in touch," he promised.

"This country needs you, Ronny, and I think that you need it. Why don't you think about finally coming home?"

"My home is in Los Angeles, and I am an American citizen," he said proudly.

"That may very well be true but you will always be a Sabra . . . and when you realize that you will come back to your roots."

"God bless you, Dina. And will you please do me a favor and lose some weight." The two embraced tenderly while tears of affection filled their eyes. Then he turned and raced up the ramp.

The flight was pleasant; the weather, beautifully calm. After finishing lunch, Lapin fully reclined his seat and placed the headset on his ears. He dialed from channel to channel until he found some classical music, then peacefully drifted off into a light sleep.

The plane was only three and a half hours away from Los Angeles. He instinctively knew this would be his last chance to get some "shut-eye" before the unrelenting, never-ending race began anew. His serene state of mind was jolted back to consciousness by a distressed voice over the P.A. system, "Is there a doctor on board? If you are a doctor or a medic, please identify yourself to one of the flight attendants."

He reluctantly left his seat, still not completely awake, and rushed to the nearest stewardess. After he

240

identified himself, she ushered him into the main cabin where an elderly man was stretched out on the floor and was experiencing a full respiratory arrest. With tears streaming down her cheeks, the man's wife anxiously begged for someone to come to his aid. Several people watched helplessly as one bystander who seemed to know what he was doing leaned over the man and offered assistance.

The scene caused Lapin to shift instantly into high gear as he pushed through the crowd to get to the victim. Ignoring the horrified expressions of passengers sitting on both sides of the aisle, Lapin kneeled at the man's head and immediately extended his neck in order to establish an airway.

"What happened to him?" he quickly asked.

"We were having lunch," the wife responded in a trembling voice, "and suddenly he started to turn blue. Then he started to choke and just collapsed. Please do something, doctor. For the love of God, please save him! He's the only thing I have."

Lapin identified himself to the other man kneeling near the victim's chest. The man in turn responded, "I'm Dr. Roberts. I'm an obstetrician and gynecologist."

"Nice to meet you." Lapin's calm demeanor under the circumstances was bewildering to those standing within earshot. "Help me raise him up a little bit," Lapin requested, glad to have another physician on board.

"What are you going to do?" Roberts asked.

"I suspect he choked on some food and that it's probably stuck in his throat. I'm going to try to get it out."

"But are we covered by any insurance if we do anything on board this aircraft?" Roberts' voice had more than a ring of concern to it.

"I don't care about insurance coverage now. This man isn't breathing! If you don't want to help me, get out of the way and I'll do it alone." Lapin proceeded to stick his fingers down the man's throat. He tried to fish out the bolus blocking the man's trachea, but try as he might, he couldn't dislodge that soft mass of chewed food. He raised the victim to a sitting position, wrapped his arms tightly under the man's ribcage, then squeezed forcefully. A gust of air . . . and then a large piece of meat shot out of the victim's mouth. As he began to breathe and moan, his bluish color started returning to normal.

241

His wife managed a sigh of relief before she passed out onto the floor beside him. She was carried to the nearest vacant seat and cared for by a flight attendant.

Dr. Roberts stood watching as the man resumed breathing at a normal rate. A few minutes later, the man was lead to the seat beside his wife to finish recovering. She grasped Lapin's hands and kissed them while the other passengers cheered. Through tears she managed to get out, "I don't know how to thank you for what you've done, but we'd love to have you visit us at our ranch in Santa Barbara any time you can. We've been married nearly forty years, and thanks to you, we'll hopefully have a few more."

Shaking hands, Lapin promised the elderly gentleman that he'd check on him from time to time during the flight's duration. Dr. Roberts followed along as Lapin headed back to his own seat. "Can I talk to you for just a minute?" he asked.

"Sure. Let's go to the upstairs lounge and have a drink. I think I could use one right about now."

They walked up the spiral staircase of the 747 and approached the bar. "What will you have?" Roberts asked.

"Oh, I think a glass of white wine would suit me just fine."

"Two glasses of white wine," Roberts ordered.

They sat across from each other near the window. Lapin raised his glass and announced, "*L'chaim.*" Lapin could see that the word was unfamiliar to Dr. Roberts, so he clarified it. "*L'chaim* . . . to life."

"I'm really sorry about what happened down there with the old man," Roberts began, "but you have to understand that I've just recently moved to California, and in a few months I'm scheduled to take my board examinations in OB-GYN. I just didn't want to do something that might hurt my chance of passing that exam." Lapin raised an eyebrow at his fellow physician. "You know, anything like a malpractice suit or an adverse report to the medical board."

"Oh, yes," Lapin replied sarcastically, "the eminent board examinations. We must not tamper with those."

"Do you have your boards?" Roberts asked.

"What's your first name, Dr. Roberts?" Lapin said, avoiding the question.

"John."

242

"Well, mine is Ron. But listen, John, if you really are interested and think you might not be able to sleep tonight without knowing, I'll tell you that I do indeed have my boards . . . in general surgery, abdominal surgery, and neurological and orthopedic surgery."

"It's probably tough for you to understand my insecurity in this matter, Ron, since you've already established yourself and achieved this goal."

"Well, I'll tell you," Lapin said with a sigh. "I guess we all march to a different drummer. But that old man down there could care less about boards and security. All he really needed right then was for somebody to care enough to help save his life and to at least establish an airway so he could breathe."

The two doctors studied each other intently. Lapin continued, "And isn't that the reason you and I went to medical school? Or have we lost the real meaning of our profession somewhere between the courses in anatomy and medical jurisprudence?"

"What makes you so tough, doctor?"

"I guess it's the rusty nails I eat every morning for breakfast," Lapin replied. "I just can't stand cornflakes."

"But aren't you afraid of being sued and losing everything you've worked so hard to get?"

"Listen, *boychik*, take my advice; you can't go through life worrying about malpractice suits. Suing doctors is becoming a favorite American pastime. It's even more prevalent in bad economic times. But it will always be around, as long as there are lawyers. You don't need to do anything wrong to be named in a suit, and there's not much you can do to gain total immunity unless you stop practicing. So why don't you quit worrying about it so much and just do your best."

Roberts, sounding somewhat naive, injected, "You can protect yourself by keeping good records. . . ."

Lapin's face softened. It was a nice thought. "There's no chart in the world that can't be taken apart by a sharp attorney and presented in a fashion that makes you appear not only negligent, but incompetent as well."

"Have you ever been sued?"

"Oh, a few times," he answered, with subtle irony.

"How did it make you feel?"

"That's a good question . . . and I'll tell you. First you get angry, then hostile, then anxious and resentful. Then as time goes on and you get back to taking care of patients, you just leave it alone and let the attorneys fight it out among themselves."

"I don't feel as complacent about that as you do, but then I guess that's part of my background."

"What about your background?" Lapin asked.

"Well, I graduated from Princeton with a B.S. degree. Then my father, a successful internist and influential alumnus, got me into Harvard Medical School. After graduation I married Diane, who's the only daughter of a Bostonian millionaire industrialist. I spent five long, hard years in postgraduate training in OB-GYN at New York University. Just recently I joined a four-man group in Beverly Hills and have been very careful to do just the right things. My wife and I belong to the right organizations and we try to be seen in the best of social circles. All this will hopefully insure us of a highly successful and very profitable future."

Lapin frowned. "Oh, my God, John, I hope your illness is curable. Being here with you is about as close to medical royalty as I've ever come. I can tell with some degree of certainty that your blue chip myopic vision distorts the way you perceive reality."

"What kind of background do you come from?" Roberts had completely missed the childish sarcasm in Lapin's exchange.

"I was raised on a farm in Israel. I came to America with stars in my eyes and a head full of fantasies about being the first one in my family to ever become a doctor. I had no money, no family, no home . . . and my English was terrible. I worked my way through Monmouth College in West Long Branch, New Jersey, then through the Indiana University School of Medicine. Actually, a good number of my classmates came from farms and they became excellent doctors even though they didn't graduate from Harvard."

"How old are you?"

"How old do you think I should be?"

"I guess you're older than you look."

"I'm forty years old," Lapin said.

"My God, that's hard to believe. Your background is so incredible. How'd you manage to do all of it alone?"

"I used an old Jewish weapon called 'chutzpah' to accomplish it."

"What's that?"

244

"*Chutzpah* is when you kill both your parents and throw yourself on the mercy of the court on the grounds that you're an orphan," Lapin mused.

Roberts chuckled and offered, "You sound so Jewish."

"You're not so bad for a '*goy*' either."

"A *goy?*" Roberts questioned, clearly not under-standing.

"Yes, anyone who buys retail."

They were both laughing as the captain came out of the cockpit and walked over to the two of them. He shook both of their hands and thanked them for saving the passenger's life.

"That's okay," Lapin replied. "We needed some excitement to break the monotony of the long flight."

"The entire flight crew wishes to extend their appreciation. We're grateful for what you did. Thanks again, gentlemen," the pilot concluded, "and God bless you." He went back off to the cockpit.

Lapin sat back in his seat, and Roberts asked, "Are you married?"

"No . . . no, I'm not."

"Boy, I have a dynamite lady for you to meet. She's good looking, high society--the whole enchilada. And she's available, too."

"Sounds great, John, thanks; but it just won't work."

"Why . . . why's that?"

"Because a bird can love a fish, but where would they build a home?"

"Oh well, it was just a thought."

"And I thank you very much for it. Really."

Roberts got up, brought the open bottle of wine from the bar, and refilled the glasses. As he sat down he asked, "Do you have a very busy practice, Ron?"

"I sure do! We have lots of 'nobody's people' coming to us from all over the United States and even abroad."

"What do you mean by 'nobody's people'?"

"I operate primarily on Jehovah's Witnesses. I've coined the term for them because they get no political and very little medical support for their stand against blood transfusions."

"My God!" Roberts exclaimed. "You're the one I've been reading about in the papers and seen on televison. You're the bloodless surgeon who's taking on the State of California to fight for the Jehovah's

Witnesses' civil rights."

"That's me," Lapin said with a grin.

"You know, my partners and I were discussing you in the office just last week. Our senior partner feels you represent a terrible threat to the medical profession and to the Red Cross by your stand against using blood transfusions. He thinks a lot of doctors view what you do as a blatant slap in the face because you have the audacity to operate on cases that they're afraid to touch."

Roberts squinted as he searched through his memory, then went on. "My partner played golf one day with an Orange County surgeon who's heavily involved politically with the Medical Association and who also knows people on the Board of Surgery. He said he'd cause you problems in Orange County and try to stop you from getting your boards."

Lapin smiled. "I'm not a newcomer to prejudice. I've tasted the bitter flavor of second-class citizenship more than once. I've had the hospital where I worked raided by the Board of Health, who in turn broke countless laws and repeatedly violated every principle of decency. I've had my patients' charts copied without authorization and given to the Board of Medical Quality Assurance--the medical Gestapo agency--for prosecution. That simple act violated the basic rights of privacy guaranteed to each and every one of us. I've had State investigators harass patients, hoping to persuade them to testify against me. I've had the Attorney General's Office withhold information they gathered about me and then deny ever having it. All I can tell you is that someone wants to get to the Jehovah's Witnesses--through me--in the worst way. And, you know, the saddest part is that we'll probably never really know who or why."

"Ron, that's terrible." Robert's voice conveyed his sincerity. "I wish I could do something to help."

"Thank you. I appreciate that. I really do."

"Why don't you just get on the staff of one of the large hospitals or universities? I'm sure that they'd love to have you and your experience." Roberts thought for a fleeting second about what he'd just said, and added, "Then again, maybe they wouldn't."

"And maybe in a few years," Lapin said, "physicians will recognize the advantages of transfusionless surgery. Hopefully they will admit to themselves, and

246

their patients, that blood can be very dangerous, especially with volunteer donors. Maybe then they'll agree that better surgical techniques and transfusion alternatives such as 'artificial blood' should be explored. Maybe then my ideas--all the things I've spent the last ten years of my life fighting for-- will be accepted in academic circles. And, maybe then, the JWs will be able to walk into any hospital and be treated with dignity and with the highest standard of medicine. Until then, I will have to endure the isolation and the personal attacks on me and my patients. Until then, I'll continue to take the least traveled road."

"Do you really feel that blood is over utilized in the United States?"

"Absolutely," Lapin replied. "I definitely do. Last year alone, twelve million units of blood were transfused into patients who were given little information by their attending physicians about the danger of blood. Basing these figures on my personal experience, I'm certain that over seventy-five percent of the blood being given is not really necessary. A lot of physicians rely on transfusions not necessarily to make the patient better, but to soothe their own consciences. I look at a blood transfusion as a liquid organ transplant with its consortium of possible complications. Two hundred years ago, the medical standard of care was blood letting; today, it is blood transfusion. Perhaps our experience will help educate other doctors to understand that it's best to work with what blood is available in the patient at that time, and not to take some out or add some back."

"Would you let a patient die on the table without transfusing him if you thought that blood might save his life?" Roberts asked cautiously.

"Fortunately, I've never had to do that. But if the situation arose and the patient had signed a release form, I would then allow him to die in accordance with his wish to uphold his religious beliefs. No doctor can guarantee beyond-the-shadow-of-a-doubt that a patient will live if he is transfused, or die if he isn't. Logically then, it's better that the chance patient die than to take away each and every patient's fundamental right to refuse a particular medical procedure."

"You really feel that strongly against blood

transfusions?"

"Yes, I do. I don't feel it's a great shame to transfuse other patients who will accept it, but neither is it a great honor. The best way a surgeon can avoid giving blood to a patient is to avoid losing so much of it in the first place."

"That makes a lot of sense to me," Roberts said. "If only our colleagues would really want to work that way. . . ."

"It's hard to understand why some doctors can't comprehend that the head bone is connected to the heart bone."

"How true," Roberts said with conviction.

"Watch out for yourself, John," Lapin said. "Once you get bitten by the 'bloodless bug,' your life will never be the same."

"If the 'bug' makes sense . . . then I welcome the challenge."

The "fasten your seatbelt" light came on, signaling the plane's preparation to land in Los Angeles. Both doctors, now friends, got up and returned to their seats below. Approaching the spiral staircase, John placed his hand on Lapin's shoulder and said, "I can't remember the last time I learned so much from one individual in such a short period of time. I'd like to thank you for taking the time to talk with me. In the near future, I'd appreciate coming to Bellflower City Hospital to watch you work."

"You will be welcomed as a friend."

"Stay well and keep on fighting. I know you'll be victorious in the end."

"Thanks, John . . . you, too. And have a safe landing."

11

Lapin landed in Los Angeles with pride in his heritage, a sense of belonging, and renewed vigor. Above all, he returned determined to continue fighting for his beliefs, regardless of the price he might have to pay.

Jodie met him at the airport and helped load his suitcases into her car. When she started the engine, he wearily asked, "What's happening?"

"Oh, not much," she replied, but her face told him differently.

"What's going on, Jodie?" he said.

"Okay," she answered as she exhaled deeply. "The State filed another accusation against you. It's based on information supplied by the two rats, Donnelly and Rana. I wish you'd have Garner sue the hell out of them. Rana took a complete chart without authorization from the patient and apparently handed it over to BMQA without even being asked. Isn't that a little unusual?"

"Highly unusual," Lapin sighed. "With regards to which patient?"

"Rusty," she replied.

"Rusty?" he said in amazement. "You can't be serious! That's the boy who accidentally shot himself four years ago and was bleeding from stomach ulcers. We transferred him from Santa Fe with a hemoglobin of six. I remember him well because I was at home when I made the arrangments for him. During one phone call, I had to listen to the boy's own doctor tell me I was a criminal for treating him without blood. That was all going on while my ex-wife roamed through the house with her clipboard, telling me which possessions I'd get to keep. Remember that?"

"That's the one," Jodie replied in agreement.

"So what's their complaint?" " "
"They allege he didn't need surgery."
"Like hell he didn't. He was unstable when he came to us. More than half of his circulating blood was gone, and he had a hemoglobin count of six grams. The diagnosis of multiple ulcers was reconfirmed before we operated on him. After we brought the bleeding ulcers under control, he did well . . . hell, he did great . . . and then he left. I suppose they would have liked me to get a court order for blood or, worse yet, just let the boy die. Great. I can just see the headlines in *The Register* now, "Lapin Lets Young JW Die Without Giving Blood Transfusion." He shook his head in dismay. At first he felt it was all starting over, but quickly realized it wasn't actually starting over, it was just continuing. "Oh, Jodie . . . what's the use. Maybe I should just give up."

"Over my dead body, you will," she said as she pulled her car to the side of the road and stopped. Lapin had just had a gigantic bubble of happiness burst in his face and now felt the tiring effects of the long flight. He was in no mood for a lecture from her, but knew it was still coming.

Trying to prevent her frontal attack, he stressed, "Jodie, I'm just tired of constantly coming home time after time to find someone else trying to stab me in the back. The State just keeps coming at me from all directions. They have an unlimited supply of money and full use of attorneys paid for by the taxpayers. Now they have Donnelly and Rana adding more fuel to the fire. They're both just trying to save their worthless skins by providing the State with absurd information that's completely false." He grimaced and shook his head again. "I'm one man alone trying to physically, emotionally, and financially mount a defense against incredible odds. It's just a little too much for me to deal with single-handedly."

"Listen, Dr. Lapin, I've worked for you for nine years because I think you're the best surgeon in the area, probably in the whole world. You love your patients, and you know they'll follow you to the end of the earth. So stop feeling sorry for yourself and go out there like the fighter you are. Beat those worthless State bureaucrats and win big!"

"You know, Jodie, you're okay . . . for a woman," he concluded as he suppressed a big smile.

Jodie stared straight ahead through the windshield,

stifling a smile of her own. "That's what I've always loved about you, doc; you're really a devout male chauvinist masquerading as a physician."

They sat in silence for a moment, savoring the reinforcement they gleaned from each other's words. Jodie started the car and weaved her way back into traffic. Lapin was on the road again.

**

Hutchins had been admitted to Skyline Hospital three days before Lapin returned from Israel, and he was being prepped to have his aortic valve replaced. Lapin was gravely concerned about his long-time friend facing major surgery at his age.

Some team members felt Herk shouldn't risk the surgery. If he died, they reasoned, Lapin would lose his major source of support and a strong voice in denouncing the unjust claims against him. But Lapin only wanted what was best for Herk. He knew Herk needed this particular surgery badly. He had even urged it for some time now.

Lapin came to the hospital early the day of the surgery and stayed with Herk until he was wheeled into the surgical suite. Herk remained jovial right up until he was put under the anesthetic, but his loving wife, Marilyn, was a nervous wreck. Lapin, again at Herk's side, held his hand and said, "Go to sleep, you old crow, go to sleep now. Everything is going to be fine."

The surgery was carried out with efficiency and speed . . . and without blood. His aortic valve had nearly filled with calcium deposits and was replaced with a mechanical valve. There was no obstruction on the under surface of the valve as was previously suspected.

Herk's recovery went so well that he was back assisting Lapin in surgery in only five short weeks.

Two days after Herk's release from Skyline, the State Board of Health descended in force on Bellflower Hospital. They professed having a serious complaint about the hospital itself, but, as usual, produced nothing to validate their statements. An onslaught was once again in the making, and now as Lapin passed their investigators in the hallway, his anger and frustration dangerously reached the boiling point. *Why can't they just leave the Witnesses alone? Why*

251

can't they pick on somebody else for a change?

He invited the principal doctor on the investigative team to observe his surgery, but only after he had received permission from the patient. "They might as well watch what we do, and hopefully they won't be so eager to criticize," he told the team.

A difficult resection of a cancerous esophagus was preformed in minimal time with little blood loss.

"He was very impressed," Dixie said as the State doctor left the surgery suite.

Lapin's face remained grim. "They said they were impressed at Esperanza, too."

Mr. Needman, the administrator, stood firm and blocked investigators from copying patients' charts without authorization. The State proceeded to serve the hospital with an endless barrage of broad, ambiguous subpoenas. They finally left after two weeks of intensive investigation, only to come back a month later, in June, with yet more subpoenas.

The administration at Bellflower, aware of Esperanza's mistake in permitting the investigators to do whatever they wished, held their ground. They restricted the State's requests to the point of protecting the patients' privacy and civil rights.

***

Pat Earley and her husband, Scott, lived in Phoenix, Arizona, with their two children. Their lives were peaceful and orderly. They spent many hours studying the Bible with various individuals who were interested in the Truth.

Helping spread the Truth to a worldly society brought them incomparable joy as their lives became enriched with real meaning and purpose. Pat was pregnant with their third child but continued to conduct her Bible studies right up until she went into labor on a Thursday late in February. She was cheerful as she checked into the hospital.

"This one is going to be a girl," she told Scott. But Scott looked worried and was rather nervous as he coached her through the pain.

Pat's labor progressed rapidly. Her pains were more intense and somehow different from her other two pregnancies. "This must be a large baby," she mumbled as she was being wheeled into the delivery room. Scott wasn't permitted to go in with her and paced relentlessly outside, biting his nails.

An hour later, the obstetrician came out with a distraught expression on his face. He informed the frantic husband of the difficult delivery, but said the infant--a good-sized baby girl--was all right. But then he said the mother's uterus might have ruptured, and that she'd lost a lot of blood and went into shock.

Scott was startled. "What can you do to stop the bleeding?"

"Nothing right now . . . she's just not stable enough to undergo an operation."

"Please, doctor, can you stabilize her?" he pleaded.

"Yes, we can. But we'll need your permission to give her at least four or five units of blood. Then she'll be ready for emergency surgery."

Scott thought about his wife and the children. He was a reasonable man, an understanding man. But to violate Jehovah's commandments . . . that he couldn't do, even if it means losing her in this system. He thought to himself, *I'll just see her in the New Order after the resurrection.* Then he said with resolve, "No, doctor, I can't do that. And she wouldn't want me to."

"Be reasonable, Mr. Earley. We can save her life with blood."

"No, doctor . . . absolutely not."

"I'm sorry then, but I think your wife's chance of survival is extremely slim. Her blood count is down to four-point-two grams and falling rapidly."

"Can you give her a blood substitute, or blood expanders, or something to build her blood back up quickly?"

"We're giving her everything we have," the doctor snapped. He was clearly angered at the suggestion.

"What about Fluosol, the new artificial blood they've used so successfully in California and other places?"

"I don't know much about it," the obstetrician replied indifferently.

"Well, can we get her out to California then?" Scott asked.

"I'm afraid she's not stable enough to move to the elevator, let alone fly four hundred miles."

"I'd like to call the doctors in California, if it's okay with you, just for some advice."

"You suit yourself, but I assure you they won't be

253

able to do anything for you." With that, the doctor angrily walked away.

***

Hutchins was helping Lapin remove a badly infected gall bladder from a seventy-three-year-old Mexican Witness. She had tried to treat her symptoms with a home remedy consisting of olive oil and lemon juice. This concoction probably helped rupture her gall bladder, but certainly didn't help dislodge the stones. Lying in the open bed of a truck, she crossed the California border illegally and came to Bellflower City Hospital.

The operation was difficult because inflammation made vital structures virtually impossible to identify. Lapin finally managed to remove the infected organ, stripping away the stones from her common bile duct and draining it to allow the infection to subside.

They were ready to close the abdominal incision when Mikie entered the room. "There's an emergency call for you in the hallway. The guy's very upset. He's crying, Dr. Lapin. Can you talk to him, please?"

"How's the patient, Fred?" he asked his trusted anesthesiologist.

"She's sure no rose, but she's stable."

"Mikie . . . tell the guy to hold, and ask Dr. Zia if he'll come in and scrub and help Hutchins close."

As Zia entered the operating room, Lapin hurried to the phone in the hallway. "This is Dr. Lapin. Can I help you?"

"I hope so, doctor, I sure hope so."

"Okay, okay, what's the problem?"

Scott quickly outlined Pat's situation and ended the conversation saying, "Her last blood count was two point five grams of hemoglobin. She looks terrible, doctor. She looks so white . . . and so hopeless."

"Listen to me, Scott, and listen very carefully. You have to be the strong one now because your wife can't help herself at this point."

"Tell me what to do."

"I suggest you make immediate arrangements for air transportation and get her out here now. We can't help her over the telephone."

"The doctor here warned me that she wouldn't make it if she was moved and that he wouldn't be responsible for her."

"Then you accept the responsibility, Scott. You sign her out of the hospital right now."

"I'll have to think about it," he said. "I'm just not sure what would be best for her."

"Okay, Scott, okay. You think about it. Then you call me back after you decide what you want to do . . . but, man, just do it quickly."

"I'll call you back," Scott promised.

When Lapin returned to the operating room, the patient's abdominal wall was nearly closed. He informed everyone that they might get another critical patient later that afternoon and asked them to stay in the hospital. No one grumbled except Garcia. "I don't know how you always manage to do it to me, Ron, but every time I have a hot date, you decide to fly in another one of your disaster cases."

"Oh, Fred," Lapin countered, "you love working here and you know it! You can't find this kind of stimulation and challenge anywhere else."

"Can't argue with that. I'll switch my date to later tonight and hang around. Maybe she'll offer to assist."

"That's great, Fred. I knew I could count on you," Lapin said with a conquering smile.

***

Scott Earley called Lapin back two hours later. "I've made the flight arrangements and we'll arrive in Long Beach at three p.m. Could you make arrangements for an ambulance to meet us there?"

"Don't worry, Scott," Lapin replied. "I'll be there with an ambulance when you land."

"Thank you, Dr. Lapin, thank you very much."

"Scott, is your wife still bleeding badly?"

"Yes, she is." He was hesitant for a second, wondering if he should continue. "Her blood count's down to two point four grams . . . her lower abdomen is real swollen."

Oh, my God, Lapin thought to himself, *how can this patient possibly still be alive? We're talking medical history here!* With much concern, he said, "Listen Scott, make sure they put a shock suit on your wife before her transfer. Then you'll have to be responsible for keeping it inflated."

"Okay, doctor, I'll do that."

Moments later, he found Garcia and Gough, the gynecologist, in the cafeteria. The three of them discussed the emergency case that was on its way. Gough reserved comment, but Garcia was vocal in his objections, saying, "Of all the crazy things I've watched you do, Ron, this is the craziest of all. Just how are you going to pull this one off?"

"Well, first, I'm trying to see if we can get some Fluosol for her. If we can't, we'll just go in through both flanks and tie off the internal iliac arteries that supply the ruptured uterus. That should shut off the blood supply to the damaged organ. Then all we can do is give her a massive dose of intravenous iron and folic acid, pray a lot, and hope for the best."

"Just that simple, huh?" Garcia responded. "I've never anesthetized a patient with a blood count that low. I want to go on record for telling you right now that I'm scared. Frankly, Ron, I'm real scared."

Lapin lowered his voice and calmly whispered, "Well, Fred, don't broadcast it over the P.A. system, but I get scared at times myself. Let's stop the bleeding. Let's just do it and get out."

Both were somewhat shaken when Gough dogmatically added, "I agree. This lady has only one chance in a million. I think she's fortunate to be coming to the surgeon who's had the greatest degree of experience with such acute problems. If surgery can possibly save her life, Ron is the one to do it."

That kind of praise from co-workers was an especially nice compliment. "Fred, why don't you and Gough stay here for a while? I'll get an ambulance and run over to Long Beach to meet the plane."

Later, as Lapin watched Pat being carried off the small private jet on a stretcher, he could only think, *Man! I've never seen anyone so white in my life.* She was coherent and somehow managed a faint smile. Her mother was along, holding her one-day-old granddaughter in her arms.

Lapin quickly assessed the situation. He confirmed that she was still losing blood vaginally and he decided to take her to surgery immediately to stop the bleeding.

Garcia was pacing the corridor of the surgical suite. "I can't believe I'm going to do this," he mumbled. "I can't believe I'm involved in this at all."

About the time that Pat was being anesthetized, Lapin went to the waiting room where about twenty Witnesses were in the midst of a Bible study. He asked the elder who was conducting the study if they could say a prayer for Pat, her family, and the operating crew. The group willingly obliged, and Lapin's confidence soared. After that prayer, he walked briskly toward the operating room. Fred had just about completed the anesthesia. Scott Earley was pacing in front of the operating room door, holding his newborn little girl in his arms. As Lapin passed by, Scott said, "Please do the best you can, doctor. I know she's in bad shape."

"Relax, Scott. She's going to be just fine . . . I know she will." Then as he began to scrub, a prayer passed over his lips.

Lapin realized that his patient couldn't tolerate a complete hysterectomy. He chose to stop the bleeding by making two flank incisions and tying off the major blood vessels that supply the uterus. The procedure was quick and virtually without blood loss since the patient had none to start with. At the time of surgery, the patient's hemoglobin had fallen to one-point-seven grams, no doubt one of the lowest blood counts in the history of modern medicine where an operation was not only successful . . . but completed without a blood transfusion.

As he and Hutchins were closing the incision, Lapin whispered, more to himself than anyone else in the room, "My God . . . I've never seen a live patient that didn't bleed when cut."

Pat was in the ICU for five days. She had received massive doses of intravenous iron, folic acid, steroids, B-12, and prayers. She recovered nicely and left the hospital with a hemoglobin count of seven-point-two grams nine days later.

Within the next ten days, Lapin received a thank you card and a picture of the entire family. He still treasures that photograph and keeps it on his office desk.

12

The alarm clock sounded on schedule at seven that Sunday morning. Lapin sat up in bed slowly and rubbed his tired eyes after yet another restless night. He forced himself into a shower of ice-cold water and instantly woke up. While drying off, he gazed out the large bedroom window overlooking sleepy Orange County. A flock of birds chirped happily in the avocado tree as they ushered in the August morning.

It's going to be a hot one today, he thought. Zipping up the jacket of his red and blue jogging suit, he sauntered down the stairs. Ethan was stretched out on the shaggy brown kitchen rug and only partially opened his honey-colored eyes when Lapin patted his head. He then rolled over lazily and continued to sleep. "You do that so well," Lapin said affectionately as he walked outside and closed the kitchen door behind him.

The heat was sweltering. A soft breeze coaxed the ageless palm trees to sway ever so gently.

He raised the garage door and slid into the gleaming white BMW. After one turn of the ignition the engine roared to life like a ferocious animal. Lapin loved the sound of a well-tuned engine. He enjoyed having the kind of power and speed behind him that was always ready to be unleashed and challenged on some unsuspecting road. He raced downhill, squeezing out every ounce of performance from the screaming motor while keeping a sharp eye open for the California Highway Patrol. He pulled up beside a late model blue Lincoln Continental with a personalized license plate, "GARNER," and parked.

Gerry's early this morning, he thought, as he pushed open the timeworn front door of Manny's Coffee Shop.

He looked for the telltale large blue cloud of cigar smoke overhanging the booths and found Garner engaged in a conversation with his favorite waitress. The two men had been meeting at Manny's every Sunday for the past fourteen months. During those brief encounters, Gerry Garner and Judy the waitress had developed a genuine, yet comical, love-hate relationship. He loved teasing her, and she hated putting up with it almost as much as she hated his cigars. As Lapin approached the booth he heard Garner say, "But, Judy, a five-dollar cigar couldn't possibly stink."

"I see nothing has changed here since last Sunday, so I must be in the right place." Lapin smiled at the frustrated young lady as he reached out warmly to shake Gerry's hand.

"No, nothing's changed, and Judy is still picking on me," Garner remarked with a suppressed smile.

"You've got to stop doing this to him, Judy," Lapin warned with a grin. "Don't you know he's a big attorney in town?"

"Big attorney, my foot," she shot back. "The next thing you'll tell me is that you're a doctor." Her winning smile beamed as she walked from the table.

Lapin wasn't quite finished with the ruse. "I was going to tell you that, Judy, but I didn't think you'd believe it."

As Lapin sat across from Garner and his fortress of paperwork, he said, "I can see by your gray and pink jogging outfit that we're not color-coordinated this morning."

"What's the matter, don't you like my tailor?" Garner replied in a deep Brooklyn accent.

"Your tailor I can live with; it's your taste I'm concerned about."

"What's wrong with my taste?" Gerry asked defiantly, relighting his soggy cigar and instantly filling the air with its pungent aroma.

"Nothing's wrong with your taste. Just do me a favor and don't wear that particular outfit to court next month when we take on the State. Heaven only knows I have enough problems already."

"Yes . . . and we'll talk about those problems this morning. But first, let's just have some breakfast."

Garner called for Judy to take their order, but she refused to walk over until he put out his cigar.

"Okay, okay, it's out," he grumbled. "I get no respect around here, no respect at all."

260

"Orange juice and coffee," Lapin said.

"Aren't you eating?" Garner asked.

"No, I'm not very hungry today."

"No wonder you always look so trim. I think it's disgusting." Garner studied the menu needlessly. After fourteen months, he knew it by heart. "Well, let's see. I guess I'll have a double order of sausage and some extra napkins. I just can't stand greasy things."

"You should talk," Judy said with a giggle.

"What did I tell you, Ron? I get no respect here at all."

After Judy walked away to place their order, Gerry called another waitress over and baited, "I just can't understand why Judy doesn't want to serve us. Just because I wouldn't leave my wife last year like she wanted me to during our affair is no excuse for not serving good-paying customers who tip well."

The waitress' ears perked up. Interest in hearing the latest gossip registered instantly on her face. Lapin was doing everything humanly possible to keep from bursting into uncontrollable laughter. As the waitress left their booth, he looked across at Garner and appreciatively remarked, "Gerry, you're something else. You're a real piece of work."

"I just try harder; that's all," he acknowledged with a grin.

Moments later, as if on cue, Judy stormed out of the kitchen, flung the food in front of them, and asked indignantly, "How could you tell that waitress such a story?"

"I just wanted to know the reason why you won't serve us."

"Well, good luck from now on," she mumbled as she disappeared behind the counter.

As they ate breakfast, Lapin recalled how he'd first met Gerry Garner two years before at Dr. Kaller's Fourth of July party. There was something about this burly guy with his Jewish modification of an Afro hair style and a mischievous smile that instantly captured Lapin's attention. As they sat around a small table near the crowded swimming pool--trying to converse over discordant sounds created by twenty children and a handful of adults frolicking in the water--Lapin had the pleasure of gaining insight into one of the sharpest legal minds around. He had always admired creative thinkers; but in Gerry, he saw the epitome, the zenith.

"You have a dissecting, diabolical mind," Lapin said, devouring a piece of barbequed roast beef. Garner seemed unimpressed by the compliment. He simply continued to drink his protein meal, determined to stick to his diet even in the thick of a hedonistic, gastronomic orgy.

He told Lapin that between his two offices--one in New York and the other in Fullerton, a distant suburb of Los Angeles--he'd amassed a flight schedule that could match or even surpass that of most commercial pilots.

In a most prophetic statement, Lapin told Garner before he left, "If I ever get into trouble, I mean real trouble, I'd like you to defend me."

"Be more than glad to. As a matter of fact, I'd be honored," Garner replied as the two shook hands.

Right then it didn't occur to Lapin just how soon he'd need Garner's services, or that they'd end up being the very closest of friends.

Their friendship sprang from deep mutual respect for one another's professional abilities, and was strengthened by their common Jewish heritage. It was brought more sharply into focus by other shared experiences: the seemingly tireless ability to be in perpetual motion and the shared background of having had a difficult childhood.

Meeting every Sunday morning in jogging suits for business and strategy sessions at a local truck stop could not be easily explained on the basis of eccentricity alone. It could, however, be viewed as part of their anti-establishment response to daily stress situations, coupled with an attempt to downplay external appearance as their fertile minds came together to plan and execute future moves.

As Lapin toyed with his coffee cup, Garner picked up one of his ever-present yellow legal pads and a black felt-tip pen.

"While you've been in Holland getting Fluosol approved over there, I've been doing some serious thinking about this whole stupid case with the State. Now I realize I'm not involved in saving lives like you are, but just the same. . . ."

"Whoa, wait just a minute, Gerry," Lapin interrupted. "In the immortal words of Robert Browning, 'All services rank the same with God. God's purpose, best and worst, are we. There is no last or first.' So do me a favor, will you, and cut out all this B.S."

"I've never known you to quote poetry before."

"And I've never known you to be self-deprecating," Lapin sternly replied.

"Well anyway," Garner said, "I'm having some problems with the case and I need your help in deciding which way to go with it . . . if we go at all."

"You're not talking about giving up and letting those pea-brain bureaucrats have their way, are you?" a startled Lapin asked.

"No, not quite, but there's one thing that concerns me most."

"And what's that?"

"I don't think you have a snowball's chance in hell to get a fair administrative hearing."

"Why not?"

"Because the administrative judge, the experts, and all the people who are after you are employed by the State."

"Can't we get a jury trial?"

"Maybe later, but not at this stage."

"Are you talking about another trial, or what?" Lapin asked, somewhat confused.

"I'm talking about another three or four trials in a legal process that could take as long as five years and that could go all the way to the Supreme Court. I'm also talking about legal fees which could cost you over a half million dollars."

"I beg your pardon."

"You heard me . . . a half million big ones."

Lapin was silent for a moment, reticent, reflective, concerned.

"What are my alternatives?"

"Well, Mr. Basket--who by the way is a bird watcher--is the assistant attorney general in charge of your case, and he admits he's had a few legal problems with it."

"Oh, yeah? What kind of problems?"

"First of all, they aquired records from Esperanza Hospital without the patients' permission. Second, not one of those patients filed a complaint or lawsuit, yet their charts are being used in an attempt to throw the book at you. Third, the Board of Health had absolutely no right to pass along patient information to the Board of Medical Quality Assurance for disciplinary action unless a patient complaint had been filed."

263

"Wait a minute, Gerry, wait just a minute. Let me get this straight. Here we have a consumer protection agency, this Board of Medical Quality Assurance, trying to protect consumers who haven't asked for any protection. Is that right?"

"That's a fair analysis of the situation."

"Can they use those patient records against me anyway--without the patients' authorization--and destroy the doctor-patient relationship in the process?"

"Uh huh. . . ."

"And they can also violate the Right of Privacy Act passed by the California voters in the early seventies?"

"Look, the law is real vague about all this, but I think some local judges would rule that, even though the State obtained the records illegally, they can use them now that they have them."

"But suppose we were talking about criminal proceedings. Could the prosecution use evidence obtained illegally in its case?"

"Absolutely not," Garner replied. "In another case, we filed a motion on this issue--together with a complaint from another surgeon's patient who doesn't want her records made public. She also doesn't want them used against her attending physician, a doctor for whom she has nothing but respect and high regards."

"Are we living in the U.S.S.R. under the thumb of the KGB or in the land of the free and the home of the brave?"

"Geography has nothing to do with the facts," Garner said, "and the facts are that when State officials hide behind badges and blatantly abuse their authority, they can do anything they want in the name of protecting the public."

"But don't they have rules or laws or guidelines that they have to follow as an enforcement agency?"

"Ron, they didn't follow the rules. In your case, they even broke their own guidelines. They gave the case to an assistant district attorney from another county in order to keep the investigation quiet. They never talked with you before filing their charges. They withheld information that you needed in order to defend yourself in court, all the while denying that they had it."

Lapin sighed and shook his head. Garner continued with much empathy, "Do you remember it taking four separate court appearances and a judge telling the A.G.'s office that they were totally wrong in the way they handled your case, and that the attorney general himself needed a defense lawyer? Only after facing a contempt-of-court rap did the records begin to slowly appear out of nowhere. Can't you see that they've placed themselves above the law by pulling all the strings and flaunting their invincibility in everyone's faces."

"Gerry, we just have to challenge them. We have to stop them, because, to me, the Board of Medical Quality Assurance is still not synonymous with God."

"No, it's not," Garner barked in controlled anger. "But they're trying hard to place it in that role."

"What if, for example, one of my Witness patients was hooked on heroin before she was baptized? What if she had had an illegal abortion and a case of syphilis? What if she later changed her way of life and chose not to let her husband know about her shady, sordid past, but did in fact tell all to her physician? Now, in comes the State. They decree that this patient has no rights when it comes to keeping her past medical history confidential. As a matter of fact, they conclude that she's even incapable of deciding for herself whether or not she needed surgery. Then the State makes her case history part of public record. Are you telling me the patient is helpless in stopping this atrocity?"

Garner emitted another heavy sigh. "Unfortunately, that's the situation."

"Gerry, you know that I have some patients like that in my practice. The way I look at it, I have a responsibility and an obligation to protect their right to privacy, no matter what it costs."

"I'm glad you feel that way, Ron. I really am. I think it's admirable."

"Why can't we simply have the patients who are involved in this case come to court and testify? Stating the facts about their condition before and after surgery should clean up this entire matter."

"Seems like a good idea, but it really won't help that much. I found out the State's position after my last case with Basket. Much to my dismay, they say a patient is incapable of deciding whether they need surgery or not. One of the State's experts testified that a patient suffering from a bad gall bladder would claim that he'd improved if the surgeon had removed

265

his arm. Think about that for a second. I'm serious."

"Okay, then how about all the medical and surgical authorities we have lined up to testify for us?"

"Well, as you already know, one well-known surgeon who operated on several Witnesses refuses to testify because he doesn't want to get involved."

"I saw his letter," Lapin said, "and I was very disappointed by his decision. I'm sure the Witnesses would share my reaction if they knew about it."

"Well, that's another problem for another day. What we need now is to concentrate on finding everything that will help us, including experts who are willing to testify. This might theoretically include testimony from the writing and directing staffs of the television show *MASH* about battlefield surgery done outside the medical standard of care. You know, it's interesting that those army surgeons got medals for trying to work with what they had available, and you get kicked in the face for trying to do the exact same thing."

"What's your overall assessment about the hearing? What do you think?"

"I think you have two chances to get a fair hearing, slim and none."

"Gosh, thanks for the encouragement."

"Listen, I'm not trying to be nice, just honest. It's about time someone spoke to you like a Dutch uncle. You'd never believe how biased the judge was in the last case I defended against Basket. Remember now that that case had nothing to do with you or the Witnesses or bloodless surgery. So . . . when out of the blue the A.G. asked one of my experts if he'd had any financial dealings with you, I was sure the judge would disallow it. But he didn't. He then proceeded to allow other unrelated questions about you in someone else's case. The other poor doctor's case--a man, by the way, who was accused of being negligent and incompetent just so the State could show that they weren't simply picking on you--should easily be won by us on the basis of facts. But who knows when you're up against a kangaroo court."

"Why don't we force the State to play fair by asking for television coverage of the entire proceedings?"

"On the surface that sounds like a great idea," Garner answered, "but be honest with yourself. What network would suddenly become interested when all three major networks have already shot entire programs

266

about the problems experienced by the Witnesses and
yourself and then shelved them? Not even one station
aired the program . . . not one. You have to face it,
Ron. This whole problem generates very little public
interest. Now if you were treating extra-terrestrial
patients, that could possibly change things a little."

"You mentioned before that there may be at least one
more trial. How do you figure that?" Lapin asked.

"Well, let's say a miracle happens and the judge
hearing your case makes his recommendation in your
favor. The Board of Medical Quality Assurance won't
have to accept it, and they can go ahead and suspend
you anyway. Even if the BMQA and the judge both rule
for you, the attorney general will no doubt appeal.
I'm quite confident about this because he has nothing
to lose except tons of the taxpayers' money."

"Then what?"

"Well, if they all rule against us, we'll appeal. So
you can see that this is only the preliminary battle.
It's by no means the main event."

"How long should the first hearing last?"

"At least nine months."

"You're kidding. That's incredible."

"That's right, but that's how the law works."

"What are our chances in an appellate hearing?"

"Excellent, providing we build a good record in the
administrative hearing."

"Well, that at least sounds good," Lapin said,
expressing relief.

"One of my deepest concerns," Garner added, "is that
they'll attempt to destroy your credibility with
tremendous adverse publicity."

"Is there any way we can stop them?"

"No, not a chance."

"That's right. No one interferes with freedom of the
press," Lapin added sarcastically.

"Just as sure as you know what sells newspapers, you
can count on seeing your name in the press for at
least nine months. And, my friend, it's bound to hurt
you. People in general believe most anything they see
in print."

Lapin was struggling, reaching, grasping. "What
about the ACLU? Have we heard from them?"

"You can forget about civil liberties . . . unless
you bus your Witness patients from L.A. to Bellflower
and operate on them while wearing Nazi uniforms--with
the Jewish community marching outside. I suspect

that might be enough to attract some help."

It was quiet for a moment. Lapin had seemingly run out of questions, but then one more came to mind. "Can anyone else help, Gerry? Anyone?"

"Maybe Jehovah will," Garner replied with a frown.

"Seriously, Gerry, seriously."

"The sad thing about this whole mess is that Witnesses don't generate any public support or sympathy. Consider the following facts: they don't vote, they don't salute the flag, they don't support political parties, they don't pledge allegiance, and they don't join the military. So I ask you seriously: who in their right mind in good old conservative Orange County is going to support them, or you for standing up for them?"

"I just can't believe in my heart that no one cares."

"Well, you'd better start believing it. Except for your team and your patients--who can at best stand up for you as private citizens rather than as a group-- and, of course, Ari and myself, you're alone . . . and I mean alone."

Depressed and visibly upset, Lapin ordered another cup of black coffee. Then he slowly spoke. "You mentioned before that you spoke with the assistant attorney general assigned to the case and that he, too, was having some problems."

"Oh yeah, you mean Basket, the bird photographer. Did you know that he now refers to me as 'the Joe McCarthy of the eighties'"? Both men laughed. Garner continued, "After the last going-over he got from me in the other physician's case against the board, he realizes he's in for the fight of his life. Even though he wants to make a name for himself by nailing you to the cross and plans to move up the ladder of success by using you as one of the rungs, he's offered to make a deal."

Lapin's eyes sprung open. "What kind of a deal?"

The words came out softly as Garner replied, "A year's probation. . . ."

"Gerry, you're not suggesting that I even consider such an option. . . ."

"It's something to think about."

"It's not something to think about. First of all, you know just as well as I that they'd leak the news about the probation and the probationary terms to every news agency they could. That kind of unchallenged, negative publicity would cause an enormous amount of damage. I haven't done anything wrong--nothing--and I don't think I should have to make any deals. And besides all that, I think that's the wrong way to deal with the law anyway."

"Ron, look," Gerry said patiently, "I had your hospital charts reviewed by world-renowned experts in the field of medicine, so I know you haven't done anything wrong; but the long, arduous process of proving all that in court may just be too much, emotionally and financially."

"Listen, my friend, I'm tougher than you think. There are times when I'm down and have my doubts about everything that's happened to me, or even times when I'm really down and question God's wisdom in this entire matter. But it's during those times that I find particular comfort in reading the Book of Job in the Bible . . . or the Prophet Amos, who I admire for his incredible blend of faith and reality."

"For God's sake," Garner said, "we're not talking about sitting in the ashes and scratching to death, or even about a realistic prophet. We're talking about the fact that, for some unknown reason, the Board of Medical Quality Assurance wants you so bad they can taste it. We're talking about potentially losing your license . . . and about your ability to withstand legal pressures that could last as long as five years. And, Ron, you won't get a fair hearing. You just won't. Even at this very minute, they're suppressing evidence. They refuse to turn over favorable reports regarding the hospital or your surgical conduct and strategies. They have such information in their possession and we're entitled to it, but BMQA keeps quiet when they want to and uses only what is convenient, not what's fair."

"But why," Lapin asked, "can't the State use somebody who's competent and unbiased, like Doctor Sheldon Zinberg or Doctor Mickey Goldsmith? That caliber of expert witness would assure a fair hearing."

"My friend," Garner replied, "the State gets whatever they want, and not what's necessarily considered a fair shake."

Lapin was unmoved. The fire grew brighter in his eyes. "My Israeli background taught me that there is only one way and that's to win, especially when the Mediterranean Sea is at your back. This training

269

allows me to tell you from my heart that I can handle anything and everything that life can throw at me."

"I wish I could be so sure," Gerry responded. "For the last two years, I've watched you age rapidly and become grayer by the minute. I've seen the lines in your face become deeper, and the bags under your sunken eyes get bigger and darker. I haven't seen a smile on your face in months. I've noticed you withdraw into your own protective shell and become a virtual recluse. I personally know that you blew at least one relationship with a great lady who could have helped you, could have made you happy. God only knows what your life would have been like without Ari. He seems to be the only person you live for . . . except, of course, your patients. Just don't ask me, your humble, trusted attorney, to stand by and watch a brilliant surgeon--who operated on my only daughter--destroy himself and everyone around him for a small group of people that nobody cares about. Damn it, Ron . . . look . . . martyrs just aren't fashionable in a callous, indifferent world!"

"Why is all this happening to me, Gerry?" Lapin asked introspectively.

"You haven't figured it out yet?"

"I guess I'm too close to the front line to be objective."

"Well, let me make it simple for you. It happens to be a fact that God gave you one of the finest pair of hands in this area and a brilliant mind to match. You operate on more patients in a week than most surgeons operate on in a month. You take care of patients that no one else wants. You see pathology that most surgeons only read about. On top of that, you handle many of your cases for nothing. You don't feel you should engage in public relations or politics, like your fellow physicians do, since the majority of your patients are referrals from other patients. What's more, you're a perfectionist, Ron. You demand a minimum of one hundred percent. You write extensively about your experiences. You've traveled extensively through the world and have gotten an incredible amount of favorable press, up until recently. As if all that weren't enough, let's not forget that you belong to an extremely carnivorous profession and that you work alone in a location that's overpopulated by doctors of every specialty. I don't want to sound like a broken record, but you take care of an unpopular religious group of people that most others classify as a cult, just like the Moonies. Are you seeing the big picture now? Are you starting to get it?"

"You do get right to the point, don't you?"

"I'm sorry, I don't know how else to do it."

"Now let me tell you something, Mr. Attorney. On my last visit to Israel, I visited Masada. As I traced the footsteps of those ancient martyrs--out of vogue as they may be today--I vowed that I would fight the State tooth-and-nail and win. You see, Gerry, if the State can eliminate me, then there will be few physicians who will ever treat the Witnesses again."

"So why should you care? You can sell your house, move to Israel, teach, retire . . . do whatever your heart desires."

"I care because if I don't defend the Witnesses' rights today, I shouldn't be surprised if no one defends mine tomorrow. I care because I've spent ten years of my life taking care of them. I care because I'm Jewish and it's in my blood. And finally, I care because I have the right to care!"

"Let me inform you that it costs extra to carve the words "Magnificent Fool" on a headstone. But in your case, my good Dr. Lapin, it just may be well worth the expense."

"Does that mean--in Brooklyn dialect--that you're still with me?" Lapin asked, smiling.

"I guess it does. I figure if you're crazy enough to go through it all, then the least I can do is help you beat the pants off those creeps. And let me tell you something else. When we beat them, I'll file the biggest lawsuit you've ever seen against the State of California for slander and defamation of character in your behalf. With the money we make from the suit, we can both retire to Israel and I'll be your chauffeur. How's that?"

"No chance, Garner."

"Why not?"

"Because you can't drive."

"Well then, I guess I'll just have to learn."

"You're a good man, Gerry," Lapin said meekly.

"Well, I'll tell you, doc, I hope someone up there is going to be watching over you. It's going to be tough going. We're not looking at a picnic up ahead. When this thing is over, I hope you'll have been successful in changing surgical techniques and the standard of care. I hope you will have opened the door

for the Witnesses to be treated as equals, regardless
of their religious beliefs. Who knows, my friend, you
might even find a wife and settle down."

Both men smiled warmly, each understanding the other
a little better, a little deeper.

"*Inshallah*. . . ."

"What did you say?" Garner asked.

"*Inshallah* . . . it's Arabic. It means 'God
willing.'"

"God willing. . . ."

The Penalty of Leadership

One can only speculate as to why physicians are
reluctant to deviate from the "standard of care" in
the community. This abstraction, although never sat-
isfactorily defined, is used by the legal profession
as a punitive measure against doctors who have, in
their estimation, strayed from its ambiguous standards. This concept of "standard of care" has also
been employed by the organized medical establishment
as a deterrent against innovation and progress.
Medical advancement seems to threaten the very
existence of "entrenched mediocrity." In every
field of human endeavor, the one taking the lead will
be cast into the lime-light of publicity. Whether
leadership be vested in a man or a product, emulation
and envy are sure to follow. In art, literature, and
industry, the reward/punishment system is always the
same. The reward is praise and widespread recogni-
tion; the punishment, fierce denial and dishonor.
Jealousy does not protrude its forked tongue at the
man who produces a common work. No one will strive to
surpass or slander him. But when a man's work becomes
a standard for the whole world, it also becomes a
target for the shafts from the envious few. History
bears this out. Those who proved to be outstanding
leaders in their own field were assailed by their
peers out of envy, personal disappointment, spite, or
ambition. The rival claimed, "it cannot be done."
The leader proved that it could.
Unable to equal or to excel, the follower seeks to
depreciate and to destroy. This only confirms the
superiority of that which he strives to supplant.

There is nothing new in this. It is as old as the world and as old as the human passions of envy, ambition, fear, greed, and competition. It all avails nothing. If the leader truly leads, he remains a leader regardless of another man's achievements.

Master-poet, master-painter, master-workman: each in turn is assailed, yet each retains his laurels through the ages. That which is exceptional makes itself known, no matter how loud the clamor of denial. That which deserves to live, lives.

***

If I or any of my family ever needed major surgery, it would be performed by Dr. Ron Lapin and his team. I believe that that's the ultimate vote of confidence I can voice for the man and the special people who assist him. They, with much patience and understanding, have shown me the way. They've shown me the light. They've shown me surgery at its finest. They've shown me dedication and loyalty not only to a man but also to a principle, an ideal, a cause that I have never before seen.

The ability to sustain and perpetuate life is an awesome responsibility. I stand in wonder as I watch these people do it on a daily basis. Their commitment to do what "can't be done" truly amazes me.

I'm proud to have known Doctors Herk Hutchins and Stanley Kaller. Their teachings, both spoken and unspoken, have been invaluable.

Eternal thanks to Jodie Langdon and Jan Jordan. Their compassion and assistance has been greater than they'll ever imagine.

To the rest of the team, Dixie Roushey, Marilyn Robinson, Smitty Harris and Mikie Waring . . . my gratitude . . . not only for the help they've given me but also for the valuable and wonderful assistance they provide in the operating room.

My deepest appreciation to B.L.C., who encouraged me when my days as well as nights became the darkest.

Now the hard part: to Ron Lapin, surgeon, who has indeed become a friend--not only to me, but also to thousands of others whose lives he has touched and affected.

I marvel at his talent, abilities, and unwavering

commitment in the face of ominous opposition. Ron
Lapin is a special human being, blessed not only with
gifted hands but also with a heart that knows no
limits when it comes to dedication to his patients and
their beliefs.

I wish you a long lifetime of success, my good
friend. I sincerely hope that all your dreams come
true and that some day you even find peace and
happiness.

"Inshallah. . . . "

Gene Church

EPILOGUE

ON MAY 16, 1986, THE ATTORNEY GENERAL OF THE STATE OF
CALIFORNIA ON BEHALF OF THE BOARD OF MEDICAL QUALITY
ASSURANCE OF THE STATE OF CALIFORNIA, THE DEPARTMENT
OF HEALTH OF THE STATE OF CALIFORNIA, AND THE STATE OF
CALIFORNIA WITHDREW AND DISMISSED ALL ACCUSATIONS
AGAINST RON LAPIN, M.D.

The Stipulation entered by the State of California
read in part:

1. The accusations heretofore filed against Ron Lapin,
M.D., including the Accusations and First Supplemental
Accusations are hereby deemed withdrawn and dismissed
with prejudice.

2. Executed Requests for Dismissals with Prejudice in
each of the following actions shall be provided to the
Office of the Attorney General, which is immediately
authorized to file such Requests for Dismissals
forthwith.

The Stipulation, dated May 16, 1986, was written seven
months after a letter was sent by Dr. Lapin's attorney
to the supervising attorney general. That letter read:

Office of the Attorney General
110 West A Street
Suite 700
San Diego, CA 92101

Attention: Al Korobkin

RE: BMQA v. Lapin

Dear Mr. Korobkin:

When you appeared, unannounced, in my office on
the evening of October 22, 1985, I was somewhat

277

surprised. I had earlier written to you explaining to you that Dr. Lapin was not intending to sign the Stipulation you had forwarded for his signature and that I had in fact written to you in that regard and had enclosed a Stipulation that would be acceptable to us and that should resolve this matter once and for all.

You explained to me that you had been involved in the Alaia case here in Orange County and had not received that letter but were desirous of understanding why Dr. Lapin was refusing to execute the agreement which would place him on a one year suspension stayed and could potentially affect his license to practice medicine in this state.

To begin with we should go back to the very beginning of this matter, more than four years ago, which serves as a glowing example as to the manner in which this case has been handled by the Department of Health Services, the Board of Medical Quality Assurance and the Attorney General's office. Please recall that Dr. Lapin learned of the charges that were filed against him by reading about them in numerous local and state wide newspapers. He had never been served with a copy of any allegations or charges against him and in fact more than a week passed from the date that he read about the alleged charges in the paper to the point where he was eventually personally served with anything in writing from the Attorney General's office. During that period of one week the Attorney General's office, essentially through Gayle Askren engaged in possibly the most deleterious smear campaign I have ever seen engaged in in my eighteen years as an attorney.

With absolutely no ability to respond, with absolutely no opportunity for Dr. Lapin to be heard or to contest the allegations, representatives from the Attorney General's office engaged in a below-the-belt punching in describing, from a soap box perspective, the claimed heinous and quasi-criminal conduct of

this terrible doctor who made it his business to
butcher and unnecessarily remove human organs.
One of your associates, M. Gayle Askren, is
quoted in two newspapers as referring to Dr.
Ronald Lapin who is board certified in four
separate specialities as "the Jimmy Jones of
Orange County." To make matters worse, Mr. Askren
not only quoted extensively in the newspapers but
was also seen on television on numerous occasions
essentially playing the "white knight" attempting
to rid the countryside of this malignant scourge
of a physician known as Ron Lapin. All that was
presented in the press was extremely negative:
nowhere were the virtues of Dr. Lapin extolled;
nowhere were any of his patients
interviewed; nowhere was it stated that none of
the accusations that were mentioned by the
Attorney General's office were based upon any
complaints by any of the patients that were
involved; nowhere was it mentioned that all of
these patients were turned down by other
physicians for treatment because of their
religious beliefs and their refusal to accept
blood transfusions; nowhere was there mention of
the number of lives that had been saved by Dr.
Lapin because of his pioneering in bloodless
surgery and in his extensive use of the BOVIE
knife and other advanced surgical techniques in
curing and in healing people that were unable,
primarily for religious reasons, to accept blood
transfusions.

With AIDS now being the subject of national
conversation it would appear that Dr. Lapin's
earlier pioneering efforts may now become the new
standard of care for all surgical procedures
unless a cure for this virulent and devastating
disease can be found.

Secondly, it should be pointed out that there
were no patient complaints. No patient of Dr. Ron
Lapin ever went to the Board of Medical Quality
Assurance, the Department of Health Services or
the Attorney General's office to ever complain in
any manner whatsoever of any of the treatment or
care rendered by this doctor to them personally
or to any member of their family. Yet, and this

has been proven beyond any doubt in this case, State Investigators had harassed patients in order to coerce them to testify against Dr. Ronald Lapin. This has been the subject of affidavits and is also contained in depositions that have been taken in this matter.

It is also axiomatic and should be understood at the outset that the investigators on behalf of the State of California (whether you call them investigators for the Department of Health Services, investigators for the Board of Medical Quality Assurance, or investigators for the Attorney General's office) did not have complete charts to review and had only partial information at the time that the interviews and reviews were taking place.

It should be also pointed out that it took numerous reviews before the "witch hunt" mentality was satisfied. It should be recalled that there were two sets of reviewers who were initially sent to Esperanza Hospital. The first set of reviewers headed by Dr. Knight gave essentially a clean bill of health to Esperanza and found nothing in Dr. Lapin's charts that they felt should be criticized. It was only after that report was available to the Attorney General's office that a second set of doctors, this time headed by the infamous Dr. Shapiro, finally did a "hatchet job" on Dr. Lapin. It is this very same Dr. Shapiro who, by his own admission, was censured by the State of New York Medical Board for performing unnecessary surgery, is now somehow qualified to comment on a standard of care which he failed to meet.

It should be further pointed out that Dr. Hardy, a third reviewing physician, found no basis for any derrogatory comments from his review of Dr. Lapin's charts. Yet, with two out of three sets of reviewers giving a clean bill of health, the powers that decided to prosecute Dr. Lapin, to ruin his reputation in the fashion described above, and, without probable cause, subpoenas or patient complaints, to cause accusations to be

280

filed on the basis of Dr. Shapiro's minority review.

It should also be pointed out that no valid subpoena was ever used to remove the records from Esperanza Hospital. It should further be pointed out that there was no authorization whatsoever for transfer of these records from the Department of Health Services to the Board of Medical Quality Assurance. It should be noted that the Department of Health Services was ostensibly present at Esperanza Hospital for an audit for Medi-Cal and Medi-Care utilization only. It was not called in to review the surgical standards or procedures or to focus on any particular physician, which it obviously did. We are not certain to this date how the records were transferred from the Department of Health Services to the Board of Medical Quality Assurance and what records were in fact transferred and what records were in fact destroyed, lost or secreted.

It should again be emphasized that no complaints were ever lodged against Dr. Lapin by his patients or any members of their family. We have provided you with case authority (two appellate decisions) indicating the patients' right of privacy under existing and current law was violated and a most recent appellate decision holding that the patients' rights are superior to those of the Board of Medical Quality Assurance. Absent patient authorization you simply cannot seize patient's confidential charts which are protected by the Constitution and make them the subject of review. You can look at bills, you can look at hospital procedures, but you may not, without prior authorization and a proper subpoena, review individual patient's charts which were done in this instance. Your entire case must be dismissed by virtue of the fact that you violated not only Dr. Lapin's Constitutional rights but the Constitutional rights of the fourteen patients who are the subject of the accusations and of all patients whose rights were violated by this unnecessary and unfounded witch hunt at Esperanza Hospital.

281

The above noted information was that which was known to us at the time that Dr. Lapin was initially charged. As time went on, new revelations of other improprieties continued to manifest themselves and the hole which the State of California, the Department of Health Services, the Board of Medical Quality Assurance and its investigators, servants, agents and employees had dug continued to gape larger and larger.

To begin with, Attorney General Gayle Askren was requested to turn over all investigative materials, pursuant to Administrative Law Judge Rulings and the laws of the State of California as embodied in the Health and Safety Code for copying by the charged defendant. Numerous requests were made of the Attorney General's office, in particular M. Gayle Askren, for copies of all investigative materials which are required, by law, to be turned over to the accused doctor. The Attorney General, M. Askren, continuously denied both in writing and before the Superior Court of the County of Orange that he had any information in his possession that was in any way exculpatory of Dr. Lapin. It was not until M. Gayle Askren was on vacation and an appearance was made on his behalf by his superior, Mr. Alvin Korobkin, that there was production of some of the exculpatory material which had previously been secreted and hidden. This revelation that the Attorney General's office had been hiding material that was relevant to this action, material to the issues presented in this case, and exculpatory of the accused doctor so enraged Superior Court Judge Linda McLaughlin that she: (1) ordered the deposition of the various state investigators and agents to be taken; and (2) advised the Attorney General to appear in court on the next occasion with separate counsel in the event additional action had to be taken.

One might think that enough was enough! That the revelations noted above, about the early handling, the early publicity, the early defamation and intent to disrupt and destroy a physician's career in this state, would be sufficient material to stop a needless and groundless prosecution. But it was not. Still additional improprieties were discovered.

It was during one of the "Court Ordered" depositions, i.e., of Rod Crabb, that it was ascertained that just the day before his deposition was scheduled, he "shredded" certain original documents and notes of the investigation at Esperanza Hospital and Dr. Lapin, <u>some of which were exculpatory</u>. He also admitted that Dr. Shapiro was brought in for a second opinion due to the fact that the local task force was really out to get Dr. Ron Lapin.

Rod Crabb also admitted in his testimony, under oath, that he publicly discussed (in barber shops, shopping centers, cocktail parties, etc.) his role and the position of the State of California in trying to stop Dr. Lapin from practicing.

Mr. Crabb's superior, Ken Galloway, took the Fifth Amendment in the case of BMQA v. Robert Bingham, M.D., rather than answer defense counsel's questions regarding the investigation that he participated in with reference to Dr. Lapin and Esperanza Hospital. It was very shortly after his assumption of the Fifth Amendment that he retired from his position as local director, and has since refused to participate in the Court Ordered discovery and depositions based on "<u>low back pain</u>."

The beat goes on! Through the use of the federal procedure known as the Freedom of Information Act counsel for Dr. Lapin was able to recover an inter-office memorandum (never formally produced) from the Department of Health Services saying that a team "familiar with Dr. Lapin's modus operendi should enter Bellflower Hospital (in Los Angeles) for purposes of investigating his activity, using a change of ownership as the basis for the investigation, the intent of charging Dr. Lapin with unnecessary operations."

In fact Bellflower Hospital and Dr. Lapin were investigated. That investigation was stopped by a Los Angeles Superior Court Order due to the fact that it was determined that the Department of Health Services and/or the Board of Medical Quality Assurance was illegally attempting to remove patient's charts without authorization from the patients. That matter was appealed by the Attorney General's office and that appeal was lost by the Attorney General's office, represented by Attorney General LaHanna, just last month.

It should further be noted that there appears to be collusion among various state agencies and individuals in the investigation of this case initially and the prosecution of this case. While Dr. Lapin's patients were all admitted to Esperanza Hospital by a Dr. Vinod Malhotra, who independently verified (1) the need for hospitalization; and (2) the need for surgery, the investigating team noted that Dr. Malhotra should have been charged with fifty-five counts of gross negligence. Mysteriously, those fifty-five counts of gross negligence were never charged nor made the subject of any accusation against Dr. Malhotra. In fact, Dr. Malhotra was encouraged by representatives of the Department of Health Services, Board of Medical Quality Assurance or Attorney General's Office to illegally remove the chart of patient Ross from Doctor's Hospital. That chart was illegally removed and found its way to the Attorney General's office of the State of California and formed the basis for the first supplemental accusation against Dr. Lapin. As of this date, no one has admitted how the chart left Doctor's Hospital, how it got into the hands of the Attorney General's office, whether any complaint was made, whether any subpoena was used. Further, no one is admitting that they encouraged Dr. Malhotra to remove the chart. Yet the fact remains that the chart is the basis for the supplemental accusation against Dr. Lapin. It should also be noted that this is one of the accusations that the Attorney General's office has agreed to dismiss. In fact the Attorney

General's office has agreed to dismiss all fourteen accusations that have been filed against this answering defendant.

Interestingly, but not surprisingly, it has come to our attention that numerous patients of Dr. Malhotra's have written to the Board of Medical Quality Assurance complaining of various charges that he made. These charges, appropriately, should have been investigated but were not investigated. In fact there has never been any accusation or any action taken against Dr. Malhotra. These charges by the various patients, which are the subject of numerous correspondence, are a matter of record and we are certain that the Board of Medical Quality Assurance is aware of these. We are wondering why no action has been taken?

It should be noted that numerous prominent physicians and surgeons of national and world renown have provided written analysis and independent reviews that they have conducted on all fourteen charts which form the basis of all accusations of Dr. Lapin. These prominent physicians of both national and world stature are unanimous in declaring that there is no negligence, no malpractice, and no conduct below the standard of care! These materials have been provided to the Attorney General's office and to the Board of Medical Quality Assurance in writing and it should be noted that the physicians also indicate, in writing, that they will be willing to testify in this matter before the administrative tribunal in defense of Dr. Lapin.

It should also be noted that none of these physicians indicate that they are afraid their testimony "will not hold up in court" which is what Dr. Moosa advised Attorney General Askren in his most recent correspondence wherein he was asked to "independently" review Dr. Lapin's charts.

Yet, the Attorney General's office chooses to continue this prosecution and to ignore the favorable reviews by world renown surgeons, just as the Attorney General's office ignored earlier exculpatory reviews by both the Dr. Knight team and Dr. Hardy. One can only conjure up an image of conspiracy in view of all that has gone on before us in this matter. It is possible that Jehovah's Witnesses are not popular people. It is possible that they are not politically popular. But it is their right, as American citizens, to receive adequate and complete medical treatment and certainly not be permitted to die by virtue of the fact that they refuse to accept blood transfusions. This is an inalienable right guaranteed to each and every American under the Constitution and Dr. Lapin is giving these individuals an opportunity for continued life, not an opportunity for anything less.

At the present time, Mr. Korobkin, you seem to be wondering why we are not signing your Stipulation. If you have read this far in this letter I am sure you must know by now why we are not signing the Stipulation. It was more than one year ago when we agreed that you would take the non-gynecological charts and have them reviewed by an "independent" physician out of the Southern California area. You agreed to do so. You agreed that you would obtain an independent review and we provided you with a complete file on these patients which included office charts and other information that were not included or available to the Attorney General's office during initial reviews. You stated that you were not interested in the gynecological cases which you intended to dismiss but only with five cases that dealt directly with general surgery.

In prolongation of Dr. Lapin's agony and in further delaying his vindication of his record, it is noted that it was more than one year later that you finally provided us with the report of your "so-called" independent consultant. After reviewing all fourteen cases--which was not our agreement--Dr. Moosa, who is located in the Southern California area, writes to Mr. Askren, not to Mr. Korobkin, a short, four page review of all the charts that he looked at, and concludes by saying "I am not sure this will hold up in court."

What we found when we looked carefully at Dr.
Moosa's report is that it was really not a
review. It was not critical of anything specific
with reference to Dr. Lapin. There was one area
of unaminity, i.e., that Dr. Moosa seemed
predisposed to wonder why Dr. Lapin's patients
were so satisfied with his care and this he
indicated was the most well documented item
contained in all of the files.

It was obvious from the letter submitted by Dr.
Moosa that he was not in fact obtained by you,
Mr. Korobkin, but rather by Mr. Askren. One
wonders why he would be writing to M. Gayle
Askren or how he would even know M. Gayle Askren
was involved in this case if, in fact, you were
the one that located him, obtained his agreement
to provide testimony, and engaged in all of the
conversations necessary to insure a truly
"independent" review of these charts.

This "independent" report speaks more like a
coach for the "team" than somebody who is truly
independent. It is clear that Dr. Moosa has been
retained as an advocate and not as an independent
and objective reviewer of these charts. You need
only look at the language employed in this chart,
the suggestions on how to close the door on Dr.
Lapin's defense, to determine that there never
was an intention that this would be an
independent evaluation.

We were never sent any cover letters, we were
never sent any materials that were submitted to
this gentleman for his review which allegedly
delineated the areas of concern, the definitions
of the various activities which were to be
evaluated, nor the criteria for determining the
compliance or non-compliance of the standard of
care.

It is apparent from Dr. Moosa's letter that Gayle
Askren (of Jimmy Jones fame) met with him on at
least one occasion and provided him with certain
definitions and other written materials that are

not being made available to us.

Further Dr. Moosa's letter demonstrates absolutely no understanding of the nature of the patients nor the environment in which Dr. Lapin worked in order to treat these patients. He does not allude to the bloodless surgery problem at any point in his report. He does not understand the environment in which Dr. Lapin works. His comments concerning the need for "more consultations" might be appropriate in a university medical center but certainly not in the small community hospital. He makes no comment about the problem with the inability to transfuse these patients during surgery and therefore the speed for which the surgeries have to be performed. Nor does he comment on the different standard of care that must be employed in the treatment and surgery performed on Jehovah's Witnesses.

Lastly, true to his advocacy, he warns Mr. Gayle Askren that his testimony "might not stand up in court."

He also apparently has not been given the information and the voluminous reports presented by various noted physicians who in fact have offered to defend Dr. Lapin and have not cautioned their defense with the caveat "it might not stand up in court." He indicates "no credible physician would be able to defend Dr. Lapin." Such is simply not the case. It is the language and misunderstanding of a man who has not been given all the information, who does not have the proper setting in mind, who has been persuaded in advance as to the need for the outcome of his report, and who has not been given any of the exculpatory materials noted in the various physicians' reports finding no negligence and no violation of the standard of care by doctors who have equal or higher standing in the community than Dr. Moosa.

And if, in fact, Dr. Moosa is truly independent, as I am sure you will have to maintain, why is it in his last paragraph that he suggests other

physicians and surgeons who can seal the fate of
Dr. Lapin as well as other methodologies through
which his conduct could be criticized?

I reviewed the Stipulation. It is the same
Stipulation you presented to us some fourteen
months ago wherein you agreed to drop all
fourteen counts in exchange for an addition of a
fifteenth count which arises from the stolen
chart of Mr. Ross from Doctor's Hospital. I can
understand your concern with the attempt to
legitimize the use of that file. It would be my
intention, if I were the recipient of stolen
property, to try to justify its use and
incorporate it in some fashion into a structured
settlement that would exculpate all those
involved from any civil or criminal liability. In
the future that may be the sanction that would
befall some of the individuals who may be found
to be responsible for "spiriting away" the Ross
file from Doctor's Hospital. The Stipulation that
you propose goes on to ask Dr. Lapin to plead no
contest to one count involving improper charting.
In return he is to be given one year suspension
stayed and five years probation. He is also to
take certain courses and to pass certain exams.

We are absolutely not agreeable to admitting that
anything that Dr. Lapin is accused of is true. We
are certainly not interested in admitting
anything with reference to a chart that was
stolen. We are also not interested in admitting
charges that are based upon illegally obtained
charts, illegally obtained evidence, illegally
destroyed evidence, and based upon the opinions
of doctors where a fishing expedition had to be
conducted in order to find physicians who would
come forward to be critical of Dr. Ronald Lapin.

I believe it is indeed a tribute to Dr. Lapin
that he is willing to "bury the hatchet" and get
on with his life, his treatment of Jehovah's
Witnesses, and with his pioneering efforts in
bloodless surgery, and to drop any and all
federal and state complaints against the various
Attorney General's and agents of the Department
of Health and Board of Medical Quality Assurance

if this case will be dismissed. He is also willing, as I have indicated in the earlier correspondence, to take fifty hours of instruction each year for the next three years to satisfy any lingering doubt you may have in your mind as to his being current on new surgical developments. I believe that, over the past four and one half years, Dr. Lapin has been put under a microscope. If, in fact, there is any reason why this man should not be practicing medicine today and not performing the service that he performs to the community at large I am certain it would have been brought to your attention by now and you would have taken steps to end his career. Certainly that was the effort that was made by the Attorney General's office early in this case. Fortunately for Dr. Lapin and the people of the State of California that unjustified effort has not been successful. I cannot see any justification to continue to spend the People's money in continuing with this witch hunt.

I will state, unequivocally, that, if this continues any longer, all involved parties to this conspiracy, all illegally obtained evidence and all individuals participating in the use of illegally obtained evidence, and all defamatory actions will be the subject of complete and total redress in both Federal and State Court. The price is simply too high for either side to continue. Dr. Lapin wants acquittal. Dr. Lapin deserves acquittal. This case deserves to be dismissed. I trust you will act accordingly.

Very truly yours,

HORTON BARBARO & REILLY

by Frank P. Barbaro

The State of California had unequivocally cleared Dr. Lapin of all accusations, and the State itself began a new era in doctor-patient relations. The confidentiality between doctor and patient as now

290

mandated by the California State Court supercedes the
right--or the corrupt power--of unnecessary investigation. With this, the State of California, Division
of the Board of Medical Quality Assurance, commenced a
new era in the supervision of doctors and maintenance
of quality care for medical patients.

Bloodless medicine and surgery has become so
predominant in medical circles that Dr. Lapin is being
considered for a Nobel Prize in Medicine. To date,
fifteen countries have recommended him for this
tribute.

AIDS (Acquired Immune Deficiency Syndrome) has now
reached epidemic proportions in the United States and
has begun to appear in almost every country in the
world. This terrifying viral disease, which has
touched the lives of 19,000 people and caused the
death of 10,000 in the United States, has terrorized
the American public and caused the cancellation of
twenty-five percent of scheduled elective surgeries.
The fear of contracting AIDS has resulted in a significant drop in volunteer blood donations, despite an
intensive campaign by the American Red Cross to assure
the public that the blood supply is now safer than
ever.

It is suspected that this killer disease originated in
the African Green monkey and was somehow passed on to
humans. It was probably brought back to the United
States by American tourists vacationing in Haiti and
then rapidly spread throughout the country. Although
it had been clearly demonstrated in 1982 that AIDS is
transmitted through blood transfusions, the blood
banking industry in the United States was extremely
slow in implementing safeguards and screening
techniques, and in developing effective testing of
blood donors.

Today, nearly three percent of the AIDS victims in
this country acquired the disease through transfusion
of blood or blood products. An antibody test was
recently instituted, but has not proven to be completely effective in screening potentially infected
donors. The official position of the Institute of
Bloodless Medicine and Surgery has always been that
unless a specific antigen test is developed to detect

AIDS carriers (estimated to be 1 - 2 million in the United States), blood still carries the danger of transmitting AIDS to the recipients.

Kenneth Galloway, the Board of Medical Quality Assurance investigator who took the Fifth Amendment during the Lapin proceedings, left the office of investigation and went on medical disability. The future of Rod Crabb, the Department of Health investigator who admitted shredding the records during the investigation, is not known. Also unknown is the fate of Dr. Vinod Maholtra--Lapin's discarded associate. Maholtra altered local hospital records and then delivered them without authorization to State agents in an attempt to prevent his own prosecution for falsification of medical records and charts which the State uncovered.

As to Dr. Ron Lapin, none of the above is his concern. He remains a dedicated physician, pledged to the concept that transfusing blood and blood products is an organ transplant which should be avoided. Coast Plaza Medical Center in Norwalk, California, has helped Dr. Lapin to continue his pioneering work in "bloodless medicine" with overseas trips. Since 1981, these trips have become commonplace in Lapin's life, as have weekend excursions to various cities in the United States for the purpose of educating both doctors and potential Jehovah's Witness patients. In the United States, the phone number 1-800-NO BLOOD has become as important as 911.

THE EDITOR

"GREAT SPIRITS HAVE ALWAYS ENCOUNTERED VIOLENT OPPOSITION FROM MEDIOCRE MINDS."
ALBERT EINSTEIN